Texts in Computing

Volume 3

Logical Reasoning
A First Course

Volume 1
Programming Languages and Semantics
Maribel Fernandez

Volume 2
An Introduction to Lambda Calculus for Computer Scientists
Chris Hankin

Volume 3
Logical Reasoning: A First Course
Rob Nederpelt and Fairouz Kamareddine

Volume 4
The Haskell Road to Logic, Maths and Programming
Kees Doets and Jan van Eijck

Volume 5
Bridges from Classical to Nonmonotonic Reasoning
David Makinson

Volume 6
Automata and Dictionaries
Denis Maurel and Franz Guenthner

Volume 7
Learn Prolog Now!
Patrick Blackburn, Johan Bos and Kristina Striegnitz

Volum 8 A Meeting of the Minds: Proceedings of the Workshop on Logic,
Rationality and Interaction, Beijing, 2007
Johan van Benthem, Shier Ju and Frank Veltman, eds.

Texts in Computing Series Editor
Ian Mackie   ian.mackie@kcl.ac.uk

Logical Reasoning
A First Course

Revised Edition

Rob Nederpelt
Technische Universiteit, Eindhoven, The Netherlands

Fairouz Kamareddine
Heriot-Watt University, Edinburgh, Scotland

© Individual author and College Publications, 2004.
Revised edition, 2007.
All rights reserved.

ISBN 0-9543006-7-X
College Publications
Scientific Director: Dov Gabbay
Managing Director: Jane Spurr
Department of Computer Science
King's College London
Strand, London WC2R 2LS, UK

Original cover design by Richard Fraser.

Contents

To the reader

This book introduces you to logical reasoning and its applications. Logic and logical reasoning have many roles in mathematics and computer science. In particular, logic can be considered as a foundational science for mathematics and computer science, but also, logic is a powerful application tool in these areas. Interest in logic dates centuries back, yet logic has never lost its influence and charm. In the twentieth century, research took new directions and logic was used to settle questions related to what can be computed and what cannot, to what machines can do, and to how efficiently these machines can do things.

Today, modern logic is considered the basis for establishing correctness of theories in mathematics, including (mathematical) proofs. Logic is also an outstanding scientific tool for the development of correct computer programs.

The book describes the necessary elementary steps in logical reasoning. The book is self-contained and presupposes no earlier knowledge from you and only elementary competence in mathematics. The book can also be followed when you do not specialize in mathematics, but for example in computer science, while still allowing you to deepen your skills further when you *are* a student of mathematics. Anything that is introduced, is explained in detail. At the end of the book, you will have developed foundational skills that will enable you to tackle more advanced books on logic and reasoning. A list of further reading is given at the end of the book which enables you to learn more about the topics you have selected as your favorites while reading this book.

The book is divided into three parts. The first gives a general introduction to logic and the methodology of logical calculations. The logical connectives and quantifiers are introduced in detail one after another together with their properties. The truth tables for connectives and the laws of calculation for connectives and quantifiers are given together with a number of standard equivalences. You can think of a step of a logical calculation to be merely a rewriting of the logical formula at hand with an equivalent logical formula, using the given standard equivalences.

The second part starts by discussing advantages and disadvantages of logical calculations and presents another method for making logical derivations, the so-called reasoning. A reasoning allows a conclusion of an inference to be derived from everything that is available (instead of just from the formula at hand). And so, the second part gives the laws of reasoning for all the logical connectives and quantifiers studied in the first part. A particular style, the so-called flag-notation (or Fitch-style), is used in this book to express this kind of reasoning. Proofs in this style are clearly structured and one is aware at any moment of every formula and fact that is available.

The third part deals with applications of logic in different areas, in particular: sets, relations, mappings, numbers and structures, and ordered sets. In this part, you can see the power of logical proofs 'at work'. In order to establish the desired properties you can now use calculations, reasonings or an intelligent mixture of both styles. The different proof techniques known under the name 'induction' are also developed in this part. Throughout, methods and concepts are illustrated with ample examples and there are further exercises which will help sharpen your skills.

After reading this book you know how logic helps you to set up an indisputably correct reasoning and you have seen many applications of how this can be done. We wish you good luck and much pleasure in the exploration of the stimulating field of science known as 'logic'.

A word from the authors

The book is, as the title explains, an introduction to logic, sets and the necessary backgrounds needed in this field for any degree in Mathematics and/or Computer Science. We introduce the students to these field from a very introductory point of view and we expect that, by studying this book, the student can develop the necessary techniques needed to work with abstract structures and correct proofs.

The approach of the book is to be as informal with the reader as possible, creating a relationship between the reader and the authors. Abstract material is explained in a friendly tone without sacrificing the precision needed to master this subject.

In every university, the subject of logics and sets is taught as a compulsory course to undergraduates. Most existing books are either too introductory or cover only one of the topics of the book in details. Our book goes in depth into logic and naive set theory, with ample examples and techniques. None of the books currently available for teaching logics and sets to undergraduates covers proofs and derivations in such details as we do.

This book can be used as a textbook for an introductory course at both the undergraduate and graduate level. The book will serve as a basis for a leisurely two-terms course or can be used in an intensive one-term course. The material of this book has been used by dr R.P. Nederpelt as an undergraduate course at Eindhoven University of Technology since 1987 until today and was modified following the students experience with it. Students following the course are freshmen in the University and they follow the course in the first three months of their first year. There has also been a long experience in teaching the material of this book to first year classes of Computer Science at Glasgow University (1987–1997), by Professor F.D. Kamareddine. She currently uses this material for teaching courses on logic and formal specifications at Heriot-Watt University whose size varies between 15 and 65 students.

Both authors have taught this subject to large classes, up to 180 students.

They concluded that this course material is suited for the modern classes and addresses modern developments.

As special features of the book we mention the following:

- The first way of proving propositions as presented in this book, is the method using so-called calculations. These calculations were coined by the computer scientist Dijkstra and his group at Eindhoven and are strongly associated to basic notions in computer science such as invariants, pre- and post-conditions and to Hoare logic. In this book we develop an easy method to work with these calculations in a transparent manner, using a format which also provides arguments for the correctness of the calculation. The method is based on a well-chosen set of standard equivalences.

- The second method of proving, being a form of what is known as natural deduction, uses the flag notation for proofs. The mathematician de Bruijn and his Automath group at Eindhoven have exploited it several decades ago in the first theorem prover which checks books of mathematics. With such a notation, it is clear which hypotheses are valid, where they are valid and when they are retracted. This avoids the possibility of using a hypothesis when it is not valid. These flags are used in developing and presenting derivations which give proofs for propositions.

- We believe that both methods of proofs need to be taught and this is what we do in this book. In addition, we compare and combine these two methods and present them coherently.

  This book contains all the above items in one single manuscript. It addresses the needs of modern day computer science and mathematics students.

The book includes many examples, questions, problems and the like. The concepts are first taught by examples, then by generalizations and then the student learning is tested by many exercises. All along, the student is asked to reflect and think about why a certain concept is introduced and why a certain definition is used.

The purpose of this book is to encourage the student to be inventive and to develop an abstract mind. So, the student needs to attempt the exercises without help. If the chapters are studied, then the exercises will be easy to solve.

We expect the book to be used mainly for undergraduate teaching as we have used it ourselves. We also expect however that the book be used at Master levels, for example: (a) in conversion courses for students converting to computer science and who hence need to learn the material and (b) for IT degrees. In addition, we expect our book to be a valuable reference for all teachers and researchers in computer science including those working in industry and who understand the value of formal methods.

Our background

Dr Rob Nederpelt is a senior lecturer in applied logic at the Technische Universiteit in Eindhoven, The Netherlands. He was one of the members of the Automath project at this university. The influence of the 'mathematical language' Automath, designed by N. G. de Bruijn, on theorem proving and automating mathematics is widely acknowledged. Rob Nederpelt has published over 40 articles and a number of books.

Professor Fairouz Kamareddine is a professor of computer science at Heriot-Watt University in Edinburgh, Scotland. Since 1980, she has been involved in teaching many subjects in Computer Science and mathematics. Fairouz Kamareddine has published over 60 articles and several books.

Addresses of the authors

Dr R.P. Nederpelt, Technische Universiteit Eindhoven, Dept of Mathematics and Computer Science, P.O. Box 513, 5600 MB Eindhoven, The Netherlands

e-mail: r.p.nederpelt@tue.nl

Professor F.D. Kamareddine, Heriot-Watt University, School of Mathematical and Computer Science, Mountbatten Building, Riccarton, Edinburgh EH14 4ASQ, Scotland

e-mail: fairouz@macs.hw.ac.uk

Revised edition

This edition differs in several places from the first edition of 2004, albeit that the changes are relatively small.

As regards the *contents*, the changes concentrate on the following items:

• A new Section 4.3, 'Equivalency of propositions', has been added.

• In Section 16.9, we added a rule for Equality of pairs.

• In Chapter 20, the lexicographic orderings have been removed from Section 20.3 and inserted into a new Section 20.4, with a slight extension of the subject.

• Throughout the whole Chapter 20, the distinction between reflexive and irreflexive orderings has been implemented in a more consistent manner. This has led to a number of changes in the text.

• Slight changes in formulation and paragraph order have been carried out throughout the book. We also seized the opportunity to eliminate a number of typo's and small errors.

As to the *lay-out* of the text in this book, good use has been made of a new and improved tool for the rendering of flag derivations ('flagderiv'). One of the many useful options in that package concerns the breaking of derivations over pages, which enabled us to remove unnecessary white in many places.

Acknowledgements

The authors are grateful to all users who informed them about mistakes, typo's and possible improvements. Their information has been used in the preparation of this revision.

In particular, we thank Bas Luttik and other members of the staff of the Computer Science Group of the Technische Universiteit Eindhoven.

Special thanks to Paul van Tilburg and his former co-students, who prepared the versatile *flagderiv* package for flag derivations, based on the first version of Jan Zwanenburg and Erik Poll.

And as a final remark: without the help of the editors of King's College London (including our contact person Jane Spurr), this book wouldn't have got the nice appearance that it has now.

Thank you all!

Part I

Logical Calculations

Chapter 1

What is 'logic'?

1.1 Aristotle and his 'Organon'

Logic is an old science. Already around 350 B.C., the Greek Aristotle wrote six collections on reasoning which together became known as the *Organon*[1]. The meaning of 'Organon' is approximately 'instrument'. In his Organon, Aristotle gave a list of fixed irrefutable rules which make it possible to derive correct conclusions. These rules give a kind of instrument that helps set up good reasoning.

In those old days, reasoning was – like it is today – of great importance. He who can reason, is in a state of carrying through convincing arguments with which he can achieve what he desires. Moreover, with a reasoning-instrument, one is capable of getting oneself rid of false reasoning, and of winning arguments against opponents.

As an example of a general rule, we give the rule of Aristotle which later, in the Middle Ages, became known as 'Barbara' (the three a's in Barbara refer to the three words 'all' in the rule) :

| All K's are L's |
| All L's are M's |
| All K's are M's |

You should read this as follows:

---

[1]See *The Cambridge Companion to Aristotle*, a book edited by Jonathan Barnes and published by Cambridge University Press in 1995.

From 'all K's are L's'
and 'all L's are M's'
we can conclude that: 'all K's are M's'.

This is elegant indeed. The rule can for example be applied as follows:

From	(1) All Scottish are British;
and	(2) All British are European;
we can derive	(3) All Scottish are European.

This rule only has a say over the validity of the *conclusion*: from (1) and (2) *conclude* (3). Whether (1) and (2) themselves hold, is not a priority for the rule. In the above example, (1) and (2) are correct: Scottish are British, and British are European. But, in the following example, both (4) and (5) are incorrect. *Nevertheless, on the basis of the rule 'Barbara', the conclusion* (6) *is still correct*: Suppose that (4) and (5) were really true, then indeed (6) follows!

From	(4) All tigers are vegetarians;
and	(5) All vegetarians are sea animals;
we derive	(6) All tigers are sea animals.

Now we must be careful with these general rules like Barbara: it is necessary that they **always** hold, no matter what you have instead of the K's, L's and M's.

Look at the following 'rule':

All K's are L's
There are L's that are M's
─────────────────────────
There are K's that are M's

This rule might look alright at first sight, but it actually isn't. Look at the following instantiation of the rule, which gives a *counterexample* against its own correctness:

From	(7) All Scottish are British;
and	(8) There are British which are Welsh;
we derive	(9) There are Scottish which are Welsh.

This is obviously an incorrect conclusion, because (7) and (8) are correct, but (9) is not. Hence, it is *not* correct 'From (7) and (8), to conclude (9)', because in that case, (9) *would* have to hold! Therefore, the 'rule' (with the K's, L's and M's) is not correct in general.

Remark 1.1.1 *The word 'logic' comes from Greek. It is the first part from the Greek expression 'logikè technè', which means: reasoning techniques,* *the technique (knowledge) of reasoning. The word 'logikè' is the adjective which comes from the Greek word 'logos', which can either mean 'word', 'understanding' or 'reason'.*

1.2   Formal logic

Logic deals with *general reasoning laws*, which you can trust. Logical laws are given in the form of formulas with *'parameters'*. When in one such law, you replace the parameters with something concrete, you get a good trustworthy reasoning. Look at the law 'Barbara' of Aristotle, given on page 3 where the parameters K, L and M appear. When you take 'Scottish' instead of K's, 'British' instead of L's and 'European' instead of M's, the formula is correct. But the formula remains correct when you replace all occurrences of K, L and M by something else (see the previous section).

Aristotle gave in total 19 rules, the so-called *syllogism*, of which 'Barbara' is one. Until the Middle Ages, the logic of Aristotle was leading. Only after then, did the basis of logic change. This was necessary because other conditions began to be imposed in *mathematics* (an important application area of logic). In his book,[2] the English mathematician George Boole (1815 – 1864) wrote logic in a way which became known as the *two-valued* or *Boolean* logic. Later, the German Mathematician Gerhard Gentzen (1909 – 1945) went a step further. He invented[3] a logical system which was connected, as closely as possible, to the method of reasoning used in mathematics. He called his logic 'natural deduction' and intended to use it to *deduce* (derive conclusions) in a *natural* way (exactly like man is used to).

Computer science imposes different conditions than mathematics. In the area of logic, computer science imposes perhaps more conditions than mathematics. A computer must be told precisely what it should do, up to the smallest details, otherwise it will not work well. If a mathematician goes quickly or lightly over some details, his fellow mathematician will still understand him. However, a computer scientist cannot permit himself to go lightly over some details. If a program is false or has some holes, it will not work ('error'!). Or, even worse: it *does* work, but will not deliver what is expected. One hopes that one discovers the mistake in time, otherwise disasters might happen.

In this book, we will not discuss Aristotle any further. His logic, although ground breaking, will no longer be needed because it does not go

---

[2]George Boole: *The Mathematical Analysis of Logic, being an Essay towards a Calculus of Deductive Reasoning.* Cambridge University Press, 1847.
[3]Gerhard Gentzen: *Untersuchungen über das logische Schliessen.* Mathematisches Zeitschrift, 1935.

far. Boolean logic on the other hand, will be discussed further (see Chapter 3), and so will natural deduction (Chapter 11 onwards). Both logical systems have had many applications, not only in mathematics, but also in computer science:

- Modern logic is used in mathematics in areas that include set theory, functional analysis, algebra and discrete mathematics.

- Modern logic is important in computer science especially in areas like programming, database theory, computer architecture and verification.

Nowadays, one prefers to use the term '*formal logic*' instead of 'modern logic', in order to express that the general science of reasoning is written as precisely as possible. This is done with logical *formulas*, and hence the use of 'formal'.

Remark 1.2.1 *Judges, politicians, philosophers, and also 'ordinary' people like you and I, use natural language when reasoning. Formal logic attempts to separate the logical laws from ordinary (spoken and written) language. This is needed, because language is often too 'rich' in meaning and hence not precise enough to avoid writing the logical laws in a manner that can be subject to double interpretations. In the following chapter, we will continuously make the association with language, in order to explain where the logical formulas come from. However, when it is a question of precision of reasoning, logic will dissociate itself from language and will often take its own separate way. This is necessary in order to preserve the consistency, which is the guarantee that as long as we keep faithful to the rules, we can never derive an incorrect conclusion. Via this process of doing our best to avoid ambiguity and double interpretations, both mathematics and computer science can be made 'trustworthy'. This leads to quality and good products.*

1.3   Exercises

1.1 Check in each of the following cases whether the given rule is correct. If it is, give arguments to show this. If it is not, give a counterexample.

(a)
$$\frac{\text{There are K's which are also M's}}{\text{All K's are L's}}$$
There are L's which are M's

(b)
$$\frac{\text{No one K is an M}}{\text{All K's are L's}}$$
No one L is an M

Chapter 2

Abstract propositions

True to the facts

2.1 Propositions

Modern, formal logic has as a basic concept the so-called *proposition*. This is a purely technical term, and you must not think of the ordinary English word 'proposition' ('proposal'), but instead, think of something like a special kind of a (linguistic) 'sentence'.

What is a proposition? It is a grammatically correct sentence which (at this moment, at this place, etc.) is either *true* or *false*. Here are some examples of propositions:

(1) It is raining.

(2) There are birds which cannot fly.

(3) $2 + 2 = 5$.

(4) π is bigger than three.

(5) $p^2 + q^2 = r^2$.

Proposition (3) is completely written in the 'language of mathematics' (and is false in our world). In proposition (4), ordinary language is mixed with the mathematical symbol π. Sentences in the language of mathematics (like (3)), or sentences which are mixed with the language of mathematics (like (4)), are allowed as propositions.

Note that proposition (5) is grammatically correct, not because of English grammar, but because of the grammar of mathematical formulas. Moreover, this sentence is only *in principle* true or false: it depends on what p, q and r are. Only when we know the *context* (hence as soon as we have enough information about p, q and r), can we say: true or false. A proposition can hence have symbols which are meaningless *in* the proposition, but are (perhaps) specified in the context.

Here are some examples of sentences that are *not* propositions, and reasons as to why they are not:

(6) Is it raining? (This is a question, which on its own cannot be true or false: there does not exist something like a 'true question' or a 'false question'.)

(7) Make sure to get away! (An order.)

(8) $x := x + 1$. (This is a command in a programming language, and also a kind of order.)

(9) All these awaiting jobs! (This is not a sentence, but a cry of despair.)

(10) Queen Netherlands Juliana of the was. (This is not a grammatically correct sentence.)

We have now seen examples of simple sentences which are propositions and of sentences which are not. Things become interesting when we try to form new propositions from old ones. This happens frequently in ordinary language.

(11) It is raining and it is windy. (This proposition can be built from the propositions 'It is raining' and 'It is windy', via the use of the connecting word 'and' which joins them together.)

(12) It is not freezing. (Built from 'It is freezing' with the negation, 'not'.)

(13) If it is raining, (then) I will stay home. (A proposition built from 'It is raining' and 'I will stay home', with the use of 'if ... then'.)

(14) $x < -1 \Rightarrow x^2 + x > 0$. (Built from the proposition $x < -1$ and $x^2 + x > 0$ with the help of the implication sign $\Rightarrow$. This sign (or symbol) $\Rightarrow$ is used in logic for expressing 'if ... then'.)

(15) The sun is shining, but I am cold. (Built by the use of the connecting word 'but' which combines the two propositions 'The sun is shining' and 'I am cold'.)

Propositions which are not built from other propositions (like examples (1) to (5)) are usually called *simple* propositions. Those built from other propositions (like examples (11) to (15)), are called *complex* propositions.

2.2 Abstract propositions and connectives

Logic deals with *patterns* of correct reasoning. This means that propositions as such are not that important. What matters is the way in which propositions are combined and what follows from them.

For example, let us look at the following proposition:

> If it is raining and windy, then I will not come.

This fits the pattern:

(*a* and *b*) implies not-*c*,

with *a*, *b* and *c* as abstractions respectively from 'It is raining', 'It is windy' and 'I will come'. (The word 'implies' is an alternative for 'if ... then'.)

Also the proposition

> If it holds that $x \geq -1$ and that $x \leq 0$, then $x^2 + x$ is not positive

fits the same pattern: take $x \geq -1$ for *a*, $x \leq 0$ for *b* and '$x^2 + x$ is positive' for *c*.

Logic is primarily the study of abstract patterns rather than the 'real' concrete propositions. This is to clarify what the essence is. We do not lose anything via the use of abstract patterns because, once we know how the reasoning laws work for abstract propositions, we can apply them without any difficulties to concrete propositions by replacing the occurrences of the *proposition variables a*, *b* etc., by the concrete propositions.

By abstracting over propositions, one goes even further. Patterns like the above mentioned '(*a* and *b*) implies not-*c*' still contain words from natural language ('and', 'implies', 'not'). In order to avoid in logic the double meanings that usually occur in natural language, we replace these words by symbols, the so-called *connectives*.

In logic, one usually limits the number of connectives to the following:

$\wedge$ This is the symbol for the word 'and'.

$\vee$ The symbol for the word 'or'.

$\neg$ Represents the word 'not'.

$\Rightarrow$ For 'if ... then' or 'implies'.

$\Leftrightarrow$ For 'if and only if'.

(In Chapter 3 we will come back to these connectives and will explain in detail what they represent. The ⇔, for example, which we have only vaguely described with 'if and only if', will be defined more precisely.)

We can now describe, with the help of these connectives, the above-mentioned pattern '(*a* and *b*) implies not-*c*' in a fully abstract form, without words from natural language:

$$(a \wedge b) \Rightarrow \neg c \ .$$

Remark 2.2.1 *Although logic only uses a limited number of connectives, this appears to be enough for many applications. Especially when it concerns reasoning, we mostly have enough with the above five symbols. Moreover, some of the nuances that exist in natural language, disappear when formalizing towards an abstract proposition. For example, the proposition 'the sun is shining, but I am cold' has the abstract logical form 'd ∧ e' (where d stands for 'The sun is shining' and e for 'I am cold'). The word 'but' is replaced by ∧ ('and'), which is a sort of weakening: the surprising aspect of 'but' (like: 'You didn't expect that I can be cold despite the sun shining, did you?') disappears.*

2.3   Recursive definitions of propositions

We will clarify what we precisely understand by 'abstract propositions'. We will assume that we have at our disposal an *infinite* collection of *proposition variables*, such as *a*, *b* and *c*. We start by giving the following definition:

Definition 2.3.1 *(Abstract proposition)*
Basis: Proposition variables (like a, b and c) are themselves abstract propositions.
Step (case 1): If P is an abstract proposition, then so is (¬*P*).
Step (case 2): If P and Q are abstract propositions, then so are (*P* ∧ *Q*), (*P* ∨ *Q*), (*P* ⇒ *Q*) *and* (*P* ⇔ *Q*).

Remark 2.3.2 *This is what we call a* recursive definition. *These definitions are also called* inductive *definitions. It consists of a* basis, *which specifies what the simplest abstract propositions are, and a* step *which is divided here in two* cases. *Through the steps, more complex abstract propositions can be formed from less complex ones.*

As an example, let us see how the abstract proposition $((a \wedge b) \Rightarrow (\neg c))$ can be 'built' or 'constructed' according to the definition:

(basis) a, b and c are proposition variables, hence following the definition, they are also abstract propositions.

(step) Because a and b are abstract propositions, then so is $(a \wedge b)$ (see case 2).

(step) Because c is an abstract proposition, then so is $(\neg c)$ (see case 1).

(step) Because $(a \wedge b)$ is an abstract proposition and also $(\neg c)$ is an abstract proposition, then so is $((a \wedge b) \Rightarrow (\neg c))$ (see case 2).

All the abstract propositions that we reach during the construction, are called *sub-formulas* of the formula that we have finally built. The sub-formulas of $((a \wedge b) \Rightarrow (\neg c))$ are hence: a, b, c, $(a \wedge b)$, $(\neg c)$ and also $((a \wedge b) \Rightarrow (\neg c))$ itself.

In this definition, you may question the number of parentheses and may rightly believe that they are used excessively. We will in Section 2.5 see how we can reduce the number of parentheses without affecting the intended meaning of the formula.

Remark 2.3.3 *The word 'recursive' literally means 'running back'. What runs back in a recursive definition? We are actually going forward in the building of our abstract propositions: from a and b to $a \wedge b$, from c to $\neg c$, etc. This word 'recursive' does not really refer to the building of the propositions, but rather to breaking them down into smaller pieces. This process of breaking down into smaller pieces is needed when we come across a ready-made formula which we want to check whether it is an abstract proposition.*

Example 2.3.4 *Look at the following formula: $((\neg(a \wedge b)) \Leftrightarrow ((\neg a) \vee (\neg b)))$. Is this an abstract proposition? We see that it has the form $(P \Leftrightarrow Q)$, with $(\neg(a \wedge b))$ for P and $((\neg a) \vee (\neg b))$ for Q. According to case 2 of the definition, the formula is a 'good' abstract proposition, provided that P and Q are too. Hence we must check whether $(\neg(a \wedge b))$ and $((\neg a) \vee (\neg b))$ are abstract propositions.*
   The first is of the form $(\neg R)$ with $(a \wedge b)$ as R. This is 'good' according to case 1 of the definition, again provided that $(a \wedge b)$ is an abstract proposition. However, this is the case (again case 2) when a and b are. And this is indeed the case due to (basis). As for the second formula, $((\neg a) \vee (\neg b))$, we can follow the same parsing process.
   Finally we decide that the formula $((\neg(a \wedge b)) \Leftrightarrow ((\neg a) \vee (\neg b)))$ is an abstract proposition because we could break it down into smaller abstract

propositions, until we reach the bottom (the level of (basis), the proposition variables). This breaks the recursion (the running back via the definition).

2.4   The structure of abstract propositions

We have seen (Definition 2.3.1) how abstract propositions can be both constructed and broken down. We can also give these formulas graphically in the form of a so-called *tree*. In Figure 2.1, we give the tree of $((a \wedge b) \Rightarrow (\neg c))$.

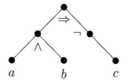

Figure 2.1: The tree of $((a \wedge b) \Rightarrow (\neg c))$

Such a tree has *nodes* (the black buttons), *branches* (the connecting lines) and *labels* (the symbols at the nodes, like b, $\neg$ and $\Rightarrow$). The nodes at the end of the tree (in this case: the nodes with labels a, b and c) are called *leaves*. At the node at the top of the tree, the so-called *root*, there is a label which is called the *main symbol* of the formula, in this case $\Rightarrow$.

Characteristic for a tree is that it has a root, that all nodes are connected to each other and that there are no *loops*. (A loop occurs, for example, when there is a branch between the nodes labeled b and c. In such a loop you can go continuously round.) As can be seen, trees in the above graphical figure, are drawn upside down. The root is in the air, the leaves grow on the ground. You can draw the horizontal mirror image of such trees, and then you get 'normal' trees.

Note that the tree of an abstract proposition does not need any parentheses in order to clarify the structure of the formula:

(1) In order to see how the tree is *built*, we begin at the bottom, with the leaves, and then we follow the branches *to the top*.

(2) In order to see how the tree can be *decomposed* or *broken down*, we begin from the top, at the root, and we follow the branches *to the bottom* in order to find the different parts.

In the tree one can also see what the subformulas are: $(a \wedge b)$ can be found as a sub-tree of the whole tree. Namely as the tree of Figure 2.2.

Figure 2.2: The tree of $(a \wedge b)$

This holds for *every* node in the tree: the tree below a node represents a sub-formula.

2.5 Dropping parentheses

An inductive definition has in general more parentheses than is needed. In order to economize on parentheses, one usually uses a *precedence* or a *priority scheme* for the connectives. So, in logic, the following priority scheme for the connectives is used (the horizontal lines separate here the different priority levels):

$$
\begin{array}{c}
\hline
\neg \\
\hline
\wedge \quad \vee \\
\hline
\Rightarrow \\
\hline
\Leftrightarrow \\
\hline
\end{array}
$$

This means that: $\neg$ has a higher priority than $\wedge$ or $\vee$, which in turn have a higher priority than $\Rightarrow$, which again in turn has a higher priority than $\Leftrightarrow$. The following three examples illustrate what this priority scheme offers:

(i) In $\neg a \wedge b$, the symbol $\neg$ has higher priority than $\wedge$, and hence one must read this formula as $(\neg a) \wedge b$ and not as $\neg(a \wedge b)$.

(ii) In $a \vee b \Leftrightarrow b \vee a$ the symbol $\vee$ has higher priority than $\Leftrightarrow$, and hence it represents $(a \vee b) \Leftrightarrow (b \vee a)$ and not for example $(a \vee (b \Leftrightarrow b)) \vee a$.

(iii) As to $a \wedge b \vee c$, there is a problem: $\wedge$ and $\vee$ have the same priority in the above mentioned priority scheme, hence it is not clear whether one means with this formula $(a \wedge b) \vee c$ or $a \wedge (b \vee c)$. We will come back to this point below.

Remark 2.5.1 *Priority schemes can also be used for non-logical symbols. So in arithmetic, the following scheme is used:*

$$
\begin{array}{c}
\hline
\uparrow \\
\hline
\times \quad : \\
\hline
\sqrt{} \\
\hline
+ \quad - \\
\hline
\end{array}
$$

It should be noted that not everyone uses the same priority scheme. Sometimes, in logic, $\wedge$ has higher priority than $\vee$ and in arithmetic $\times$ may be stronger than $:$.

In the case where priorities do not give a definite answer (as in example (iii)), one usually applies the *left-associativity rule*: 'left is applied first', or: first come, first serve. Then we read $a \wedge b \vee c$ as $(a \wedge b) \vee c$. Be careful however. Sometimes we also see the *right-associativity rule*: right is applied first. That this can make a lot of difference can be seen in the formula $a \wedge b \vee c$: right-associativity represents it as $a \wedge (b \vee c)$, which is very different from $(a \wedge b) \vee c$ (as we will see in Section 3.2). See also the following example:

(l) With the left-associativity rule, $9 - 5 + 3$ must be read as $(9 - 5) + 3$, and hence results in 7.

(r) With the right-associativity rule, one gets a different formula, namely $9 - (5 + 3)$, which results in 1.

The priority scheme for connectives and the associativity rules enable one to economize on parentheses. In addition, it is common to leave out the outside parentheses.

Summary: You can cut down the number of parentheses by

(1) applying a priority scheme,

(2) using the left- (or right-)associativity rule and

(3) removing the outside parentheses.

Convention 2.5.2 *In the rest of this book we will use the priority scheme from the beginning of this section. Also, we will remove the outside parentheses. However, we will neither use the left- nor the right-associativity rule. Instead, we will when necessary, keep the extra parentheses needed to avoid ambiguity. Hence, in the formula $a \wedge b \vee c$, we add parentheses to describe what we mean exactly. This could be either $(a \wedge b) \vee c$ or $a \wedge (b \vee c)$.*

Example 2.5.3 *By applying (1) and (3) given above, we can write the abstract proposition $((a \wedge b) \Rightarrow (\neg c))$ completely without parentheses, as follows: $a \wedge b \Rightarrow \neg c$. Note that for readability, it is sometimes useful to keep some parentheses; hence for this example, we may write $(a \wedge b) \Rightarrow \neg c$.*

Remark 2.5.4 *Parentheses remain however necessary, for distinguishing for instance between the formulas $\neg(a \wedge b)$ and $\neg a \wedge b$. For example, replace a by 'It is raining' and b by 'It is cold', then the first formula says: 'It is not* *the case that it is both raining and cold' and the second (which is actually* $(\neg a) \wedge b)$*: 'It is not raining and it is cold'. (In the first case, it can very* **well** *not be cold, and perhaps it can* also *be raining.)*

2.6 Exercises

2.1 Check in each of the following cases whether the given expressions are propositions or not. If yes, say whether this proposition is simple or complex. If no, give reasons why not.

(a) It is freezing and yet it is not cold, because it is not windy.

(b) <u>if</u> $x < 0$ <u>then</u> $x := x + 1$ <u>else</u> $x := x - 1$.

(c) The queen of Great Britain lives in Liverpool.

(d) Either $x < 0$, or $x = 0$ and $y < 0$.

(e) How is this.

(f) Romeo and Juliet.

(g) Elephants don't exist.

(h) If $x = 0$, then x.

2.2 For each of the following concrete propositions, write an abstract proposition which corresponds to it:

(a) I love you and will always be true to you.

(b) If it is raining, then I will stay home and will open a bottle of wine.

(c) $x \leq 1$ or $x > 2$.

(d) I will go to play tennis, if you bring balls with you.

(e) I will go to the movies, unless something happens.

(f) $x^2 > 4$ if, and only if, $x > 2$ or $x < -2$.

2.3 Give the following propositions in words again, with 'it is raining' for a, 'it is windy' for b and 'I am wet' for c.

(a) $a \wedge \neg b$

(b) $\neg(a \wedge b)$

(c) $(a \Rightarrow c) \wedge (b \Rightarrow \neg a)$

(d) $c \vee \neg c$

(e) $c \Leftrightarrow a$

(f) $\neg\neg a$.

2.4 Show how the following abstract propositions are built according to Definition 2.3.1.

    (a) $(a \Rightarrow (b \Rightarrow a))$

    (b) $((\neg(a \Rightarrow b)) \Leftrightarrow (a \wedge (\neg b)))$

    (c) $((\neg(\neg a)) \Rightarrow ((\neg a) \wedge b))$

    (d) $(a \Rightarrow ((b \wedge a) \vee c))$.

2.5 Show that:

    (a) In every abstract proposition in which the symbol '$\neg$' does *not* appear, the number of proposition variables is one more than the number of connectives.

    (b) In every abstract proposition where no parentheses are dropped out, the number of parentheses is equal to twice the number of connectives.

2.6 (a) Draw the trees of the abstract propositions of Exercise 2.4.

    (b) For each of the abstract propositions of Exercise 2.4, give the main symbol.

2.7 Give all the sub-formulas of the abstract proposition

$$((a \wedge (\neg b)) \Rightarrow ((\neg c) \Rightarrow d)).$$

2.8 Drop as many parentheses as possible from the abstract propositions given in Exercise 2.4. Use the left-associativity rule.

Chapter 3

Truth tables

The truth and nothing but the truth

3.1   The conjunction $P \wedge Q$

The simplest logical connective is $\wedge$, the symbolic reproduction of the word 'and'. It leads to little confusion. Assume that P and Q are abstract propositions. The meaning of $P \wedge Q$ is: 'P *and* Q are true', hence, if we want to know if $P \wedge Q$ holds, we need to know
(1) whether P is true, and
(2) whether Q is true,
and only when this is the case for *both*, we can say that $P \wedge Q$ is true.

We can express this in one *standard truth-table for* $\wedge$, which specifies how the truth or falsity of $P \wedge Q$ follows from the truth or falsity of P and that of Q. We use the symbol 0 for 'false' and 1 for 'true'. These symbols 0 and 1 are called in logic the *Boolean values* or *truth-values*. There are four possible cases, depending on the values of P and Q from the list of values 0 and 1:

P	Q	$P \wedge Q$
0	0	0
0	1	0
1	0	0
1	1	1

It is obvious that $P \wedge Q$ is true *only*, when P is true *and* Q is true: we only get 1 as value for $P \wedge Q$ in the last row of the table.

Note that such a truth-table follows the inductive construction of an abstract proposition. We begin first with the truth-values of P and Q, based on which we decide the truth-value of the proposition $P \wedge Q$ which is *built* out of P and Q. (Compare with case (2) of Definition 2.3.1.)

Remark 3.1.1 *An abstract proposition of the form $P \wedge Q$ is called a con-junction. The Latin prefix* con *means 'together' or 'both' and* junction *means 'connection'. One calls $(a \Rightarrow b) \wedge c$ the conjunction of $a \Rightarrow b$ and c. With the symbol $\wedge$ you can think of two legs with strong standing feet on the ground: To stand strong on one's feet, one needs to stand on* both *feet, hence both on the left foot* and *on the right foot.*

3.2   The disjunction $P \vee Q$

With the logical connective $\vee$, the symbolic reproduction of 'or', there is ambiguity. Roughly speaking, there are *two* forms of 'or':

- *the inclusive 'or'.* You say: 'I feel hungry. I'll fetch a roll or a sand-wich'. This can mean that you come back with a roll *and* a sandwich, without you uttering a false statement. So the word 'or' means here: the one or the other *or both.* The both-option is 'open' (inclusive). In order to precisely express the inclusive character of 'or', a combination of 'and/or' is used in language (especially the official language): 'The information meeting is for the benefit of travelers to France and/or Italy'.

- *the exclusive 'or'.* On lottery tickets one finds: 'Congratulations. You have won a TV or 500 pounds'. In this case you have a right for one of the two, but not to both. You should therefore understand here: one *or* the other (and not both). The both-option is 'closed' (exclusive). Also here, language provides possibilities for avoiding ambiguity. When we mean the exclusive 'or', we use 'either ... or ... (but not both)': 'You have won either a tv or 500 pounds (but not both)'.

In natural language, it usually depends on circumstances or on the reason-ing, which of the two 'or's is meant. Such imprecisions cannot be tolerated nor permitted in logic.

Hence the following convention. In logic the symbol $\vee$ is used for the *inclusive or* (i.e. with an open possibility for 'both'). Hence $P \vee Q$ means: P is true or Q is true *or both are true.*

The *standard truth-table for* $\vee$ is now straightforward:

P	Q	$P \vee Q$
0	0	0
0	1	1
1	0	1
1	1	1

Here one can see that $P \vee Q$ is *only* false, when both P and Q are false. As soon as (at least) one of the two is true, $P \vee Q$ becomes true too.

In this book we don't use any separate standard symbol for exclusive 'or'.

Those who want to express in logic 'either P or Q (but not both)', can for example use: $(P \vee Q) \wedge \neg(P \wedge Q)$ (i.e.: P or Q, but not: P and Q). A shorter way is: $\neg(P \Leftrightarrow Q)$, but in order to show that this expresses 'the same' formula, we must wait till Section 3.5.

Remark 3.2.1 *An abstract proposition of the form $P \vee Q$ is called a dis-junction. The Latin prefix* dis *means 'away from each other' or 'separated'. And in $P \vee Q$ there is indeed often a separation of ways, a choice. With the symbol $\vee$ you can think of two arms which in hesitation shoot in the air: 'I don't know, should I now go left or right (or in both directions at the same time...)'.*

With truth-tables, we can also calculate the truth-values of complex abstract propositions. As an example, we give the truth-tables of $(a \wedge b) \vee c$ and of $a \wedge (b \vee c)$:

a	b	c	$a \wedge b$	$(a \wedge b) \vee c$
0	0	0	0	0
0	0	1	0	1
0	1	0	0	0
0	1	1	0	1
1	0	0	0	0
1	0	1	0	1
1	1	0	1	1
1	1	1	1	1

a	b	c	$b \vee c$	$a \wedge (b \vee c)$
0	0	0	0	0
0	0	1	1	0
0	1	0	1	0
0	1	1	1	0
1	0	0	0	0
1	0	1	1	1
1	1	0	1	1
1	1	1	1	1

In these tables, it is clear that $(a \wedge b) \vee c$ and $a \wedge (b \vee c)$ 'calculate' different things. The first three columns in both tables (the 'input'-possibilities for a, b and c) are the same. But the 'results', which appear in the last column, are different. The last column of the left table differs in two places from the last column of the right table. For example, when the values of a and b

are both 0 and that of c is 1, then the value of proposition $(a \wedge b) \vee c$ is 1, whereas the value of $a \wedge (b \vee c)$ is 0. We say that $(a \wedge b) \vee c$ and $a \wedge (b \vee c)$ are *not equivalent*.

Note how during the calculations in the truth-tables, the structure of the formula is followed precisely (compare Section 2.4)!

3.3   The negation $\neg P$

The negation 'not' is expressed with the sign $\neg$. It has in principle a simple meaning: the negation of 'true' is 'false', and the negation of 'false' is 'true'. In other words: 1 becomes 0 and 0 becomes 1. Hence the *standard truth-table for* $\neg$ is:

P	$\neg P$
0	1
1	0

This truth-table is shorter than that of $P \wedge Q$ resp. $P \vee Q$. The reason is that $\wedge$ and $\vee$ have *two* arguments, P and Q, for which four Boolean truth combinations become possible: (0,0), (0,1), (1,0) or (1,1). Whereas $\neg$ has only *one* argument, P, with two Boolean choices: 0 of 1.

Remark 3.3.1 *In ordinary language, negation is less clear, because there usually are more choices than simply yes or no. When it is not cold, it does not necessarily mean that it is warm: it can be 'in between'. This has consequences for the* double negation *in ordinary language: 'It is not that I do* not *believe in this' does not in general mean: 'I (do) believe in it', but more likely: 'I believe in it a little bit'.*

In standard logic (see also Section 5.4) there is no ambiguity concerning this point: with 'not-not' we are simply back where we started, as is seen in the following truth-table:

P	$\neg P$	$\neg\neg P$
0	1	0
1	0	1

This implies that: when P has the truth-value 0, then also $\neg\neg P$ has the truth-value 0; and when P has the truth-value 1, then also $\neg\neg P$ has the truth-value 1. Therefore P and $\neg\neg P$ have the same truth-values *or are equivalent, whatever P is.*

3.4   The implication $P \Rightarrow Q$

The connective $\Rightarrow$ is called *arrow* or *implication arrow* and it is the formal symbol for *if ... then*. Hence $P \Rightarrow Q$ expresses: 'If P, then Q'. One can also say: 'P *implies* Q' or '*From* P *follows* Q'. In logic we simply say: 'P *arrow* Q'.

It is not immediately obvious how the truth-value of $P \Rightarrow Q$ can be calculated from the truth-values of P and Q. This is especially the case if P is false. Example: is the proposition $(2 > 3) \Rightarrow (2 > 3)$ true or false? And what about $(2 > 3) \Rightarrow (4 > 3)$?

To get a feel for how things work, we will study the following proposition, where n and i are natural numbers:

$$\text{If } n > 3, \text{ then } n + i > 3.$$

We have absolutely no difficulties in declaring that this proposition is *true*, independently of what n and i are. Hence the truth-value of the whole proposition is 1, independently of what the truth-values of its sub-propositions $n > 3$ and $n + i > 3$ are.

We will look now at three cases: (1) $n = 2$, $i = 0$, (2) $n = 2$, $i = 2$ and (3) $n = 4$, $i = 0$. In these cases, three different combinations of $n > 3$ and $n + i > 3$ take place:

	$n > 3$	$n + i > 3$	If $n > 3$, then $n + i > 3$.
$n = 2, i = 0$	0	0	
$n = 2, i = 2$	0	1	always 1
$n = 4, i = 0$	1	1	

Hence, it makes sense that in logic, the truth-value of $P \Rightarrow Q$ is calculated as follows:

P	Q	$P \Rightarrow Q$
0	0	1
0	1	1
1	1	1

We still have one case left, namely when P is true (1) and Q is false (0). (This case does not occur in the example above.) Take the example: 'If 4 is bigger than 3, then $2 + 2$ is equal to 5'. Now, there is no possibility for ambiguity. In this case, $P \Rightarrow Q$ says that from something true, something false must follow, and this can never be the case. So, in this case, the truth-value of $P \Rightarrow Q$ is equal to 0.

When we summarize the above, we reach the following *standard truth-table for* ⇒:

P	Q	$P \Rightarrow Q$
0	0	1
0	1	1
1	0	0
1	1	1

Hence an implication $P \Rightarrow Q$ is always true, *except* when P is true but Q is false.

In ordinary language, 'if ...then' has a double meaning. Imagine that you say: 'If it is raining, then I will not come'. Often this *also* means: 'But if it is *not* raining, then I *will* come'. It is true that you have not uttered this last sentence, however, a little common sense can lead to the conclusion of this last sentence.

In logic this is *not* the case: 'If it is raining ⇒ I will not come' simply means what it says; what happens if it is *not* raining is not discussed at all.

Furthermore, in ordinary language, there often is a *consequential relation* in an implication. For example: 'If I drink a lot tonight, then I will be ill tomorrow'. This being ill tomorrow is a *direct consequence* of over-drinking.

In logic, such a consequential relation is not necessary. For this reason, some implications may look strange on first sight: 'If penguins can fly, then two plus two equals five'. This is a true implication (because penguins don't fly), which can be seen by looking at the truth-table.

Finally, one last remark about 'if ... then'. In ordinary language, 'if' has a double role: It can mean 'in case' and hence leads to an implication, but it can also mean 'when'. For example: 'If the sun is shining, I feel happy'. This means: '*When* the sun is shining, I feel happy'. And hence, this is not an implication in the true sense.

The difference between 'if = in case' and 'if = when' is rather subtle. We will not go further into such details.

Remark 3.4.1 *The word 'implication' comes from the Latin 'implicere', which is 'to fold in'. The proposition 'P implies Q' means hence something like 'By P, we fold in Q', i.e. 'if P holds, then automatically Q holds too'.*

3.5   The bi-implication $P \Leftrightarrow Q$

The connective ⇔ will also be called *double arrow*. You can treat it as the combination of an implication arrow from left to right and an implication arrow from right to left. Hence, $P \Leftrightarrow Q$ can be described as: 'If P then Q, and if Q then P'. Written as an abstract proposition: $(P \Rightarrow Q) \wedge (Q \Rightarrow P)$. This allows us to calculate the truth-table for $\Leftrightarrow$:

P	Q	$P \Rightarrow Q$	$Q \Rightarrow P$	$(P \Rightarrow Q) \wedge (Q \Rightarrow P)$
0	0	1	1	1
0	1	1	0	0
1	0	0	1	0
1	1	1	1	1

So now, we can distill the following *standard truth-table for* $\Leftrightarrow$:

P	Q	$P \Leftrightarrow Q$
0	0	1
0	1	0
1	0	0
1	1	1

Hence $P \Leftrightarrow Q$ is only true when P and Q have the *same* truth-value (both 0, or both 1).

The abstract proposition $P \Leftrightarrow Q$ is pronounced as follows: 'P *if and only if* Q'. This is a combination of 'P if Q' and 'P only if Q'. With the first, 'P if Q', we have no difficulties. It is the usual 'if Q then P' (be careful about the exchange of the order of P and Q). Formally: 'P if Q' is expressed as $P \Leftarrow Q$, another way of writing $Q \Rightarrow P$.

But now the part 'P *only if* Q' is more difficult. It costs some headaches before understanding what one means here, namely: 'if P then Q', or, in formula-form: $P \Rightarrow Q$.

We illustrate the latter one with an example. Look at: '$x > 5$ only if $x > 4$'. We can read this as: 'x is greater than 5 (only) if also x is greater than 4' or as: 'For $x > 5$, it is needed that $x > 4$'. This is a true proposition, which expresses the same thing as $x > 5 \Rightarrow x > 4$.

Therefore, we repeat the general conclusion: 'P only if Q' is the same as $P \Rightarrow Q$.

Hence 'P if and only if Q' is the combination of $Q \Rightarrow P$ and $P \Rightarrow Q$, which we have expressed above with $P \Leftrightarrow Q$.

As a shorthand notation for 'P if and only if Q' one uses: 'P iff Q'.

Remark 3.5.1 *The connective $\Leftrightarrow$ is called the* bi-implication *symbol, with the Greek prefix 'bi' which means 'double'. Indeed, like we saw above, $\Leftrightarrow$*

expresses a mutual implication, one from left to right and one from right to left.

In this respect, one also speaks of equivalence, *which is 'having the same value' ($P \Leftrightarrow Q$ is true when P and Q always have the* same *value, both 0 or both 1). (See also the end of Section 3.2 and Chapter 5).*

3.6 Other notations

There are alternative notations in use for the various connectives. In this section we describe some of these alternative notations. We use the same order in which the connectives in this book have been listed so far: $\wedge$, $\vee$, $\neg$, $\Rightarrow$ and $\Leftrightarrow$.

For $\wedge$, especially in the field of electro-technology, one also uses the multiplication sign '$\cdot$', for $\vee$ the plus sign '$+$'. This is because the truth-values of $P \wedge Q$ and $P \vee Q$ can be *calculated* from those of P and Q via the multiplication respectively the addition of the values 0 and 1.

For example: When P has value 0 and Q has value 1, then $P \wedge Q$ has the value $0.1 = 0$ and $P \vee Q$ has the value $0 + 1 = 1$. We should hence use the convention that $1 + 1 = 1$, see the table below.

Another possibility to calculate the value of $P \wedge Q$ resp. $P \vee Q$, is to take the *minimum* resp. the *maximum* of the values of P and Q. (We denote the minimum of x and y by $x \downarrow y$, the maximum by $x \uparrow y$.)

We summarize this in the following tables:

P	Q	$P \wedge Q$	$P \cdot Q$	$P \downarrow Q$	$P \vee Q$	$P + Q$	$P \uparrow Q$
0	0	0	0	0	0	0	0
0	1	0	0	0	1	1	1
1	0	0	0	0	1	1	1
1	1	1	1	1	1	1+1=1	1

One can take the truth-value of $\neg P$ to be *one* minus the value of P:

P	$\neg P$	$1 - P$
0	1	1
1	0	0

Remark 3.6.1 *Abstract propositions with only $\wedge$, $\vee$ and/or $\neg$ have a* mathematical structure *which is called a* Boolean algebra. *The calculations that belong to such an algebra are better executed with '$\wedge$' written as '$\cdot$' and '$\vee$' written as '$+$', in the same way we demonstrated above. (In so-called Boolean* rings, *however, it is customary to use $P + Q$ not for $P \vee Q$ (the* inclusive or), *but for $(P \vee Q) \wedge \neg (P \wedge Q)$ (the* exclusive or; *see Section 3.2).)*

The truth-value of $P \Rightarrow Q$ can be calculated by taking the sum of $1 - P$ and Q. In order to calculate the value of $P \Leftrightarrow Q$, one needs a more complex operation, which we don't give here.

The following alternative notations are also in use for $\neg$, $\Rightarrow$ and $\Leftrightarrow$:

- $\sim P$ or $\overline{P}$ for $\neg P$,

- $P \rightarrow Q$ or $P \supset Q$ for $P \Rightarrow Q$,

- $P \leftrightarrow Q$ or $P \equiv Q$ for $P \Leftrightarrow Q$.

3.7 Exercises

3.1 Give the truth-tables of the abstract propositions of Exercise 2.4.

3.2 For which values of a, b and c one gets 0 in the truth-table of

$$(a \wedge (b \Rightarrow c)) \Rightarrow ((b \Rightarrow a) \wedge c)?$$

Chapter 4

The Boolean behaviour of propositions

`Truth is stranger than fiction`

4.1 Truth-functions

We have seen that for each abstract proposition, we can make a *truth-table*. Such a truth-table shows how different truth-values of the proposition *variables* lead to the truth-value of the *whole* proposition. The number of lines in such a truth-table depends on the number of proposition variables:

(1) For an abstract proposition with *one* proposition variable, one needs *two* lines (one for 0 and one for 1). For example:

a	$\neg a$	$a \Rightarrow \neg a$
0	1	1
1	0	0

(2) For an abstract proposition with *two* proposition variables, one needs *four* lines. For example:

a	b	$\neg a$	$\neg a \vee b$
0	0	1	1
0	1	1	1
1	0	0	0
1	1	0	1

(3) For an abstract proposition with *three* proposition variables, one needs *eight* lines. See the two tables at the end of Section 3.2.

In general: a complete truth-table for an abstract proposition with k proposition variables needs 2^k lines for 0 and 1. This means that the number of lines is *exponential* in the number of proposition variables.

To each truth-table, one can associate a *function*, which expresses how the final result depends on the choice at the beginning. The above example (2) gives the following function:

$$\begin{cases} a\ b \\ (0,0) \mapsto 1 \\ (0,1) \mapsto 1 \\ (1,0) \mapsto 0 \\ (1,1) \mapsto 1. \end{cases}$$

Such a function is called a *truth-function* or a *Boolean function*, because the *values* (right of $\mapsto$) can only be 0 or 1. The *domain* is in this case the four-elements set $\{(0,0),(0,1),(1,0),(1,1)\}$, which is the set of *all* pairs (a,b) where $a \in \{0,1\}$ and $b \in \{0,1\}$.

The set of all pairs (a,b) with $a \in A$ and $b \in B$, is called the *Cartesian product* $A \times B$. In our case we have $A = B = \{0,1\}$. Hence we can write $\{0,1\} \times \{0,1\}$ instead of $\{(0,0),(0,1),(1,0),(1,1)\}$.

Remark 4.1.1 *The Cartesian product is called after the French philosopher René Descartes (1596 – 1650), whose name is written in Latin as: Cartesius. He wrote a famous book[1] in which he explained what the 'scientific method' is and why it is important. The character of the book is mainly philosophical, but in an appendix, he applies his own ideas to develop a relevant new area for that time: the analytical method, which is the theory of algebraic similarities and their relation with geometry.*

Let us call the above function f. Then for example, it holds that $f(0,1) = 1$. From this, we see that the choice $a = 0$ and $b = 1$ leads to the value 1 for the whole proposition $\neg a \vee b$.

If we do the same for the abstract proposition $(a \wedge b) \vee c$ (see Section 3.2), then we get as domain for (a,b,c) a set of eight elements:

$\{(0,0,0),(0,0,1),(0,1,0),(0,1,1),(1,0,0),(1,0,1),(1,1,0),(1,1,1)\}.$

(We can also see this as a collection of all the *sequences* of 0s and 1s, with length 3. Such a sequence of length 3 is also called a *triple*. In general: the

---

[1]R. Cartesius: *Discours de la méthode pour bien conduire sa raison et chercher la vérité dans les sciences*, Leiden, 1637.

collection of all triples (a, b, c) with $a \in A$, $b \in B$ and $c \in C$, is called the Cartesian product $A \times B \times C$. Above, we have dealt with the special case that $A = B = C = \{0, 1\}$. Hence, the above set of eight elements can be denoted in a compact manner by $\{0, 1\} \times \{0, 1\} \times \{0, 1\}$.)

It can happen that *different* abstract propositions lead to the *same* Boolean function. For example:

- The abstract propositions $\neg a$ and $a \Rightarrow \neg a$ have the same Boolean function, namely:

$$\left\{ \begin{array}{l} a \\ 0 \mapsto 1 \\ 1 \mapsto 0 \end{array} \right.$$

See the above example (1).

- Also the abstract propositions a and $\neg\neg a$ have the same Boolean function:

$$\left\{ \begin{array}{l} a \\ 0 \mapsto 0 \\ 1 \mapsto 1 \end{array} \right.$$

(See Section 3.3.)

- Naturally, the same holds for b and $\neg\neg b$:

$$\left\{ \begin{array}{l} b \\ 0 \mapsto 0 \\ 1 \mapsto 1 \end{array} \right.$$

But be careful: this Boolean function ranges over the proposition variable b and is therefore *different* from the previous one, which ranged over a.

- The abstract propositions $a \Rightarrow b$ and $\neg a \vee b$ lead to the same Boolean function. See the truth-table for $\Rightarrow$ in Section 3.4 and the above example (2), which we could summarize as follows:

a	b	$a \Rightarrow b$	$\neg a \vee b$
0	0	1	1
0	1	1	1
1	0	0	0
1	1	1	1

$$\left\{ \begin{array}{l} a\ b \\ (0,0) \mapsto 1 \\ (0,1) \mapsto 1 \\ (1,0) \mapsto 0 \\ (1,1) \mapsto 1. \end{array} \right.$$

It is not difficult to see that this table implies that *any* abstract proposition *of the form* $P \Rightarrow Q$ is equivalent to one of the form $\neg P \vee Q$.

Take for example $P = c \vee d$ and $Q = \neg\neg e$. Then $P \Rightarrow Q$ is equal to $(c \vee d) \Rightarrow \neg\neg e$ and $\neg P \vee Q$ is equal to $\neg(c \vee d) \vee \neg\neg e$. If we now choose values for c, d and e, then P gets a value (0 or 1) and so does Q. But the value of $P \Rightarrow Q$ is then *equal* to that of $\neg P \vee Q$, exactly like that of $a \Rightarrow b$ is equal to that of $\neg a \vee b$ for given values of a and b. Hence, $(c \vee d) \Rightarrow \neg\neg e$ (of the form $P \Rightarrow Q$) has – for every triple of values of c, d and e – the same value as $\neg(c \vee d) \vee \neg\neg e$ (of the form $\neg P \vee Q$).

4.2   Classes of equivalent propositions

In the previous section, we saw that, given a truth-table of an abstract proposition, one can build a corresponding truth-*function*. Different abstract propositions can however give the same truth-function.

We will now turn this around. Suppose we have a truth-function. Which propositions will then represent the truth-table to which this truth-function applies?

For example, take the truth-function f of the previous section:

$$\begin{cases} a\ b \\ (0,0) \mapsto 1 \\ (0,1) \mapsto 1 \\ (1,0) \mapsto 0 \\ (1,1) \mapsto 1. \end{cases}$$

We saw already that the abstract propositions $a \Rightarrow b$ and $\neg a \vee b$ correspond to this truth function. Are there any more? The answer is: yes, even infinitely many. For example: $b \vee \neg a$ (which is not surprising), but also $\neg b \Rightarrow \neg a$. We can still go further: $\neg a \vee (a \Rightarrow b)$, $(a \Leftrightarrow b) \vee b$, etc. (Can you give a few more?)

The set of *all* abstract propositions with the above truth-function f is called the *class* of abstract propositions with this truth-function. We say that all propositions in such a class are *equivalent* (i.e.: lead to the same – Latin: *aequus* – column of *values*, namely the column that you find behind the $\mapsto$'s in the description of the truth-function).

Every truth-function can be related as above to a class of propositions. This class is never empty, and contains an *infinite* number of propositions.

Let us look at another example, of a truth function that we call g, and which ranges over propositions with proposition variables b and c:

$$\begin{cases} b \ c \\ (0,0) \mapsto 1 \\ (0,1) \mapsto 0 \\ (1,0) \mapsto 1 \\ (1,1) \mapsto 0. \end{cases}$$

Also this function corresponds to a class of propositions, all being equivalent by definition. We give some examples: $(b \vee \neg b) \wedge \neg c$, $\neg (b \wedge \neg c) \Rightarrow (\neg b \wedge \neg c)$. If you don't believe it, then follow the above process to check it for yourself.

There is an interesting abstract proposition in this class, namely $\neg c$. That is, there is one in which the proposition variable b does not occur! Still, this proposition satisfies the above scheme, as can easily be checked:

b	c	$\neg c$
0	0	1
0	1	0
1	0	1
1	1	0

So also $\neg c$ corresponds to truth function g! Of course, $\neg c$ fits also in a simpler scheme, namely:

c	$\neg c$
0	1
1	0

Remark 4.2.1 *In this section we always began with the truth-function and afterwards we looked for 'suitable' abstract propositions which fit this truth-function.*

Those who do not want to search wildly like above, can instead look for such suitable propositions in a canonical *(or standard) way. We give here the canonical propositions that can be found from f and g. Detect, with the use of these examples, the standard recipe for finding such propositions. Check also that both examples 'make sense'.*

For f: $((\neg a \wedge \neg b) \vee (\neg a \wedge b)) \vee (a \wedge b)$.

For g: $(\neg b \wedge \neg c) \vee (b \wedge \neg c)$.

You see that this principle works (except when the result is always 0, *see for this case Section 4.4), but the drawback is that you get fairly complex formulas.*

4.3   Equivalency of propositions

We called abstract propositions which lead to the same Boolean function, *equivalent* (Section 4.2). We can also describe this notion of 'equivalence' directly, by means of *truth tables* only (and not truth-*functions*). Suppose P and Q are abstract propositions. How can we decide whether P and Q are equivalent or not? The new procedure is as follows:

(1) Firstly, determine the set of *all* proposition variables occurring in P or Q (or in both). Assume there are n different ones, say a_1 up to a_n.

(2) Secondly, start a truth table, with all of these n variables on top of the n leftmost columns (the columns between the 'double bars'). This table obviously has 2^n lines.

(3) Thirdly, determine in this truth table what the truth values are for the abstract proposition P, and also for Q.

(4) Finally, compare the two obtained columns, belonging to P and Q respectively. If these columns are *equal* – so P has a 0 wherever Q has one, and similarly for the ones – then P and Q are equivalent. If, however, the columns are *different* (even if this is the case in only one position!), then they are *not* equivalent.

From this procedural description it is clear, that $a \Rightarrow b$ is equivalent to $\neg a \vee b$ (see the last table of Section 4.1). Moreover, $(a \wedge b) \vee c$ is *not* equivalent to $a \wedge (b \vee c)$ (see the final tables in section 3.2).

Another consequence of this procedure is, that $a \wedge b$ is equivalent to $b \wedge a$, but *not* equivalent to $b \wedge c$. The latter observation needs some consideration, so think this over carefully!

So now we have two ways to determine equivalency of two proposition P and Q:

(i) Find out whether P and Q correspond to the same *truth-function*.

(ii) Apply the procedure given above, on the basis of a *truth table*.

Of course, these two methods have much in common; both focus on the columns of truth values which belong to the propositions.

Equivalence is important when you are not interested in the abstract propositions themselves, but in their behavior as Boolean functions, i.e. when you are only interested in how the truth/falsity of the whole proposition depends on the truth/falsity of its proposition variables – which is expressed in the column of truth values belonging to the proposition. This is frequently the case in science, particularly in mathematics and computer science: it does not matter much what the proposition looks like; important is what its *Boolean behavior* is.

This means for example that, in practice, a proposition having the form $P \Rightarrow Q$ can be *exchanged* with the equivalent proposition $\neg P \vee Q$, and vice versa. This exchange of one proposition by an equivalent one, is called *calculating with propositions*. We return to this point in detail in Chapter 6.

4.4 Tautologies and contradictions

For a given domain, for example $\{(0,0), (0,1), (1,0), (1,1)\}$ (which is also written as $\{0,1\} \times \{0,1\}$, see Section 4.1), there are *two* truth-functions which have a special place: the function whose value is *always 0* and the function whose value is *always 1*. We consider first the latter function: the function which always gives function-value 1.

For $(a, b) \in \{0,1\} \times \{0,1\}$, this function is as follows:
$$\begin{cases} a\ b \\ (0,0) \mapsto 1 \\ (0,1) \mapsto 1 \\ (1,0) \mapsto 1 \\ (1,1) \mapsto 1. \end{cases}$$

Such a function exists in every domain, for example, if $c \in \{0,1\}$:
$$\begin{cases} c \\ 0 \mapsto 1 \\ 1 \mapsto 1. \end{cases}$$

All abstract propositions that have a truth-function which always returns 1, are called *tautologies*. These are abstract propositions which are *always* true, no matter which proposition variables we use.

When working with logical formulas, it is useful to have a special abstract proposition *without any proposition variables* and which always returns the value 1. We call this proposition True. The proposition True is hence a tautology (always true).

Here are some examples of abstract propositions which are tautologies:

(0) With 0 proposition variables, we only have True.

(1) As tautologies with *one* proposition variable we take:
$b \vee \neg b$ ('to be or not to be'), $a \Rightarrow a$, $a \Leftrightarrow a$, $c \Leftrightarrow \neg\neg c$.

(2) Of the tautologies with two proposition variables we give:
$a \Rightarrow (b \Rightarrow a)$ and $(a \Rightarrow b) \Leftrightarrow (\neg b \Rightarrow \neg a)$

Check that these abstract propositions always return 1, *no matter what* you use instead of a (or b or c).

At the beginning of this section we have also mentioned the other special truth-function, namely the function which *always* gives 0.

For $(a, b) \in \{0, 1\} \times \{0, 1\}$ such a function looks like:

$$
\begin{cases}
a\ b \\
(0,0) \mapsto 0 \\
(0,1) \mapsto 0 \\
(1,0) \mapsto 0 \\
(1,1) \mapsto 0.
\end{cases}
$$

Also here the domain can vary.

Abstract propositions which always return the truth-value 0, are called *contradictions*. We also introduce a new abstract proposition *without any proposition variables* and which is always false: `False`. The proposition `False` is hence a contradiction.

We give now examples of abstract propositions which are contradictions:

(0) With 0 proposition variables, we have only `False`.

(1) As contradictions with *one* proposition variable we take:
$b \wedge \neg b$, $\neg(a \Rightarrow a)$ and $a \Leftrightarrow \neg a$.

(2) As a contradiction with *two* proposition variables we give:
$(a \wedge b) \wedge \neg a$.

Check that these propositions always return 0.

There is also a name in use for the abstract propositions (these are most of the propositions!) which have in the last column of their truth-tables *at least* one 1 and *at least* one 0. These propositions are called *contingent* propositions ('contingent' = 'possibly', 'it depends').

Examples of contingent propositions (see the previous section):
$a \Rightarrow \neg a$ and $\neg a \vee b$;

other examples include:
a, $a \wedge b$, $a \vee b$, $a \Rightarrow b$, $a \Leftrightarrow b$, $(a \wedge b) \vee c$ and $a \wedge (b \vee c)$.

Remark 4.4.1 *In some computer science books one expresses the fact that an abstract proposition is a tautology, by writing it inside (left and right) brackets. Hence, one writes: $[b \vee \neg b]$, $[a \Rightarrow (b \Rightarrow a)]$, but not: $[b \wedge \neg b]$ or $[a \Rightarrow \neg a]$.*

Note the following:

- All tautologies are equivalent. For example, take the tautologies $a \Rightarrow a$ and $a \Rightarrow (b \Rightarrow a)$:

a	b	$a \Rightarrow a$	$b \Rightarrow a$	$a \Rightarrow (b \Rightarrow a)$
0	0	1	1	1
0	1	1	0	1
1	0	1	1	1
1	1	1	1	1

- In the same way, we can see that all contradictions are equivalent (or have the same truth-values).

- However, not all contingent propositions are equivalent. See for example, the truth-tables of $a \wedge b$ and $a \vee b$.

With the introduction of True and False, we can extend our definition of abstract propositions (Definition 2.3.1) with a second *basis case*:

Definition 4.4.2 *(Abstract proposition, extension)*
Basis (case 2): True *and* False *are abstract propositions.*

(The original basis-step of this definition, which said that all proposition variables are abstract propositions, has now become *Basis (case 1)*.)

The words True and False are called *proposition constants*. They can 'take part' in the building of abstract propositions, in the same way as proposition *variables*. The abstraction goes actually less far than with proposition variables like a and b, which can be substituted by well-formed propositions. It will be clear that True can only be substituted by a proposition which is always true (like $0 = 0$ or $x \geq x$) and False can only be substituted by a proposition which is always false (like $0 = 1$ or $x < x$).

Examples of abstract propositions according to the new definition include:

$a \Rightarrow$ False, $(a \wedge$ True$) \Leftrightarrow a$.

We can, for example, specialize $a \Rightarrow$ False to: 'If it is raining, then 0=1', but not to: 'If it is raining, then 0=0' (because '0=0' can only be true) and also not to 'If it is raining, then $x > 2$' (because $x > 2$ can either be true or false).

Below we give the truth-tables for the above propositions. By doing so, we see that the first example is a contingent proposition, and the second is a tautology:

a	False	$a \Rightarrow$ False	True	$a \wedge$ True	$(a \wedge$ True$) \Leftrightarrow a$
0	0	1	1	0	1
1	0	0	1	1	1

Note that $a \Rightarrow$ False has the same truth-values as $\neg a$.

On page 38 we give a diagram where each block represents a class of equivalent propositions. There is *one* class of tautologies, *one* class of contradictions, but there are *infinitely many* classes of contingencies. These infinitely many classes cannot all be drawn, of course: we use a dotted line to express this infinite number.

4.5   Exercises

4.1 Which Boolean functions correspond to:

(a) $a \Rightarrow \neg b$

(b) $\neg(a \wedge b)$

(c) $a \wedge (b \vee c)$

(d) $\neg a \vee (a \wedge \neg c)$

4.2 Which abstract propositions in Exercise 4.1 are equivalent?

4.3 Look at the 16 truth-functions

$$\left\{ \begin{array}{l} a\ b \\ (0,0) \mapsto k \\ (0,1) \mapsto l \\ (1,0) \mapsto m \\ (1,1) \mapsto n \end{array} \right.$$

with $k, l, m, n \in \{0, 1\}$.

Give for each of these truth-functions a (simple) corresponding abstract proposition.

4.4 Show the equivalence of

(a) $\neg(b \vee \neg c)$ and $\neg b \wedge c$

(b) $\neg(a \Leftrightarrow b)$ and $\neg a \Leftrightarrow b$

(c) $(a \wedge b) \vee a$ and a

(d) $(a \vee b) \wedge a$ and a

(e) $a \Rightarrow (b \Rightarrow a)$ and $a \Rightarrow a$

(f) $(a \wedge b) \vee b$ and $(b \wedge c) \vee (b \wedge \neg c)$.

4.5 Give an example of a tautology with only proposition letter a, without `True` or `False`, and with only parentheses and

(a) connective $\Rightarrow$

(b) connectives $\vee$ and $\neg$

(c) connectives $\wedge$ and $\neg$

(d) connective $\Leftrightarrow$

4.6 Show the equivalence of

(a) `False` $\Rightarrow a$ and   `True`

(b) `True` $\Rightarrow a$ and a

(c) $a \Rightarrow$ `False`   and $\neg a$

(d) $a \Rightarrow$ `True`   and   `True`

4.7 Show that every abstract proposition which is built only with proposition letter a and connective $\Rightarrow$, is either a tautology, or equivalent to a (hence a contingency).

4.8 (a) Show that there are infinitely many classes of equivalent propositions.

(b) Show that every class of equivalent propositions has infinitely many propositions.

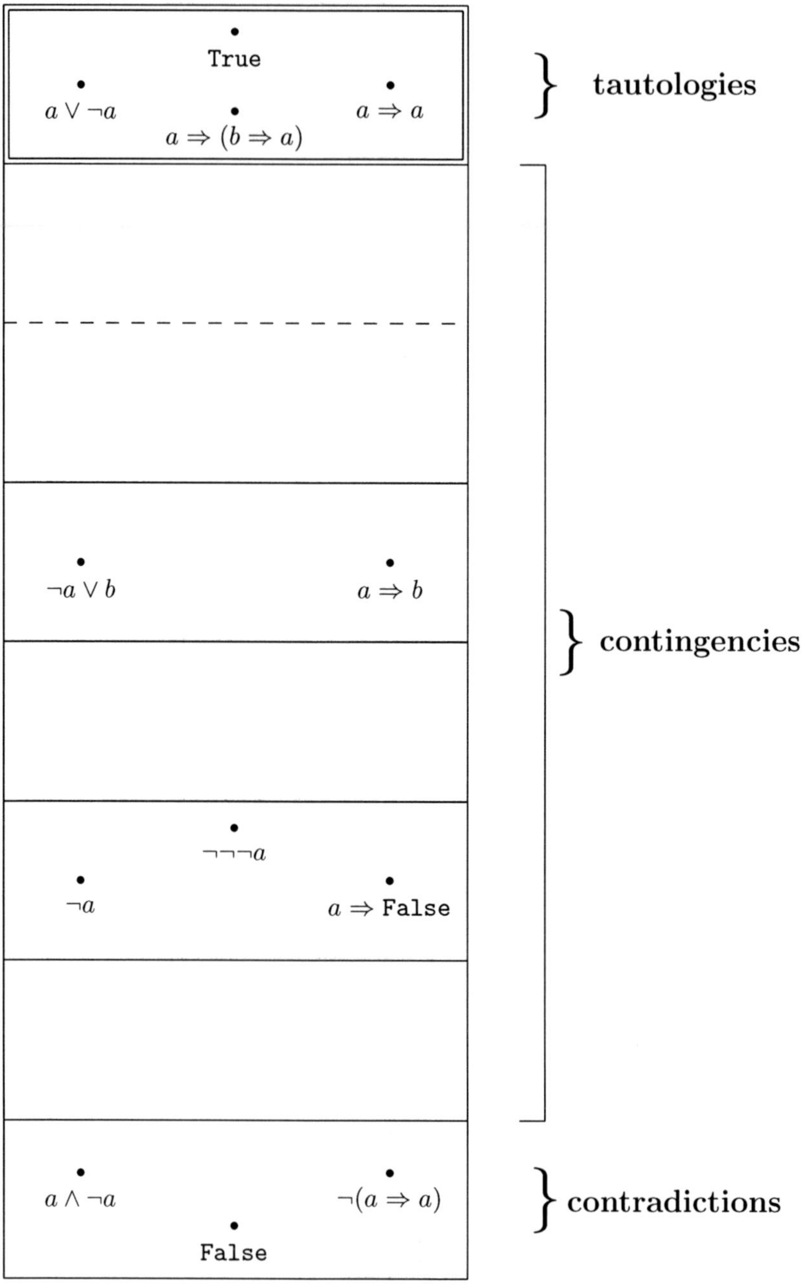

True
$a \vee \neg a$
$a \Rightarrow a$
$a \Rightarrow (b \Rightarrow a)$
tautologies
$\neg a \vee b$
$a \Rightarrow b$
contingencies
$\neg\neg\neg a$
$\neg a$
$a \Rightarrow$ False
$a \wedge \neg a$
$\neg(a \Rightarrow a)$
False
contradictions

Chapter 5

Standard equivalences

```
Too good to be true
```

5.1 Commutativity, associativity

In this chapter we discuss a few cases of *equivalences* between abstract propositions. In order to remain as general as possible, we use capital letters: P, Q, etc., to denote 'arbitrary' abstract propositions. The letter P can hence represent every abstract proposition, from `True`, `False`, a or b to $\neg a \vee (a \Rightarrow b)$ etc. With the letters P, Q, etc. we can introduce complex abstract propositions by adding connectives, for example $P \wedge Q$.

We use in this book the symbol $\overset{val}{=\!=\!=}$ to express the concept 'has the same truth-value as' or 'is equivalent to'. Be careful: $\overset{val}{=\!=\!=}$ is not a symbol of the logic itself, but a symbol from the so-called *meta-logic*. We insert it as a symbol *between* logical formulas, in order to to speak *about* these logical formulas. (The Greek word 'meta' means 'about'). So $\overset{val}{=\!=\!=}$ specifies a relation holding between logical formulas. Hence formulas of the form $P \overset{val}{=\!=\!=} Q$ are *not* abstract propositions themselves. They only express that propositions P and Q have always the same truth-values: when the *one* has truth-value 1 then the other will also have truth-value 1, the same holds for the truth-value 0. ('val' is a shorthand for 'value'.)

Remark 5.1.1 *One usually gives a meta-symbol such as $\overset{val}{=\!=\!=}$ a lower priority (see Section 2.5) than all 'language symbols', such as the connectives. Hence we should read $P \overset{val}{=\!=\!=} Q \wedge R$ as $P \overset{val}{=\!=\!=} (Q \wedge R)$.*

We start with simple cases of propositions that have the same truth-values, and which are also intuitively obvious:

> **Commutativity:**
> $$P \wedge Q \overset{val}{=\!=} Q \wedge P,$$
> $$P \vee Q \overset{val}{=\!=} Q \vee P,$$
> $$P \Leftrightarrow Q \overset{val}{=\!=} Q \Leftrightarrow P.$$

Note that the $\Rightarrow$ is missing here: $P \Rightarrow Q$ does *not* have the same truth-value as $Q \Rightarrow P$; see the corresponding truth-tables, which differ in the last column:

P	Q	$P \Rightarrow Q$
0	0	1
0	1	1
1	0	0
1	1	1

P	Q	$Q \Rightarrow P$
0	0	1
0	1	0
1	0	1
1	1	1

The Commutativity rules are easy to remember because as you may have noticed, the connectives $\wedge$, $\vee$ and $\Leftrightarrow$ are their own mirror image on the vertical axis. (This is not the case though for the connective $\Rightarrow$.)

Remark 5.1.2 *The word 'commutativity' comes from the Latin word 'commutare', which is 'to exchange'.*

Other very common cases of 'having the same truth-values as' or 'being equivalent to' include:

> **Associativity:**
> $$(P \wedge Q) \wedge R \overset{val}{=\!=} P \wedge (Q \wedge R),$$
> $$(P \vee Q) \vee R \overset{val}{=\!=} P \vee (Q \vee R),$$
> $$(P \Leftrightarrow Q) \Leftrightarrow R \overset{val}{=\!=} P \Leftrightarrow (Q \Leftrightarrow R)$$

Again, $\Rightarrow$ is missing here.

Remark 5.1.3 *The word 'associativity' comes from the Latin word 'associare', which means 'to associate', 'to relate'.*

We illustrate the last of the three Associativity equivalences with a truth-table (see below: under the headings $(P \Leftrightarrow Q) \Leftrightarrow R$ and $P \Leftrightarrow (Q \Leftrightarrow R)$ there are two equal columns):

P	Q	R	$P \Leftrightarrow Q$	$(P \Leftrightarrow Q) \Leftrightarrow R$	$Q \Leftrightarrow R$	$P \Leftrightarrow (Q \Leftrightarrow R)$
0	0	0	1	0	1	0
0	0	1	1	1	0	1
0	1	0	0	1	0	1
0	1	1	0	0	1	0
1	0	0	0	1	1	1
1	0	1	0	0	0	0
1	1	0	1	0	0	0
1	1	1	1	1	1	1

Remark 5.1.4 *We will soon explain a method with which we can 'exchange' a formula with another equivalent one. There, we shall use as much as necessary the Commutativity rule and the Associativity rule, but without saying so. For example, we write $b \vee (a \Rightarrow c)$ instead of $(a \Rightarrow c) \vee b$ without giving a reason (this reason would have been: 'Commutativity').*

With the Associativity rule, we will even go further: we write for example: $P \wedge Q \wedge R$ without explaining how the parentheses are written: $(P \wedge Q) \wedge R$ or $P \wedge (Q \wedge R)$. This is justified because these two propositions have the same truth-values.

For the same reason, one writes $P \vee Q \vee R$ and $P \Leftrightarrow Q \Leftrightarrow R$ without parentheses. Be careful: outside logic $P \Leftrightarrow Q \Leftrightarrow R$ usually means something different! (See the following section.)

Remark 5.1.5 *With the last sentences, we depart from Chapter 2. There, we made sure that a formula can only be 'read' in one way, even if the parentheses were dropped. With formulas like $a \wedge b \wedge c$, this cannot work any more, and hence we avoided such formulas. (Unless we assume the left or right associativity, but we did not want to commit ourselves to these in Section 2.5).*

This is no longer the case. The formula $a \wedge b \wedge c$ can now equally mean $(a \wedge b) \wedge c$ or $a \wedge (b \wedge c)$. These are two different propositions, although they are equivalent, i.e. have the same truth-values! (That they are different shows even more clearly by drawing their trees.)

5.2 Intermezzo: ⇒ and ⇔ as meta-symbols

It is time now to point out that it is common to use the arrow '⇒' as a *meta*-symbol in science, and then not for 'if ... then', but for 'therefore'.

What is the difference?

- *if ... then.* The proposition '*If* I come, *then* I will bring a bottle of wine with me' expresses only the implication. The first proposition, 'I come', can be true *or* false. *I don't need to come at all.* But *if* I come, I will bring a bottle of wine with me (at least, I promise this). I would only have said a falsity if I *do* come and *don't* bring with me any bottle of wine.

- *therefore.* The word 'therefore' is a meta-symbol. It creates a relation between two propositions *of which the first must be true.* Via a *conclusion* the second will also be true. Such a conclusion can be derived on logical grounds, but can also for example have mathematical, philosophical or scientific reasons.

  Example: 'I think, therefore I exist' (Descartes). This means:

  (1) It is true that I think.

  (2) From this I can deduce (on philosophical grounds) the following *conclusion*: It is true that I exist.

The word 'therefore' between two propositions expresses hence much more than only the truth of the implication: it also gives the *truth* of the first proposition and as a conclusion *the truth* of the second proposition.

For this reason it is confusing that '$\Rightarrow$' is not only used for 'if ... then', but also for 'therefore'. Moreover, it happens *in sequence*. For example:

$$x^2 \geq 0 \;\Rightarrow\; x^2 + 2x + 1 \geq 2x + 1 \;\Rightarrow\; (x+1)^2 \geq 2x + 1$$

This is not an example of a string of two implications, but of a 'truth at the beginning' followed by two (mathematical) conclusions. In order to be precise, we have:

(1) It is true that (always) $x^2 \geq 0$.

(2) From this, the truth of $x^2 + 2x + 1 \geq 2x + 1$ follows on the grounds of mathematical laws.

(3) And from this, again on mathematical grounds, the truth of the final conclusion $(x + 1)^2 \geq 2x + 1$ follows.

In short: '$P \Rightarrow Q \Rightarrow R$' in this example means 'P therefore Q, and therefore R'. In other words: we give a *fact* (P), followed by a *conclusion* (namely that Q), followed by another *conclusion* (R). The connective '$\Rightarrow$' is hence used here for a 'conclusion', and not for an 'implication'.

Another example illustrates that it is often more complex than this:

$x > 5 \Rightarrow x^2 > 25 \Rightarrow x^2 - 25 > 0.$

This must be read as follows: *Suppose* that x is greater than 5, then it follows via an intermediate step that $x^2 - 25$ is greater than zero. Hence, the first proposition, $x > 5$, is not a *fact* here, but an *assumption*. The other propositions are *conclusions* which follow from the assumption. $P \Rightarrow Q \Rightarrow R$ here means: '*Assume* P, then *it follows* that Q and therefore *follows* in turn that R'. Again '$\Rightarrow$' is *not* an implication here.

On the other hand, in logic, '$P \Rightarrow Q \Rightarrow R$' means with the left-associative assumption that: '$(P \Rightarrow Q) \Rightarrow R$' *and this is very different*, namely: 'if it holds that: *if P then Q*, then it holds that R'. With the right-associativity convention, this means *again* something different, namely '$P \Rightarrow (Q \Rightarrow R)$' which does not have the same truth-value.

A similar confusion can occur with '$\Leftrightarrow$', which does often not represent the 'bi-implication' from logic, but a symbol for *having the same truth-values*, an alternative for our meta-symbol $\overset{val}{=\!=}$.

Look at a mathematical reasoning of the form '$P \Leftrightarrow Q \Leftrightarrow R$', for example: '$x^2 = y^2 \Leftrightarrow x^2 - y^2 = 0 \Leftrightarrow (x+y)(x-y) = 0$',

with which we mean:

(1) $x^2 = y^2$ is equivalent to (or: always has the same truth-value as) $x^2 - y^2 = 0$,

(2) and $x^2 - y^2 = 0$ is equivalent to $(x+y)(x-y) = 0$,

(3) *from which it follows* that $x^2 = y^2$ is equivalent to $(x+y)(x-y) = 0$.

The last is not immediate in the original formulation, even when we realize that the formula '$P \Leftrightarrow Q \Leftrightarrow R$' is *in this case* a shorthand for '$(P \Leftrightarrow Q) \wedge (Q \Leftrightarrow R)$'.

But be careful: in *logic* (see the previous section) '$P \Leftrightarrow Q \Leftrightarrow R$' is a shorthand for '$(P \Leftrightarrow Q) \Leftrightarrow R$' or of (the equivalent) '$P \Leftrightarrow (Q \Leftrightarrow R)$'. In this case we have a choice, because the last two formulas are equivalent. So remember that '$P \Leftrightarrow Q \Leftrightarrow R$' means in logic something very different from '$(P \Leftrightarrow Q) \wedge (Q \Leftrightarrow R)$'.

5.3 Idempotence, double negation

In Section 5.1 we discussed the commutativity and associativity of '$\wedge$', '$\vee$' and '$\Leftrightarrow$'. We will continue now with other equivalences. The first is called 'Idempotence':

> **Idempotence:**
>
> $P \wedge P \stackrel{val}{=\!=\!=} P,$
>
> $P \vee P \stackrel{val}{=\!=\!=} P.$

Remark 5.3.1 *The word 'idempotence' comes from Latin. 'Idem' means 'the same' and 'potentia' means 'power'. It is actually the case for both $\wedge$ and $\vee$ that the 'second power' of P is equal to P itself. You see this better when you replace '$\wedge$' by the multiplication sign (see Section 3.6): $P \wedge P \stackrel{val}{=\!=\!=} P$ becomes in that case $P \cdot P = P$, and hence $P^2 = P$. In the same way you can write $P \vee P \stackrel{val}{=\!=\!=} P$ as $P + P = P$, again a kind of second-power, but then for '+'. (In Section 3.6 we saw that not only $0 + 0 = 0$ in Boolean logic, but also that $1 + 1 = 1$!)*

Another useful equivalence is called 'Double Negation':

> **Double Negation:**
>
> $\neg\neg P \stackrel{val}{=\!=\!=} P.$

Remark 5.3.2 *'Double Negation' is also called 'involution', after the Latin 'involvere', which is 'to wrap': when P becomes wrapped in two $\neg$'s, it keeps its own truth value.*

5.4   Rules with `True` and `False`

Because `True` and `False` play a principal role in abstract propositions (see Section 4.4), we see them again in standard equivalences. The simplest are:

> **Inversion:**
>
> $\neg\texttt{True} \stackrel{val}{=\!=\!=} \texttt{False},$
>
> $\neg\texttt{False} \stackrel{val}{=\!=\!=} \texttt{True}.$

The rules below say what happens with `True` and `False` if they come across an $\wedge$ or an $\vee$:

> **True/False-elimination:**
>
> $P \wedge \texttt{True} \stackrel{val}{=\!=\!=} P,$
>
> $P \wedge \texttt{False} \stackrel{val}{=\!=\!=} \texttt{False},$
>
> $P \vee \texttt{True} \stackrel{val}{=\!=\!=} \texttt{True},$
>
> $P \vee \texttt{False} \stackrel{val}{=\!=\!=} P.$

Remark 5.4.1 *In* Boolean algebra *(see Section 3.6 and Remark 3.6.1) where* $\wedge$ *is written as '.' and* $\vee$ *is written as '+',* True *stands for the number* 1 *and* False *for* 0. *The above* True-False-*laws then become:*

$P \cdot 1 = P$,
$P \cdot 0 = 0$,
$P + 1 = 1$,
$P + 0 = P$.

Check that this is indeed the case, both for $P = 1$ *and for* $P = 0$.

Another important rule which involves False, is the following:

Negation:
$\neg P \stackrel{val}{=\!=\!=} P \Rightarrow$ False

(Remember when reading this formula that $\stackrel{val}{=\!=\!=}$ has the lowest priority!)

We already saw the equivalence of $\neg P$ and $P \Rightarrow$ False at the end of Chapter 4. The above rule expresses that 'not-P' 'means' the same as 'P implies falsity'.

Other important rules with True and False are:

Contradiction:
$P \wedge \neg P \stackrel{val}{=\!=\!=}$ False
Excluded Middle:
$P \vee \neg P \stackrel{val}{=\!=\!=}$ True.

Comment on these rules:

- $P \wedge \neg P \stackrel{val}{=\!=\!=}$ False:
  P can never be true at the same time as its negation $\neg P$, hence the conjunction of a proposition with its negation is always False.

- $P \vee \neg P \stackrel{val}{=\!=\!=}$ True:
  P or its negation $\neg P$ is true, one or the other. (The $\vee$ is the *inclusive* 'or', therefore in principle P and $\neg P$ can well be true *together*, if it was not for the previous rule which says that this cannot be the case.)

  One speaks of the rule (or law) of the Excluded Middle or the law of the Excluded Third, because a *third* possibility next to 'P is true' or 'P is not true' (somewhere 'in the *middle*', for example 'P is half-true') is *excluded* in the logic that we consider in this book (the so-called 'classical' logic). There are, however, logics where this third possibility is present.

5.5 Distributivity, De Morgan

The standard equivalences from the previous section took care of *simplifi-cations*. This will not always be the case with the rules of this section.

We begin with two rules which deal with a 'confrontation' between the connectives $\wedge$ and $\vee$:

Distributivity:

$P \wedge (Q \vee R) \overset{val}{=\!=} (P \wedge Q) \vee (P \wedge R),$

$P \vee (Q \wedge R) \overset{val}{=\!=} (P \vee Q) \wedge (P \vee R).$

Remark 5.5.1 *The word 'distributivity' comes from the Latin 'distribuere', which is: 'to distribute' or 'to divide'. In the first rule, for example, P and $\wedge$ are together divided over Q and R, because Q becomes $P \wedge Q$, and R becomes $P \wedge R$. One usually says by the first equivalence that $\wedge$ distributes over $\vee$. By the second it is the case that $\vee$ distributes over $\wedge$. Both are hence the case.*

We can of course again check the distributivity rules via truth-tables. That they are acceptable, can be seen by the following example:

(1) 'I come by bike and (I take with me either a bottle of wine or a bottle of whiskey)' $\overset{val}{=\!=}$ '(I come by bike and I take with me a bottle of wine) or (I come by bike and I take with me a bottle of whiskey)'.

(2) 'I take my sister with me or (I take my brother and his friends with me)' $\overset{val}{=\!=}$ '(I take my sister with me or I take my brother with me) and (I take my sister with me or I take the friends of my brother with me)'. This is much more difficult than the previous one! It's a good thing that you have the abstract logic, which can help you in case you still doubt the equivalence of these two sentences.

Note that Distributivity is applicable to *all* cases of direct confrontation between $\wedge$ and $\vee$. For example, in $(P \vee R) \wedge Q$: after applying Commutativity one gets $Q \wedge (P \vee R)$, and this falls under the first distributivity rule.

The following two rules treat the confrontation of $\neg$ on one hand with $\wedge$ resp. $\vee$ on the other. Also $\neg$ distributes in a certain sense, but it 'exchanges $\wedge$ and $\vee$' (this means: $\wedge$ becomes $\vee$ and vice versa):

De Morgan:

$\neg(P \wedge Q) \overset{val}{=\!=} \neg P \vee \neg Q,$

$\neg(P \vee Q) \overset{val}{=\!=} \neg P \wedge \neg Q$

Remark 5.5.2 *These rules are called after Augustus De Morgan, a mathematics lecturer at the University College London, who published in 1847 the book 'Formal Logic'.*[1]

We give now examples from mathematics:

(1) $\neg(x > 0 \wedge x < 10) \overset{val}{=\!=\!=} \neg(x > 0) \vee \neg(x < 10)$, which is $x \leq 0 \vee x \geq 10$.

(2) $\neg(x < 0 \vee x > 10) \overset{val}{=\!=\!=} \neg(x < 0) \wedge \neg(x > 10)$, which is $x \geq 0 \wedge x \leq 10$, or in other words: $0 \leq x \leq 10$.

5.6 Rules with $\Rightarrow$

There are many equivalences that can be constructed with '$\Rightarrow$', we only give the most important ones.

First we give the rules which change $\Rightarrow$ into $\vee$, and vice versa. There, one always sees the appearance of $\neg$:

Implication:

$P \Rightarrow Q \overset{val}{=\!=\!=} \neg P \vee Q,$

$P \vee Q \overset{val}{=\!=\!=} \neg P \Rightarrow Q.$

(Already in Section 4.1 we saw the equivalence of $a \Rightarrow b$ and $\neg a \vee b$. The first implication rule is the general form of this equivalence. In order to check the correctness of the second rule, we can again construct a truth-table, or we can use the first rule: The righthand side $\neg P \Rightarrow Q$ has according to the first rule, the same truth-values as $\neg\neg P \vee Q$, and then we can make $P \vee Q$ with Double Negation.)

Be careful that $\neg$ is always next to the *first* sub-formula. If $\neg$ is next to the second sub-formula, then we lose the equivalence:

(1) $P \vee \neg Q$ is by Commutativity equivalent to $\neg Q \vee P$, therefore to $Q \Rightarrow P$, which is *not* equivalent to $P \Rightarrow Q$.

(2) $P \Rightarrow \neg Q$ is according to the first rule equivalent to $\neg P \vee \neg Q$, which is very different from $P \vee Q$.

The following rule says something about the 'permutation' of both sides of an implication $P \Rightarrow Q$. This can only happen properly if both sub-formulas get a $\neg$:

---

[1] A. De Morgan: *Formal Logic: or, The Calculus of Inference, Necessary and Probable*. London, 1847.

Contraposition:

$P \Rightarrow Q \overset{val}{=\!=} \neg Q \Rightarrow \neg P.$

We can check this with the truth tables. But we can also check it as follows:

(1) $P \Rightarrow Q$ is equivalent to $\neg P \vee Q$ (by one of the Implication rules)

(2) and this is equivalent to $Q \vee \neg P$ (by Commutativity),

(3) which in its turn is equivalent to $\neg Q \Rightarrow \neg P$ (by the other Implication rule).

(In Chapter 6 we shall write such an argument with more structure.)

Remark 5.6.1 *A common mistake is to declare $P \Rightarrow Q$ to be equivalent to $\neg P \Rightarrow \neg Q$ (instead of $\neg Q \Rightarrow \neg P$). One can check that this is not correct by using a truth-table. One can also see this by the following counterexample:*

For x an arbitrary real number, the implication '$x > 10 \Rightarrow x > 0$' is true, but '$\neg(x > 10) \Rightarrow \neg(x > 0)$' (or: '$x \leq 10 \Rightarrow x \leq 0$',) is not: take for x the value 5. However, by Contraposition, the formula '$\neg(x > 0) \Rightarrow \neg(x > 10)$' is true.

5.7   Rules with $\Leftrightarrow$

An important rule about $\Leftrightarrow$ is already written in the first line of Section 3.5. We repeat it here as a standard equivalence:

Bi-implication:

$P \Leftrightarrow Q \overset{val}{=\!=} (P \Rightarrow Q) \wedge (Q \Rightarrow P).$

A useful rule which follows as a consequence is the following:

Self-equivalence:

$P \Leftrightarrow P \overset{val}{=\!=}$ **True**.

This can be seen as follows: First look at the formula $P \Rightarrow P$, the 'self-implication', with *unique* arrow. It holds that:

(1) $P \Rightarrow P$ is equivalent to $\neg P \vee P$, by Implication, and

(2) $\neg P \vee P$ is in its turn equivalent to **True**, by (Commutativity and) Excluded Middle, therefore

(3) $P \Rightarrow P \overset{val}{=\!=}$ **True**.

Take now the formula $P \Leftrightarrow P$, with *double* arrow. This is equivalent to the formula $(P \Rightarrow P) \wedge (P \Rightarrow P)$ by the rule Bi-implication, therefore according to what we just explained above, also to `True` $\wedge$ `True`, therefore to `True` (apply the first True/False-elimination-rule).

5.8 Exercises

5.1 Prove that:

(a) $P \Rightarrow Q$ is not equivalent to $Q \Rightarrow P$.

(b) $P \Rightarrow Q$ is not equivalent to $\neg P \Rightarrow \neg Q$.

(c) $P \Rightarrow (Q \Rightarrow R)$ is not equivalent to $(P \Rightarrow Q) \Rightarrow R$.

(d) $P \Leftrightarrow Q \Leftrightarrow R$ is not equivalent to $(P \Leftrightarrow Q) \wedge (Q \Leftrightarrow R)$.

5.2 In a mathematics book we read:

$$y = x^2 + 2x + 2 \Rightarrow y = (x+1)^2 + 1 \Rightarrow y \geq 1.$$

What is meant here? Are the arrows, implication arrows?

5.3 Check if $\Rightarrow$ respectively $\Leftrightarrow$ are idempotent.

5.4 Give shorter propositions which are equivalent to:

(a) `True` $\Leftrightarrow$ `True`

(b) `True` $\Leftrightarrow$ `False`

(c) $P \Leftrightarrow$ `True`

(d) $P \Leftrightarrow$ `False`

5.5 Show that:

(a) The $\Rightarrow$ distributes over the $\wedge$.

(b) The $\Rightarrow$ distributes over the $\vee$.

(c) The $\vee$ distributes over the $\Leftrightarrow$.

(d) The $\wedge$ does *not* distribute over the $\Leftrightarrow$.

5.6 Show that Contraposition also holds for $\Leftrightarrow$, that is:

$$P \Leftrightarrow Q \overset{val}{=\!=} \neg Q \Leftrightarrow \neg P.$$

Chapter 6

Working with equivalent propositions

As true as a die

6.1 Basic properties of $\overset{val}{=\!=}$

We begin with a proof of a lemma (i.e., an auxiliary theorem), which says that the meta-symbol $\overset{val}{=\!=}$ is *reflexive*, *symmetric* and *transitive*:

Lemma 6.1.1
(1) Reflexivity: $P \overset{val}{=\!=} P$.
(2) Symmetry: If $P \overset{val}{=\!=} Q$, then also $Q \overset{val}{=\!=} P$.
(3) Transitivity: If $P \overset{val}{=\!=} Q$ and if $Q \overset{val}{=\!=} R$, then $P \overset{val}{=\!=} R$.

- **Proof of part (1)** The column of P in the truth-table is equal to the column of P (which is the same) in the truth-table.

- **Proof of part (2)** When the columns of P and Q in the truth-table are equal, then so are those of Q and P.

- **Proof of part (3)** When in the truth-table, P and Q have the same columns, and also Q and R have the same columns, then the columns of P and R must also be equal.

Remark 6.1.2 *The name 'Reflexivity' for (1) means something like 'refer-ring back to oneself': P is in relation with itself (P). The name 'Symmetry' for (2) does not need any explanation. With 'Transitivity' one means in mathematics a* 'transfer-of-property': *if P is related to Q and Q is related to R, then P is also related to R. ('Trans-ire' is Latin for 'to continue'.)*

Now we give an important relation between the *meta*-symbol $\overset{val}{=\!=}$ and the connective $\Leftrightarrow$:

Lemma 6.1.3 *If $P \overset{val}{=\!=} Q$, then $P \Leftrightarrow Q$ is a tautology, and vice versa.*

Proof: When $P \overset{val}{=\!=} Q$, then P and Q have the same column of zeros and ones in the truth-table. Hence, at the same height in these columns, P and Q always have *the same* truth-value (either both 0, or both 1). In the column of $P \Leftrightarrow Q$ there is hence always a 1, and so this is a tautology.

On the other hand, when $P \Leftrightarrow Q$ is a tautology then in the column of $P \Leftrightarrow Q$ there is everywhere a 1, hence at the same height in the columns of P and Q the same truth-values must appear (either both 0, or both 1). Hence, these columns must be completely equal, and so $P \overset{val}{=\!=} Q$.

Example: we compare the standard equivalence $\neg(P \vee Q) \overset{val}{=\!=} \neg P \wedge \neg Q$ (one of the two rules of De Morgan) with formula $(\neg(P \vee Q)) \Leftrightarrow (\neg P \wedge \neg Q)$, denoted φ in the table below:

P	Q	$P \vee Q$	$\neg(P \vee Q)$	$\neg P$	$\neg Q$	$\neg P \wedge \neg Q$	φ
0	0	0	1	1	1	1	1
0	1	1	0	1	0	0	1
1	0	1	0	0	1	0	1
1	1	1	0	0	0	0	1

Since the two columns under $\neg(P \vee Q)$ and $\neg P \wedge \neg Q$ are equal, it follows that $\neg(P \vee Q) \overset{val}{=\!=} \neg P \wedge \neg Q$. The last column shows that the formula $\varphi \equiv (\neg(P \vee Q)) \Leftrightarrow (\neg P \wedge \neg Q)$ is a tautology.

Remark 6.1.4 *The symbol '$\equiv$' is usually reserved for 'being identical to'. It is a* meta-*symbol, used to 'talk about' formulas. Similarly, $\not\equiv$ means 'being not identical to'.*

So we have for example: $1 + 2 \equiv 1 + 2$, because the two formulas are identical; but $1 + 2 \not\equiv 2 + 1$, $1 + 2 \not\equiv (1 + 2)$, $1 + 2 \not\equiv 3$.

Just above the present Remark, we noted in passing that the formula represented by φ is identical to the formula $(\neg(P \vee Q)) \Leftrightarrow (\neg P \wedge \neg Q)$. This is because we introduced φ – right above the table – as a kind of 'name' for the latter formula.

6.2   Substitution, Leibniz

We have introduced in the previous chapter some standard equivalences. We will now see how we can use them.

For this purpose we give two very important *lemmas* about equivalence. The proofs are complex and technical, and so we will not write them down.

We begin with a lemma on *substitution*, which is the *consistent replacement of one special letter (or symbol) by a formula*. We give examples to show what substitution is:

(1) Consider the formula $P \lor (Q \Rightarrow P)$. If in this formula we substitute $P \land Q$ for P, we get: $(P \land Q) \lor (Q \Rightarrow (P \land Q))$. Hence, during the substitution, *all* (old) P's get replaced by $P \land Q$. (Note that we must add parentheses around $P \land Q$.)

(2) If in the same formula $P \lor (Q \Rightarrow P)$ we first substitute $P \land Q$ for P and afterwards R for Q, we get, $(P \land R) \lor (R \Rightarrow (P \land R))$. This is called *sequential substitution*, which is one substitution *after* the other.

(3) Another case is the *simultaneous* substitution, which is the carrying out of two or more substitutions *at the same time*. This usually gives a different result: the simultaneous substitution of $P \land Q$ for P together with that of R for Q in the formula $P \lor (Q \Rightarrow P)$, gives as result: $(P \land Q) \lor (R \Rightarrow (P \land Q))$. Compare this with the previous example.

Remark 6.2.1 *The word 'substitution' comes from the Latin 'substituere', which means 'to put in place' or 'to replace'. But in mathematics and computer science substitution has the special meaning which we have just explained. It is this process of repeatedly replacing one letter by the same formula. (This replacement formula can of course be itself a single letter, but this is not necessary, see the above examples.) With simultaneous substitution more than one letter gets replaced at the same time.*

Now it holds that equivalence is preserved when one substitutes for meta-symbols P, Q and the like (Actually, this is a major reason why one uses these meta-symbols!):

Lemma 6.2.2 (Substitution) *Suppose that a formula is equivalent to another, and that, for example, the letter P occurs many times in both formulas. Then it holds that: If in both formulas, we substitute one (and the same) thing for P, then the resulting formulas are also equivalent. This holds for single, sequential and simultaneous substitutions.*

We have seen at the end of the previous chapter two examples of this:

- $P \vee Q \stackrel{val}{=\!=} Q \vee P$ (Commutativity), hence also $\neg P \vee Q \stackrel{val}{=\!=} Q \vee \neg P$.
  Here we have substituted $\neg P$ for the P in the first equivalence.

- $P \vee Q \stackrel{val}{=\!=} \neg P \Rightarrow Q$ (Implication), hence also $Q \vee \neg P \stackrel{val}{=\!=} \neg Q \Rightarrow \neg P$.
  Here we have substituted Q for P and *at the same time* we have
  substituted $\neg P$ for Q.

Substitution is not as simple as it seems. We must carry it out consistently (for all P's, for example, none can be forgotten and not be substituted for). And we may do it simultaneously as in the last example.

The following lemma does not deal with substitution (for a letter P, Q, ...), but with *a single replacement* of a sub-*formula* of a bigger formula. (Be careful: such a sub-formula can be a single letter like P, but this is not at all necessary!) When we replace this sub-formula by an equivalent one, the resulting 'whole' formulas are also equivalent:

Lemma 6.2.3 (Leibniz) *If in an abstract proposition ϕ, sub-formula ψ_1 is replaced by an equivalent formula ψ_2, then the old and the new ϕ are equivalent.*

In the notation of Chapter 1 this is written as follows:

$$\frac{\psi_1 \quad \stackrel{val}{=\!=} \quad \psi_2}{\ldots \psi_1 \ldots \quad \stackrel{val}{=\!=} \quad \ldots \psi_2 \ldots}$$
$$\text{(the old } \phi) \qquad \text{(the new } \phi)$$

In this picture you must read $\ldots \psi_1 \ldots$ and $\ldots \psi_2 \ldots$ as being *literally the same* formulas, except for that one part where in the one we have ψ_1 and in the other we have ψ_2.

Remark 6.2.4 *This lemma is called 'the rule of Leibniz' or 'Leibniz's law' in honor of G. W. Leibniz, a German mathematician who lived from 1646 to 1716. Gottfried Leibniz developed the principles of differential and integral analysis, approximately at the same time as the Englishman Isaac Newton. With these principles, the foundation of 'modern' mathematics was set up. In addition, Leibniz is also considered as the originator of modern (formal) logic, because he was the first to search for the fundamental properties of the connectives. For centuries, the work of Leibniz has had a great influence on the development of logic and mathematics.*[1]

---

[1]See for example: Bertrand Russell: *A Critical Exposition of the Philosophy of Leibniz*, London, 1900.

Example 6.2.5

- *Because $P \overset{val}{=\!=\!=} \neg\neg P$, then by Leibniz also $P \vee Q \overset{val}{=\!=\!=} (\neg\neg P) \vee Q$. Here, the sub-formula P in $P \vee Q$ is replaced by the equivalent sub-formula $\neg\neg P$, which results in $(\neg\neg P) \vee Q$. Because the sub-formulas are equivalent, then so are the whole formulas.*

- *Because $\neg(P \wedge Q) \overset{val}{=\!=\!=} \neg P \vee \neg Q$, the following equivalence holds by applying Leibniz: $P \Rightarrow (Q \Rightarrow \neg(P \wedge Q)) \overset{val}{=\!=\!=} P \Rightarrow (Q \Rightarrow (\neg P \vee \neg Q))$.*

- *Leibniz and Substitution can occur together: Because $P \wedge \mathsf{True} \overset{val}{=\!=\!=} P$, we also have $((Q \vee R) \wedge \mathsf{True}) \vee S \overset{val}{=\!=\!=} (Q \vee R) \vee S$. We can see this as follows:*

  - *Here, first $Q \vee R$ is substituted for P in $P \wedge \mathsf{True} \overset{val}{=\!=\!=} P$; because of Substitution, it is the case that $(Q \vee R) \wedge \mathsf{True} \overset{val}{=\!=\!=} Q \vee R$.*
  - *Thereafter, Leibniz is applied to $((Q \vee R) \wedge \mathsf{True}) \vee S$ as follows: the sub-formula $(Q \vee R) \wedge \mathsf{True}$ is replaced by the equivalent $Q \vee R$.*

6.3 Calculations with equivalence

In the previous section we saw how the rule of Leibniz allows us to replace one proposition by an equivalent one. This happens very often with the intention of turning the original proposition into a more useful form.

This technique, of replacing one formula by another, is well-known from mathematics. Think of examples like: $(a^3)^5 = a^{3 \cdot 5} = a^{15}$. We will now apply these techniques in logic.

The 'rewriting' of one *proposition* into another equivalent one is called *calculating with propositions*. In order to present clearly the general idea, we will use a scheme, developed by W.H.J. Feijen and A.J.M. van Gasteren. We demonstrate this scheme via the following example:

$$\neg(P \Rightarrow Q)$$
$$\overset{val}{=\!=\!=} \quad \{ \text{ Implication} \}$$
$$\neg(\neg P \vee Q)$$
$$\overset{val}{=\!=\!=} \quad \{ \text{ De Morgan } \}$$
$$\neg\neg P \wedge \neg Q$$
$$\overset{val}{=\!=\!=} \quad \{ \text{ Double Negation } \}$$
$$P \wedge \neg Q$$

Here we have:

(1) $\neg(P \Rightarrow Q) \overset{val}{=\!=\!=} \neg(\neg P \vee Q)$ by applying Leibniz to one of the Implication rules (namely: $P \Rightarrow Q \overset{val}{=\!=\!=} \neg P \vee Q$),

(2) $\neg(\neg P \vee Q) \overset{val}{=\!=\!=} \neg\neg P \wedge \neg Q$ by selecting one of the rules of De Morgan, namely: $\neg(P \vee Q) \overset{val}{=\!=\!=} \neg P \wedge \neg Q$, and applying Substitution of $\neg P$ for P,

(3) $\neg\neg P \wedge \neg Q \overset{val}{=\!=\!=} P \wedge \neg Q$ by the Double Negation rule ($\neg\neg P \overset{val}{=\!=\!=} P$) and Leibniz.

Between the braces, the reason (or the *hint*) for the equivalence of the formula above and the formula below is given. As we already said, Substitution and/or Leibniz are rarely named in the hint.

Note that Lemma 6.1.1 has as a consequence that *each* pair of propositions in the above scheme are equivalent, especially the first with the last. Often, this work begins in order to establish the equivalence of the first and last propositions. Hence, the scheme above can have the following *conclusion*:

$$\neg(P \Rightarrow Q) \overset{val}{=\!=\!=} P \wedge \neg Q.$$

It describes the interesting observation that the implication $P \Rightarrow Q$ is *not* true if and only if P is true and Q is not. (But we knew this already.)

We give a second more involved example. With this example, we show that the proposition $P \Leftrightarrow Q$ is equivalent to $(P \wedge Q) \vee (\neg P \wedge \neg Q)$. In words: $P \Leftrightarrow Q$ holds if and only if P and Q are both true or none of them is true.

$$P \Leftrightarrow Q$$
$\overset{val}{=\!=\!=}$ { Bi-implication }
$$(P \Rightarrow Q) \wedge (Q \Rightarrow P)$$
$\overset{val}{=\!=\!=}$ { Implication, twice }
$$(\neg P \vee Q) \wedge (\neg Q \vee P)$$
$\overset{val}{=\!=\!=}$ { Distributivity }
$$(\neg P \wedge (\neg Q \vee P)) \vee (Q \wedge (\neg Q \vee P))$$
$\overset{val}{=\!=\!=}$ { Distributivity, twice }
$$(\neg P \wedge \neg Q) \vee (\neg P \wedge P) \vee (Q \wedge \neg Q) \vee (Q \wedge P)$$
$\overset{val}{=\!=\!=}$ { Contradiction, twice }
$$(\neg P \wedge \neg Q) \vee \mathsf{False} \vee \mathsf{False} \vee (Q \wedge P)$$
$\overset{val}{=\!=\!=}$ { True/False-elimination, twice }
$$(P \wedge Q) \vee (\neg P \wedge \neg Q)$$

This whole calculation depends on repeatedly applying Leibniz and Substitution, without mentioning these applications! Sometimes this may not be obvious, like the first application of Distributivity above. Remark furthermore that in the above calculation, Commutativity and Associativity were used at many places without being mentioned in the 'hint' (between the braces). In the braces, we may also give more than one reason to explain that we have carried out more than one step.

Moreover, one sees that during calculations, the formulas, especially in the beginning, tend to grow *bigger*. Only afterwards one gets a simplification.

We calculated above with 'abstract' propositions, in which the letters P, Q etc. appeared. This gives general results because substitution (see Lemma 6.2.2) allows us to fill in *arbitrary* propositions, both abstract and concrete, for these letters.

6.4 Equivalence in mathematics

So far, we have only spoken of equivalences in logic: proposition P is equivalent to proposition Q when in the truth-tables, the columns of P and Q are equivalent, this means:

(1) Whenever the truth-value of P is equal to 1, then the truth-value of Q is equal to 1.

(2) Whenever the truth-value of Q is equal to 1, then the truth-value of P is equal to 1.

(Here we have: *When the* one *has truth-value* 1, *then so does the other*. A consequence of this is that: *When the* one *has truth-value* 0, *then so does the other*.)

We can also speak *in more general terms* about equivalence by not speaking about 0 or 1, but about 'true' or 'false', respectively. In such a general case we may have all sorts of domains. Hence, not only domains with zeros and ones, but also domains with for example $\mathbb{N}$ or $\mathbb{Z}$. (The symbol $\mathbb{N}$ is used for the set of all *natural numbers*, i.e. the set with elements 0, 1, 2, and so on. The symbol $\mathbb{Z}$ stands for the set of *integers* or *integer numbers*, consisting of 0, 1 and −1, 2 and −2, …. See also Part III, Section 19.1.)

If we admit this kind of domains as well, this means that truth-tables are no longer suitable, because there are now too many (even infinitely many) possibilities, instead of 2^n.

P and Q are then *equivalent* when:

(1) Whenever P is true in the domain, then so is Q,

(2) Whenever Q is true in the domain, then so is P.

Now we can for example say that '$x^2 < 4$' and '$-2 < x < 2$' are equivalent in the domain $\mathbb{R}$, because for $x \in \mathbb{R}$ it is the case that: '$x^2 < 4$' is true *if and only if* '$-2 < x < 2$' is true. (The set $\mathbb{R}$ contains all *real numbers*. See again Part III, Section 19.1.) The domain $\mathbb{R}$ is infinite again, so it is impossible to check the above equivalence with a truth table, for all x's. We have to rely on other means, in this case the reason would be of a *mathematical* nature.

With this generalization of the concept 'is equivalent to' we can also, as described in the above method, 'calculate' with *mathematical* formulas where in the hints we can have 'Mathematics' (or 'Algebra', or something like that) to express that a certain equivalence has its justification not on *logical* grounds, but on *mathematical* ones. See the following example, where we use (among other things) the mathematical motivation that the formula $0 < x < 2$ is equivalent to the formula $0 < x < 1 \lor x = 1 \lor 1 < x < 2$:

$$0 < x < 2 \land x \neq 1$$
$$\overset{val}{=\!=\!=}\qquad \{\text{Mathematics}\}$$
$$(0 < x < 1 \lor x = 1 \lor 1 < x < 2) \land \neg(x = 1)$$
$$\overset{val}{=\!=\!=}\qquad \{\text{ Distributivity }\}$$
$$(0 < x < 1 \land \neg(x = 1)) \lor (x = 1 \land \neg(x = 1)) \lor$$
$$(1 < x < 2 \land \neg(x = 1))$$
$$\overset{val}{=\!=\!=}\qquad \{\text{ Mathematics (left and right), Contradiction (middle) }\}$$
$$0 < x < 1 \lor \textsf{False} \lor 1 < x < 2$$
$$\overset{val}{=\!=\!=}\qquad \{\text{ True/False-elimination }\}$$
$$0 < x < 1 \lor 1 < x < 2$$

The final conclusion is that:

$$0 < x < 2 \land x \neq 1 \overset{val}{=\!=\!=} 0 < x < 1 \lor 1 < x < 2.$$

This can of course also be seen without a 'calculation' like the one we have just done. However, for more complex situations, calculations like the above can be very useful. This is the case in particular for a research area in computer science to construct *correct computer programs*. This research area deals with 'the derivation of correct programs'.

(A computer program is 'correct' if it does what it was written for. In other words: if the program meets the 'specification', which is the description of what the program must output for a given input. Such a specification can for example be: 'This program calculates the greatest common divisor of two natural numbers different from 0'. These two natural numbers are then the input of the program, and the greatest common divisor is the output.)

6.5 Exercises

6.1 Show that:

(a) If $P \stackrel{val}{=\!=\!=} Q$ and $Q \stackrel{val}{=\!=\!=} R$ and $R \stackrel{val}{=\!=\!=} S$, then $P \stackrel{val}{=\!=\!=} S$.

(b) If $P \stackrel{val}{=\!=\!=} Q$ and $Q \stackrel{val}{\neq} R$, then $P \stackrel{val}{\neq} R$.

(c) If $P \Leftrightarrow Q$ is a tautology and $Q \Leftrightarrow R$ is a tautology, then $P \Leftrightarrow R$ is a tautology.

($P \stackrel{val}{\neq} Q$ means: P is *not* equivalent to Q.)

6.2 Show the following equivalences by calculating with propositions. Always state precisely:

(1) which standard equivalence(s) you use,

(2) whether you apply Substitution or Leibniz, or both,

(3) and how you do this.

(a) $\neg P \wedge \neg P \stackrel{val}{=\!=\!=} \neg P$

(b) $P \stackrel{val}{=\!=\!=} \neg P \Rightarrow \mathtt{False}$

(c) $(P \Rightarrow Q) \vee \neg (P \Rightarrow Q) \stackrel{val}{=\!=\!=} \mathtt{True}$

(d) $P \wedge (Q \vee Q) \stackrel{val}{=\!=\!=} P \wedge Q$

(e) $P \Rightarrow \neg Q \stackrel{val}{=\!=\!=} \neg (P \wedge Q)$

6.3 Show with calculations that:

(a) $P \Rightarrow Q \stackrel{val}{=\!=\!=} (P \wedge Q) \Leftrightarrow P$

(b) $P \wedge (P \vee Q) \stackrel{val}{=\!=\!=} P$

(c) $P \vee (P \wedge Q) \stackrel{val}{=\!=\!=} P$

(d) $P \wedge (P \Rightarrow Q) \stackrel{val}{=\!=\!=} P \wedge Q$

(e) $P \vee (\neg P \wedge Q) \stackrel{val}{=\!=\!=} P \vee Q$

6.4 Show with calculations that $0 < x^2 - 2x + 1 < 9$ is equivalent to

$$x \neq 1 \wedge -2 < x < 4.$$

6.5 Show with a calculation that the following formulas are tautologies:

(a) $\neg (P \Rightarrow Q) \Leftrightarrow (P \wedge \neg Q)$

(b) $((Q \Rightarrow P) \Rightarrow \neg Q) \Leftrightarrow (\neg P \vee \neg Q)$

(c) $P \vee \neg ((P \Rightarrow Q) \Rightarrow P)$

6.6 As Exercise 6.5.

(a) $(P \wedge Q) \Leftrightarrow (\neg P \vee Q) \Leftrightarrow P$

(b) $((P \wedge Q) \Rightarrow R) \Leftrightarrow ((P \Rightarrow R) \vee (Q \Rightarrow R))$

(c) $((P \wedge \neg R) \vee (\neg P \wedge R)) \Leftrightarrow (P \Leftrightarrow \neg R)$

Chapter 7

Strengthening and weakening of propositions

In the truest sense of the word

7.1 Stronger and weaker

In the previous two chapters, the notion of *equivalence* of propositions was the heart of the matter: two propositions P and Q are equivalent if the truth/falsity of P 'runs in parallel' with the truth/falsity of Q. We gave the following characterization:

'P is equivalent to Q' holds if:

(1) Whenever the truth-value of P is equal to 1, then also the truth-value of Q is equal to 1, and

(2) Whenever the truth-value of Q is equal to 1, then also the truth-value of P is equal to 1.

Now it can also occur that for two propositions only (1) holds, but not (2). Example: look at $\neg P \wedge Q$ resp. $P \Rightarrow Q$, with truth tables:

P	Q	$\neg P$	$\neg P \wedge Q$	$P \Rightarrow Q$
0	0	1	0	1
0	1	1	1	1
1	0	0	0	0
1	1	0	0	1

See the last two columns: whenever in the column of $\neg P \wedge Q$ there is a 1, then there is also a 1 in the column of $P \Rightarrow Q$.

We say in such a case that $\neg P \wedge Q$ is *stronger* than $P \Rightarrow Q$ (or also that $P \Rightarrow Q$ is *weaker* than $\neg P \wedge Q$).

Take care however: things go from 'strong' to 'weak', on one hand: a 1 for the 'stronger' implies a 1 for the 'weaker' (as soon as the stronger is true, so is the weaker too). However, when the 'stronger' has the value 0, the 'weaker' can still have value 1. This means that the 'weaker' proposition has *more* possibilities of being true than the 'stronger' one, and this may not be what you intuitively expected.

It is better to look at it this way: *a stronger proposition excludes in general more possibilities*. This means that one can find more zeros in the column of the stronger than in the column of the weaker. (One could say: $0 = \texttt{False} = $ 'excluded'.)

Therefore, the more cases can be ruled out, the stronger the proposition can be.

In order to aid the intuition around 'P is stronger than Q', we give two examples:

- $P \wedge Q$ is stronger than $P \vee Q$ (check this!). In particular, when your god-mother tells you: 'You get a hundred pounds *and* a kiss', she is uttering a stronger sentence than when she says 'You get a hundred pounds *or* a kiss'. (In the last case you may perhaps only end up with a wet cheek.)

  You can also look at it as follows: if $P \wedge Q$ has for value 1, then so does $P \vee Q$ (this can actually only be the case if '$P = 1, Q = 1$'). Hence, in $P \wedge Q$ the cases '$P = 0, Q = 1$' and '$P = 1, Q = 0$' are closed: they return 0. Whereas they give $P \vee Q$ a 1.

- '$x > 10$' is stronger than '$x > 0$'. This holds on *mathematical* grounds: if x is greater than 10, then x is greater than 0, but not vice versa (take $x = 5$). You can also say: '$x > 10$' gives *more information* than '$x > 0$', because if $x > 10$ then you know, apart from x is greater than 0, *also* that x is not between 0 and 10, and also that x is not precisely 10.

Note that with the above definition of 'stronger', it can happen that P is called *stronger* than Q, when in fact it is *as strong as* (i.e.: equivalent to) Q. Something similar holds for 'weaker'.

We express that 'P is stronger than Q' with $P \overset{val}{\models} Q$, and '$Q$ is weaker than P' with $Q \overset{val}{\Longrightarrow\!\mid} P$. The symbols $\mid\!\overset{val}{\Longrightarrow}$ and $\overset{val}{\Longrightarrow\!\mid}$ are again *meta*-symbols, exactly like $\overset{val}{=\!=}$.

In addition, the concept 'stronger' can, exactly like 'equivalent to', be generalized independently of zeros and ones. This is expressed in the following sentence:

> P *is stronger than* Q means: in every case where P is true, Q is also true.

We give now a couple of alternative formulations for saying that 'P is stronger than Q':
– the being true of P implies the being true of Q
– from P it follows that Q (although this 'follows from' must not be taken literally)
– if you know P, then you can derive the conclusion Q.

It is important to realize that some propositions are equivalent to others ('as strong as'), that some are really stronger than others, and that some are really weaker than others, *but that for the majority of propositions none of these three properties hold.* Take as a simple example $P \Rightarrow Q$ and $P \vee Q$. These two propositions are not equivalent, but also neither is stronger (or weaker) than the other. (Check this via the corresponding truth-tables.) These propositions are called *incomparable*.

Remark 7.1.1 *In logical sciences, the symbol* $\models$ *is usually used instead of the symbol* $\mid\!\overset{val}{\Longrightarrow}$, *therefore one writes:* $\neg P \wedge Q \models P \Rightarrow Q$, *where we write:* $\neg P \wedge Q \mid\!\overset{val}{\Longrightarrow} P \Rightarrow Q$ *(see above). One also says in logic:* '$P \Rightarrow Q$ *is a* logical consequence *of* $\neg P \wedge Q$'.
Because we also intend in this book to use the concept 'stronger' outside the logic, we have chosen another notation: $\mid\!\overset{val}{\Longrightarrow}$.

(A side-remark: the same symbol $\models$ is used in logic in order to express that a formula is a tautology. Example: $\models b \vee \neg b$. See also the Remark in Section 4.4 about how a tautology is sometimes denoted in *computer science*.)

7.2 Standard weakenings

As we described in Chapter 5 some standard equivalences, we will in this chapter explain some *standard weakenings*. We only describe the most important ones.

∧-∨-weakening:

$P \wedge Q \overset{val}{\models} P,$

$P \overset{val}{\models} P \vee Q.$

With Substitution (Q for P and at the same time P for Q) and with Commutativity the following follows (see Proposition 7.4.1):

$P \wedge Q \overset{val}{\models} Q$ and

$Q \overset{val}{\models} P \vee Q.$

Recalling the earlier discussion about 'stronger' and 'weaker' ('The truer something is, the weaker it is') it is no longer surprising that False is the *strongest* proposition and True is exactly the *weakest* ('The truest is the weakest'):

Extremes:

False $\overset{val}{\models} P,$

$P \overset{val}{\models}$ True.

We show this with a truth table:

False	P	True
0	0	1
0	1	1

The second is not problematic at all: when P has truth-value 1, then so does True. The first however is more subtle. Does it hold that: 'In all cases where False has truth-value 1, than also P has truth-value 1'? Yes, because the case 'False has truth-value 1' does not arise, and hence there is nothing to check.

The standard weakening rules 'Extremes' show one that, from the point of view of stronger/weaker, nothing is *stronger* than False and nothing is *weaker* than True. The strongest sentence that you can hence utter is a contradiction (for example: '0 = 1!'), the weakest: a tautology ('It can freeze or it can thaw')...

7.3   Basic properties of $\overset{val}{\models}$

In Section 6.1 we gave the basic properties for $\overset{val}{=\!\!=}$. We give now lemmas describing the properties of $\overset{val}{\models}$ and $\overset{val}{\dashv}$ and the connection with $\overset{val}{=\!\!=}$.

We begin with a lemma which says that 'stronger' is the opposite of 'weaker' (2) and that 'stronger' and 'weaker' are reflexive (1a, b) and transitive (3a, b):

Lemma 7.3.1
(1a) Reflexivity of $\overset{val}{\models}$: Always, $P \overset{val}{\models} P$.
(1b) Reflexivity of $\overset{val}{=\!\mid}$: Always, $P \overset{val}{=\!\mid} P$.
(2) If $P \overset{val}{\models} Q$, then $Q \overset{val}{=\!\mid} P$, and vice versa.
(3a) Transitivity of $\overset{val}{\models}$: If $P \overset{val}{\models} Q$ and $Q \overset{val}{\models} R$, then $P \overset{val}{\models} R$.
(3b) Transitivity of $\overset{val}{=\!\mid}$: If $R \overset{val}{=\!\mid} Q$ and $Q \overset{val}{=\!\mid} P$, then $R \overset{val}{=\!\mid} P$.

The proofs are simple. Note that (3b) follows from (3a) and (2).

The following lemma says that 'equivalence' is a special case of 'stronger' *and* of 'weaker':

Lemma 7.3.2 *If $P \overset{val}{=\!\!=} Q$, then $P \overset{val}{\models} Q$ and $P \overset{val}{=\!\mid} Q$. And vice versa: if both $P \overset{val}{\models} Q$ and $P \overset{val}{=\!\mid} Q$, then necessarily $P \overset{val}{=\!\!=} Q$.*

There is a kind of 'transitive relation' between $\overset{val}{=\!\!=}$ and $\overset{val}{\models}$:

Lemma 7.3.3
(1) If $P \overset{val}{=\!\!=} Q$ and $Q \overset{val}{\models} R$, then $P \overset{val}{\models} R$.
(2) If $Q \overset{val}{\models} R$ and $R \overset{val}{=\!\!=} S$, then $Q \overset{val}{\models} S$.

Also these proofs are simple. Give similar lemmas for $\overset{val}{=\!\mid}$.

We saw in Lemma 6.1.3 the relation between the meta-symbol $\overset{val}{=\!\!=}$ and the connective $\Leftrightarrow$ which stated that: $P \overset{val}{=\!\!=} Q$ if and only if $P \Leftrightarrow Q$ is a tautology.

A similar relation exists between the meta-symbol $\overset{val}{\models}$ and the connective $\Rightarrow$, respectively between $\overset{val}{=\!\mid}$ and $\Leftarrow$:

Lemma 7.3.4
(1) If $P \overset{val}{\models} Q$, then $P \Rightarrow Q$ is a tautology, and vice versa.
(2) If $Q \overset{val}{=\!\mid} P$, then $Q \Leftarrow P$ is a tautology, and vice versa.

The proof of (1) follows from the truth-tables: if at every 1 in the column of P also a 1 occurs in the corresponding place in the column of Q, then we can never have the situation where 'the truth-value of P is 1 and the truth-value of Q is 0', in other words, the truth-value of $P \Rightarrow Q$ is never 0, therefore it is always 1. A similar argument applies for the other direction.
Part (2) follows from part (1) and Lemma 7.3.1, part (2).

7.4   Calculations with weakening

In this section we show how one can 'calculate' with weakening, according to a similar kind of scheme to that described in Section 6.3. There are similarities, but also important differences:

Substitution (Lemma 6.2.2) also works for $\overset{val}{\models}$ and $\overset{val}{=\!\!\!\mid}$.

Leibniz (Lemma 6.2.3) works well for $\overset{val}{=\!\!=}$, but **not** for $\overset{val}{\models}$ or $\overset{val}{=\!\!\!\mid}$.

First we give the Substitution-rule for $\overset{val}{\models}$:

Lemma 7.4.1 (Substitution) *Suppose that a formula is stronger than another, and that, for example, the letter P occurs one or many times in the formulas. Then it holds that: If in both formulas, we substitute something for P, then it remains that the one formula is stronger than the other. This holds for single, sequential and simultaneous substitutions.*

Be careful that here, we are talking about *substitution*, and this means that: *all* letters P must be replaced by one and the same formula.

Example 7.4.2 *One of the standard weakening rules expresses the fact that* $P \wedge Q \overset{val}{\models} P$. *From this, it follows with Substitution that for example also* $(Q \Rightarrow R) \wedge (P \vee Q) \overset{val}{\models} Q \Rightarrow R$.

But now the case 'Leibniz'. You would expect that the following general rule holds for $\overset{val}{\models}$ (a kind of 'Leibniz for weakenings', see also Section 6.2), but this does *not* appear to be the case:

$$\frac{\psi_1 \overset{val}{\models} \psi_2}{\underset{\text{(the old } \phi)}{\ldots \psi_1 \ldots} \overset{val}{\models} \underset{\text{(the new } \phi)}{\ldots \psi_2 \ldots}}$$

We give two examples, one where things work and the other where things go wrong:

- $P \overset{val}{\models} P \vee Q$ and also $P \wedge R \overset{val}{\models} (P \vee Q) \wedge R$.

- $P \overset{val}{\models} P \vee Q$, but *not* $\neg P \overset{val}{\models} \neg(P \vee Q)$
  (*instead:* $\neg P \overset{val}{=\!\!\!\mid} \neg(P \vee Q)$).

These examples can be checked with the corresponding truth-tables. For the part between parentheses we also give a *calculation*:

$$\neg P$$
$$\overset{val}{\rightleftharpoons}\quad\quad \{\ \wedge\text{-}\vee\text{-weakening}\ \}$$
$$\neg P \wedge \neg Q$$
$$\overset{val}{\rightleftharpoons}\quad\quad \{\ \text{De Morgan}\ \}$$
$$\neg(P \vee Q)$$

Note that we have used here the symbol $\overset{val}{\rightleftharpoons}$ in the margin in order to express that $\neg P$ is weaker than $\neg P \wedge \neg Q$. This follows (exclusively) by Substitution (hence *without* Leibniz!) from the first $\wedge$-$\vee$-weakening rule.

The final conclusion from this calculation (use Lemma 7.3.3) is indeed:

$$\neg P \overset{val}{\rightleftharpoons} \neg(P \vee Q).$$

The rule of Leibniz does therefore *not* work in general for calculations like the above one with $\overset{val}{\models}$ or $\overset{val}{\rightleftharpoons}$ in the margin. We therefore reserve the rule of Leibniz for the case that $\overset{val}{=}$ appears in the margin.

As an exception, we add the following standard equivalences, which make things easier in some cases. Both standard equivalences *are* an application of the rule of Leibniz for $\overset{val}{\models}$, which *does* hold in these special cases:

Monotonicity:

If $P \overset{val}{\models} Q$, then $P \wedge R \overset{val}{\models} Q \wedge R$,

If $P \overset{val}{\models} Q$, then $P \vee R \overset{val}{\models} Q \vee R$.

These rules are also valid with $\overset{val}{\rightleftharpoons}$ everywhere instead of $\overset{val}{\models}$. This follows from part (2) of Lemma 7.3.1.

Above we gave a calculation with $\overset{val}{\rightleftharpoons}$ in the margin. Such calculations are useful if we want to reach a final conclusion of the form $\ldots \overset{val}{\rightleftharpoons} \ldots$. Similarly, one can make calculations with $\overset{val}{\models}$ in the margin.

Of course it is not useful to use both $\overset{val}{\models}$ and $\overset{val}{\rightleftharpoons}$ *together* in *one* calculation, because this stands in the way of reaching a final conclusion. Example: the following calculation is correct:

$$P \wedge Q$$
$$\overset{val}{\models}\quad\quad \{\ \wedge\text{-}\vee\text{-weakening}\ \}$$
$$P$$
$$\overset{val}{\rightleftharpoons}\quad\quad \{\ \wedge\text{-}\vee\text{-weakening}\ \}$$
$$P \wedge R,$$

but no conclusion can be reached. It even holds that $P \wedge Q$ and $P \wedge R$ are incomparable!

Remark 7.4.3 *One may compare the rule of Leibniz with what happens when calculating in algebra. There for example, for multiplication, a sort of 'Leibniz' holds with equality (if $x = y$, then also $x \cdot z = y \cdot z$), but not with greater-than-or-equal: if $x \geq y$, then we don't know for sure that $x \cdot z \geq y \cdot z$. This depends on the 'sign' of z: if z is positive or 0, then this holds. If z on the other hand is negative, then it does not follow that $x \cdot z \geq y \cdot z$, but that $x \cdot z \leq y \cdot z$.*

A special case of this is multiplication with -1: if $x = y$, then $-x = -y$, but if $x > y$, then $-x < -y$. Hence, also in this last case Leibniz does not apply.

7.5   Exercises

7.1 Check for every pair of the propositions given below whether they are comparable (one is stronger than the other), or whether they are incomparable.

   (a) $P \lor Q$ and $P \land Q$

   (b) False and True

   (c) P and $\neg(P \lor Q)$

   (d) P and $\neg(P \Rightarrow Q)$.

7.2 Check whether the following propositions are valid:

   (a) If $P \overset{val}{\models} Q$, $Q \overset{val}{\models} R$ and $R \overset{val}{\models} S$, then $P \overset{val}{\models} S$

   (b) If $P \overset{val}{\models} Q$ and $Q \overset{val}{\models} P$, then $P \overset{val}{=\!=\!=} Q$

   (c) If $P \overset{val}{\models} Q$ and $P \overset{val}{\models} R$, then $Q \overset{val}{=\!=\!=} R$

   (d) If $P \overset{val}{\models} Q$ and $P \overset{val}{\models} R$, then Q and R are incomparable.

7.3 Show with a calculation:

   (a) $P \Rightarrow Q \overset{val}{\models} (P \land R) \Rightarrow (Q \land R)$

   (b) $\neg(P \Rightarrow \neg Q) \overset{val}{\models} (P \lor R) \land Q$

7.4 Show with calculations that the following formulas are tautologies:

   (a) $(R \land (P \Rightarrow Q)) \Rightarrow ((R \Rightarrow P) \Rightarrow Q)$

   (b) $((P \Rightarrow (Q \lor R)) \land (Q \Rightarrow R)) \Rightarrow (P \Rightarrow R)$

7.5 Show with calculations:

(a) $(P \Rightarrow Q) \Rightarrow \neg P \overset{val}{\models} \neg P \vee \neg Q$

(b) $P \Rightarrow \neg((P \wedge Q) \Rightarrow (P \vee Q)) \overset{val}{\models} \neg P$

7.6 Show with calculations that the following formulas are tautologies:

(a) $(P \Rightarrow (Q \wedge R)) \Rightarrow (P \Rightarrow (Q \vee R))$

(b) $(P \vee (Q \Rightarrow R)) \Rightarrow (R \vee (Q \Rightarrow P))$

7.7 Show with calculations that the following formulas are tautologies:

(a) $(P \wedge \neg P) \Rightarrow Q$

(b) $(P \Rightarrow ((\neg P \vee Q) \wedge (P \Leftrightarrow Q))) \Rightarrow (P \Leftrightarrow P)$

7.8 Show the correctness of the Monotonicity rules.

Chapter 8

Predicates and quantifiers

There is some truth in it

8.1 Sorts of variables

In the previous chapters we looked at abstract propositions. There, we used special 'letters' in order to talk in general terms about propositions.

- The letters a, b, etc. served as *proposition variables*, which we use as basic building blocks for abstract propositions like for example $a \vee \neg b$. Letters like a and b are abstractions of concrete propositions. This means that you can use instead of a and b any 'real' propositions, such as: 'It is raining' or '$x + y = 2$' (for given variables x and y).

- The letters P, Q etc. are *meta*-variables. They are not intended to cover real propositions, but *abstract* propositions. You can therefore replace all occurrences of P by a, but also by $\neg a$ or $a \vee \neg b$. Letters like P and Q are therefore *abstractions of abstractions*, they 'live' at a higher level than a and b.

We can therefore say that a is a variable of abstraction level 1 and that P is a variable of abstraction level 2. (The word 'variable' ('changing') means that it is still not clear what the symbol precisely represents – this can still *vary*. Only when you use something more concrete instead of the variable, it becomes clear what you mean.)

The above letters like a and P act as variables from *logic*. But variables are also used in mathematics and computer science. Even more, this use of variables gives power to these two disciplines. Without variable-letters like

x, y, n, m for numbers (as an example), you can't go far in mathematics. Also computer science depends on these letters: a modern program needs x's and y's in order to carry out commands.

Variables in mathematics and computer science don't usually represent propositions, but *objects*, like numbers, functions or vectors. These variables are therefore *object variables*. They are used in mathematical formulas like $3m + n > 3$ and in computer programs.

Remark 8.1.1 *In programming, one also needs a second kind of object variables which serve to 'calculate' with the help of a computer. These variables, the so-called* program variables, *point to an address in memory. They serve to keep accounts of intermediate results in calculations.*

Values of program variables are also themselves not fixed, they change during the running of the program. Like this, the program variable x can first have the value 15, whereas after the running of the program the value has become 18. One speaks in such cases of different states *of the computer. A state is characterized by the values which the program variables have at a certain point in the calculation, for example $S_1 = \langle x = 15, \ y = -2, \ z = 30 \rangle$. If then the value of x changes from 15 to 18 (and nothing else happens), then S_1 changes to $S_2 = \langle x = 18, \ y = -2, \ z = 30 \rangle$.*

Example: look at the 'assignment statement' $y := x + 5$. This is a *command*, which when run, does the following:

- The program variable x points to a memory location, where a value is present. We look at this memory location to find out what this value is (the answer is 25 for example).

- To that value, 5 must be added (this gives in this case the value 30).

- This new value must be put in the memory location to which the program variable y is pointing; the earlier value in the memory location where y is pointing to is hence overwritten.

By this command, the state of the computer has changed from for example $S' = \langle x = 25, y = 12 \rangle$ to $S'' = \langle x = 25, y = 30 \rangle$.

8.2   Predicates

We divert our attention from propositions of everyday life 'It is a beautiful day today') to propositions in mathematics and computer science. As we explained already, object variables occur regularly in these latter propositions as for example in: $3m + n > 3$ and $x^2 + p.x + q = 0$. Therefore, the *truth* of such propositions cannot be immediately determined. Only when we know what m and n are, can we decide whether the proposition $3m + n > 3$ holds or not. For this reason, one prefers to speak about *predicates* instead of propositions: a predicate like $3m + n > 3$ only becomes a proposition *after the filling* of number-values for m and n. For example: with $m = 1$ and $n = 2$ we get the proposition $3 \cdot 1 + 2 > 3$, which is (by the way) true. With $m = -1$ and $n = 2$ we get $3 \cdot (-1) + 2 > 3$ (which is false).

One can also say this differently: a predicate is a *function* which depends on the values used for the object variables, and which after *saturation* (i.e., replacement of all the occurrences of object variables by values) leads to a real proposition. We shall often give a name to a predicate like $3m + n > 3$ where we express what the object variables are, for example: $A(m, n)$. This is actually done in order to be able to write $A(1, 2)$ for the 'saturation' with $m = 1$ and $n = 2$ (that is the proposition $3 \cdot 1 + 2 > 3$). Therefore *the predicate $A(m, n)$ is a function in m and n*, with 'real' propositions like $A(1, 2)$ as *function-values*. Because a real proposition is always either equivalent to `True`, or equivalent to `False`, we can also say: *a predicate is a function on its object variables, ultimately leading to values in* $\{$`True, False`$\}$.

For a predicate it is also important to say what the *domain* of the object variables is, i.e., what is the set from which the m's and the n's can be chosen. For the predicate $3m + n > 3$ this can for example be $\mathbb{Z}^2$, which means that m comes from $\mathbb{Z}$ and so does n (so both m and n are *integers*), but it can also be $\mathbb{N}^2$ or $\mathbb{R} \times \mathbb{N}$. (In the last case m is a real number and n is a natural number.)

It is always informative to draw for a predicate, a *graph* where it is shown which part of the domain returns the value `True` and which part returns the value `False`. For the predicate $3m + n > 3$ on domain $\mathbb{R} \times \mathbb{N}$, one has for example the graph of Figure 8.1, where the part with `True` corresponds to the fat horizontal lines.

The predicate $3m + n > 3$ has *two* object variables and hence it is called a *two-place* or a *binary* predicate. The corresponding graph is hence two-dimensional.

A predicate with *one* object variable, like $m \neq 4$ on $\mathbb{R}$, is called a *one-place* or a *unary* predicate. The graph which corresponds to it is one-dimensional. In this case the graph consists of the reals (e.g. represented as a horizontal line) where the point with coordinate 4 is excluded. The predicate $m \neq 4$ is always `True`, except if $m = 4$.

For predicates with three or more variables it becomes more difficult to draw the graphs, because we will need to go to third or higher dimensions.

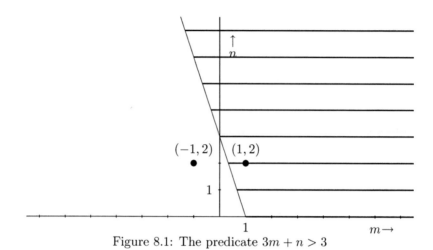

Figure 8.1: The predicate $3m + n > 3$

Remark 8.2.1 *We can also have predicates where* program variables *play a role, for example take the two-place predicate $B(x, y)$ defined by $y = x + 5$ (here '=' is used instead of ':='). The truth of this predicate depends on the state, and hence on the values which are given in the memory to x and y.*

The importance of states and state changes are evident in the assignment statement $x := x + 3$. The corresponding predicate is not $x = x + 3$, with the same x repeated twice, but rather the following: x-new $= x$-old $+ 3$, with different variables x-old and x-new. The variable x-old has the value from the old *state (for example 15), but x-new gets its value in the* new *state (in this case: the value 18). During the execution of the statement $x := x + 3$ the program moves from the old state to the new one.*

*Before being able to work with program variables we must give them a domain, exactly as we do for mathematical variables. For example, **int** for integers (whole numbers), **nat** for naturals (natural numbers) and **bool** for Booleans (the truth-values* True *and* False*). One usually uses the term type instead of domain. For a given list of program variables with their types, we can define the state space as the space occupied by all the types. For example, if x, y and z are the program variables with types respectively **int**, **int** and **bool**, then the state space is **int** × **int** × **bool**. Every 'good' value for x, y and z must come from this state space. For example, if we take $x = 15$, $y = -2$ and $z =$ False, then indeed $(15, -2,$ False$) \in$ **int** × **int** × **bool**.*

8.3   Quantifiers

In Chapter 2 we have seen how one can build new propositions from old
ones by using the connectives. In this section we explain another method
of building propositions. Such a method is based on the use of *predicates*.

First, we give a couple of examples: Look at the predicate $m \neq 4$, where
m has the domain $\mathbb{Z}$. This is not a proposition, it will become one only
after filling a value for m.

Now there are also two other methods of making a proposition from
$m \neq 4$.

- *universal* Put at the *beginning* of the predicate the words: 'For every
  m it holds that...'. This gives here : 'For every m it holds that $m \neq 4$'.
  This is a *proposition*, because it can only be true or false (in this case,
  with m an arbitrary integer number, it is false).

  We write this as follows: $\forall_m [m \in \mathbb{Z} : m \neq 4]$, which should be read as
  the proposition: 'For all m, with m an element of $\mathbb{Z}$, it holds that m
  is different from 4'.

- *existential* Put at the *beginning* of the predicate the words: 'There is
  an m such that it holds that ...'. Hence we get in our example: 'There
  is an m such that it holds that $m \neq 4$'. Also this is a *proposition*
  which is true or false (in this case, it is true).

  We write this as follows: $\exists_m [m \in \mathbb{Z} : m \neq 4]$, which should be read
  as: 'There is an m, with m an element of $\mathbb{Z}$, such that m is different
  from 4'.

The signs $\forall$ and $\exists$ are called *quantifiers*, respectively the *universal quantifier* and the *existential quantifier*. Propositions starting with a quantifier,
like $\forall_m [m \in \mathbb{Z} : m \neq 4]$ and $\exists_m [m \in \mathbb{Z} : m \neq 4]$, are called *quantified
predicates*.

It is worth noting that $\forall_m [m \in \mathbb{Z} : m \neq 4]$ is no longer a 'real' predicate.
You can actually no longer fill a value for m in the whole formula. Try it
out with $m = 5$. Then you get $\forall_5 [5 \in \mathbb{Z} : 5 \neq 4]$ which doesn't make any
sense. To sum up, the one-place predicate $m \neq 4$ (where you could replace
m by 5 say) is made by the $\forall$-quantification into a 'zero-place or *nullary*
predicate', in other words, into a proposition.

One says in this case that the variable m, which was first *free* (hence
'replaceable'), became *bound* by quantification. It is important to classify
in a complex formula which variables are bound and which are free. As an
example of such a formula we take $\exists_k [k \in \mathbb{Z} : k^2 + l^2 = 8]$, in which the k is

bound, but the l is free. This means that the formula is a *unary* predicate ('in l'), and therefore it is not a proposition.

Remark 8.3.1 *The symbol $\forall$ is nothing more than an A upside down, with the 'A' of 'All'. Similarly, $\exists$ is a mirror-image of an E, with 'E' standing for 'Exists'. The word 'quantifier' is derived from the Latin 'quantitas' which means 'quantity'. Indeed, both 'For all...' and 'There exists...' have a lot to do with quantity. 'For all...' is concerned with* total *quantity, 'everything', the 'universal' quantity. For this reason $\forall$ is called the 'universal quantifier'. 'There is...' is concerned with the fact that the quantity is not-empty, there must exist* at least one. *From this fact, the name 'existential quantifier' follows.*

Take some domain $\mathbf{D}$ and let $A(x)$ be a predicate over $\mathbf{D}$ (this means that the variable x has domain $\mathbf{D}$). Then the following holds:

- The proposition $\forall_x[x \in \mathbf{D} : A(x)]$ is *true* if the proposition $A(d)$ is true for *every* concrete $d \in \mathbf{D}$. (Only the d's in $\mathbf{D}$ matter, it is not important what happens to $d \notin \mathbf{D}$.) If $A(d)$ is *not* true for at least one $d \in \mathbf{D}$ then $\forall_x[x \in \mathbf{D} : A(x)]$ is not true either.

- The proposition $\exists_x[x \in \mathbf{D} : A(x)]$ is *true* if $A(d)$ is true for *at least* one concrete d in $\mathbf{D}$. If *no* such d can be found in $\mathbf{D}$, then it is false.

Examples:

- $\forall_m[m \in \mathbb{N} : m \geq 0]$ is *true*, because $0 \geq 0$, $1 \geq 0$, $2 \geq 0$, ...

- $\forall_m[m \in \mathbb{Z} : m \geq 0]$ is *false*, because it does *not* hold for instance that $-3 \geq 0$.

- $\exists_m[m \in \mathbb{N} : m < 0]$ is *false*, because there is *no* natural number m for which it holds that $m < 0$.

- $\exists_m[m \in \mathbb{Z} : m < 0]$ is *true*, because for instance $-3 < 0$.

From these examples it is clear that the domain of the quantifier is very important: the truth/falsity of the proposition depends on the domain.

It is also important to note that the truth of a quantified predicate (i.e., a predicate which starts with $\forall$ or $\exists$) cannot, in general, be decided with a truth-table. If the domain is not too big, i.e. *finite* then we can indeed make a list of all the possibilities for the values of the variables, on the basis of which we can reach a conclusion, but for an *infinite* domain this is no longer possible.

Example 8.3.2 *For the proposition $\forall_m [m \in \{0, 1, 2, 3\} : m^2 < 10]$ we can make the following list:*

m	$m^2 < 10$	*truth value*
0	$0^2 < 10$	True
1	$1^2 < 10$	True
2	$2^2 < 10$	True
3	$3^2 < 10$	True

From this we see that $\forall_m [m \in \{0, 1, 2, 3\} : m^2 < 10]$ is true, because filling any value for m from the set $\{0, 1, 2, 3\}$, gives as truth value: True. Note however, that the construction of such a list only works because the set $\{0, 1, 2, 3\}$ is finite.

Remark 8.3.3 *With this example we can see that $\forall$ is actually a repeated $\wedge$: instead of $\forall_m [m \in \{0, 1, 2, 3\} : m^2 < 10]$ we can also write a repeated conjunction, namely: $0^2 < 10 \wedge 1^2 < 10 \wedge 2^2 < 10 \wedge 3^2 < 10$. Of course, this is only the case when the domain is finite. (If the domain is infinite we get a conjunction of* infinitely *many propositions, which is not allowed as a formula in our logic. Albeit that $\forall_m [m \in \mathbb{N} : m \geq 0]$ can be written in a suggestive manner as $0 \geq 0 \wedge 1 \geq 0 \wedge 2 \geq 0 \wedge \ldots$, this latter expression is no longer a 'legitimate' proposition.)*

Similarly, one can see $\exists$ as a repeated $\vee$. As an example: take the proposition $\exists_k [k \in \{0, 1, 2, 3\} : k^3 = 8]$. It is not hard to see that this is equivalent to the proposition $0^3 = 8 \vee 1^3 = 8 \vee 2^3 = 8 \vee 3^3 = 8$.

8.4 Quantifying many-place predicates

With $\forall$ and/or $\exists$, we can also make propositions from predicates with more than *one* variable, but then we must quantify over every variable.

Example: Look again at the predicate $3m + n > 3$ with $(m, n) \in \mathbb{R} \times \mathbb{N}$. From this predicate we can make a proposition with two quantifiers in eight different ways:

[1] $\forall_m [m \in \mathbb{R} : \forall_n [n \in \mathbb{N} : 3m + n > 3]]$
'For all m in $\mathbb{R}$ *and* for all n in $\mathbb{N}$ it holds that $3m + n$ is greater than 3'),

[2] $\forall_m [m \in \mathbb{R} : \exists_n [n \in \mathbb{N} : 3m + n > 3]]$
'For all m in $\mathbb{R}$ there is an n in $\mathbb{N}$ such that $3m + n$ is greater than 3'),

[3] $\exists_m [m \in \mathbb{R} : \forall_n [n \in \mathbb{N} : 3m + n > 3]]$
'There is an m in $\mathbb{R}$ such that for all n in $\mathbb{N}$ it holds that $3m + n$ is greater than 3'),

[4] $\exists_m[m \in \mathbb{R} : \exists_n[n \in \mathbb{N} : 3m + n > 3]]$
    'There is an m in $\mathbb{R}$ *and* an n in $\mathbb{N}$ such that $3m+n$ is greater than 3'),

[5] $\forall_n[n \in \mathbb{N} : \forall_m[m \in \mathbb{R} : 3m + n > 3]]$,

[6] $\forall_n[n \in \mathbb{N} : \exists_m[m \in \mathbb{R} : 3m + n > 3]]$,

[7] $\exists_n[n \in \mathbb{N} : \forall_m[m \in \mathbb{R} : 3m + n > 3]]$,

[8] $\exists_n[n \in \mathbb{N} : \exists_m[m \in \mathbb{R} : 3m + n > 3]]$.

Note that the truth/falsity of these formulas is no longer obvious! (Find out why [2], [3], [4], [6] and [8] are true, but [1], [5] and [7] are not.)

In quantified predicates with more than *one* variable, we will use a shorthand for the case when a number of $\forall$'s, or a number of $\exists$'s, occur next to each other.

For example:

- For [1] we write $\forall_{m,n}[(m, n) \in \mathbb{R} \times \mathbb{N} : 3m + n > 3]$,

- For [4] we write $\exists_{m,n}[(m, n) \in \mathbb{R} \times \mathbb{N} : 3m + n > 3]$.

The order is not important in these cases, because swapping quantifiers in a *direct succession* of $\forall$'s or a *direct succession* of $\exists$'s gives equivalent formulas. For example, [1] and [5] above are equivalent, and so are [4] and [8]. But take care: a $\forall$ and an $\exists$ may not be interchanged. For example, formula [2] is *not* equivalent to [7]!

In addition, we sometimes omit the *domain description* (which appears between the square brackets, *before* the colon). For example if we have a fixed domain for m and a fixed domain for n in mind, then:

- Formula [1] becomes $\forall_{m,n}[3m + n > 3]$,

- Formula [2] becomes $\forall_m[\exists_n[3m + n > 3]]$, or (omitting an irrelevant pair of square brackets): $\forall_m\exists_n[3m + n > 3]$.

Remark 8.4.1 *It is also usual to omit the domain description* True, *because* True *does not give any 'information' (recall what we said about this in Section 7.2). So for example, we write* $\forall_x[$True$: A(x)]$ *as* $\forall_x[A(x)]$. *Hence, in the case of such an 'empty' domain description, where there is no domain mentioned between the square brackets, there are two possibilities:*

    – There is a sensible, informative domain description, but since 'everybody' knows what that is, we omit it for convenience's sake. Or:

    – The domain is described with True *and hence does not restrict the rest of the formula in any way, therefore we omit it.*

Predicates and propositions, with or without quantifiers, can be combined via connectives with other predicates or propositions. Also the domain descriptions can be combined. We give some examples:

- $\forall_m[m \in \mathbb{N} : m + n < 6] \wedge n > 1$. This is a one-place predicate (in n). (Note that this is a *conjunction* of two predicates: the 'scope' of the $\forall$-quantifier ends *before* the $\wedge$-sign.)

- $\neg\exists_k[k \in \mathbb{Z} : k > 5 \wedge k^2 < 10]$. This is a (true) proposition.

- $\forall_m[m \in \mathbb{N} \wedge m \leq 3 : m^2 < 10]$. The domain description is given here by the formula $m \in \mathbb{N} \wedge m \leq 3$, which is equal to $m \in \{0, 1, 2, 3\}$. The proposition as a whole is therefore equivalent to the proposition $\forall_m[m \in \{0, 1, 2, 3\} : m^2 < 10]$. Both propositions are true.

- $\forall_{m,n}[(m, n) \in \mathbb{Z}^2 : m < n \Rightarrow \exists_k[k \in \mathbb{Z} : m < k < n]]$. This is a false proposition.

Remark 8.4.2 *The notation for universal and existential quantification that we use is particularly useful when proving the correctness of programs (see also Section 6.4). In that case one often employs a slightly different notation, the so-called 'Dijkstra-style'* [1] *format:*

- *Instead of* $\forall_x[x \in \mathbf{D} : A(x)]$, *one writes:* $(\forall x : x \in \mathbf{D} : A(x))$,
- *instead of* $\exists_x[x \in \mathbf{D} : A(x)]$, *one writes:* $(\exists x : x \in \mathbf{D} : A(x))$.

In mathematics one uses other variants, for example:

- *For universal quantification:* $\forall x \in \mathbf{D} : A(x)$ *or* $\forall_{x \in \mathbf{D}}(A(x))$,
- *for existential quantification:* $\exists x \in \mathbf{D} : A(x)$ *or* $\exists_{x \in \mathbf{D}}(A(x))$.

Sometimes, particularly in formal logic, the domain is omitted and one writes something like: $\forall_x[A(x)]$. *(Cf. Remark 8.4.1.)*

Hence, our notation is somewhere in the middle between what is used in logic, mathematics and computer science.

8.5   The structure of quantified formulas

The structure of quantified or not quantified predicates can be expressed in a tree form. This is more involved however than that of abstract propositions (see Section 2.4). We show this with examples.

Figure 8.2: The tree of $\neg(m = 4)$

First, take the one-place predicate $m \neq 4$, which we read as $\neg(m = 4)$. The tree is given in Figure 8.2.

The universal quantification of this one-place predicate is the (false) proposition $\forall_m[m \in \mathbb{Z} : \neg(m = 4)]$. Its tree is given in Figure 8.3.

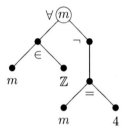

Figure 8.3: The tree of $\forall_m[m \in \mathbb{Z} : \neg(m = 4)]$

The 'main connective' of the formula, $\forall$, appears at the root. The variable associated with $\forall$, namely m, appears in the circle at the root. This expresses the special position that this m has. On the left under the root, one finds the domain description $(m \in \mathbb{Z})$. On the right under the root one finds the predicate $(\neg(m = 4))$ over which quantification takes place.

For predicates with two variables, quantified or not, we can give the structure in a similar manner. As an example we give the tree of proposition number [2] from Section 8.4: $\forall_m[m \in \mathbb{R} : \exists_n[n \in \mathbb{N} : 3m + n > 3]]$ (see Figure 8.4).

Note that the two-place predicate $3m + n > 3$, which is a *sub-formula* of the whole formula, results in a tree which is a *sub-tree* of the whole tree. The same holds for the one-place predicate $\exists_n[n \in \mathbb{N} : 3m + n > 3]$.

---

[1] After Edsger W. Dijkstra (1930-2002), a well-known Dutch pioneer of the science of computing and structured programming. See e.g. his book *A Discipline of Programming*, New Jersey, 1976.

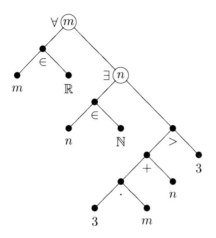

Figure 8.4: The tree of $\forall_m[m \in \mathbb{R} : \exists_n[n \in \mathbb{N} : 3m + n > 3]]$

8.6   Exercises

8.1 The two-place predicate $A(m, n)$ on $\mathbb{R}^2$ is given by:

$$m < 3 \wedge m > n + 1.$$

(a) Check whether $A(2,0)$, $A(2,1)$ or $A(2,2)$ return the truth-values False or True.

(b) Draw a graph of the predicate.

(c) Give a simple formula for the one-place predicate $A(2, n)$. Draw a graph for this predicate too.

(d) Do the same for $A(m, 1)$, $A(m, 4)$ and $A(m, m - 2)$.

8.2 **M** is the set of all people. The following predicates are given on **M** respectively $\mathbf{M}^2$:

$Man(x) \equiv$ 'x is a man',
$Woman(x) \equiv$ 'x is a woman',
$Child(x, y) \equiv$ 'x is a child of y',
$Younger(x, y) \equiv$ 'x is younger than y'.

Give the following expressions in the form of formulas:

(a) Anna is a woman, Bernard is a man and Bernard is younger than Anna.

(b) Bernard has a child.

(c) All children of Anna are girls.

(d) No child of Anna is a child of Bernard.

(e) Bernard has a younger brother.

8.3 Write the following sentences as formulas with quantifiers:

(a) All natural numbers are greater than -1.

(b) All squares of real numbers are greater than or equal to 0.

(c) All real numbers that are greater than 10, are also greater than 5.

(d) If all real numbers are greater than 10, then 0 is equal to 1.

8.4 The same as the previous exercise. $\mathbf{D}$ is a subset of $\mathbb{R}$.

(a) All elements of $\mathbf{D}$ are not equal to 0.

(b) All elements of $\mathbf{D}$ are greater than 10 and smaller than 25.

(c) All elements of $\mathbf{D}$ are greater than 10 or all elements of $\mathbf{D}$ are smaller than 25.

(d) Every pair of different elements of $\mathbf{D}$ differ by at least 1.

8.5 As Exercise 8.3.

(a) There is a natural number which is greater than 1000.

(b) There is a natural number which is equal to its own square.

(c) There is a real number which is greater than 0 and there is a real number which is smaller than 0.

(d) There is no real number which is both greater than 0 and smaller than 0.

8.6 As Exercise 8.3.

(a) For each natural number, there is a natural number which is greater than it by 1.

(b) There is no natural number which is greater than all other natural numbers.

(c) The sum of two natural numbers is greater than or equal to each of these two numbers.

(d) There are two natural numbers the sum of whose squares is 58.

8.7 As Exercise 8.3. **D** is a subset of $\mathbb{R}$.

    (a) If x is an element of **D**, then so is $x + 2$.

    (b) There is an element of **D** which is greater than or equal to all the elements of **D** (i.e. **D** has a maximum).

    (c) **D** has precisely one element.

    (d) **D** has precisely two elements.

8.8 Draw the trees of the following predicates. Write x^2 as $x \uparrow 2$ before drawing the tree.

    (a) $m < 3 \wedge m > n + 1$

    (b) $x^2 + y^2 = z^2 \wedge x \leq 10 \wedge y \leq 10 \wedge z \leq 10$

8.9 Draw the trees of the following propositions:

    (a) $\forall_m [m \in \mathbf{D} : m \leq 10]$

    (b) $\exists_m [(m \in \mathbf{D}) \wedge (m > 2) : m^2 < 15]$

    (c) $\forall_x [x \in \mathbb{R} : \exists_y [y \in \mathbb{R} : y > x^2]]$

    (d) $\forall_m [m \in \mathbb{N} \Rightarrow m^2 > m] \vee (2 + 2 = 4)$

Chapter 9

Standard equivalences with quantifiers

To tell the truth

9.1 Equivalence of predicates

In Chapter 4, and especially in Chapters 5 and 6, the equivalence of two propositions was a very important subject. Everything we said there can also be applied to *concrete* propositions. These concrete propositions are obtained by filling (or replacing) the proposition variables P, Q, etc. by concrete propositions.

The same also holds for propositions in which quantifiers occur. In order to derive the equivalence of propositions with quantifiers, we can no longer use truth-tables (see also Section 8.3). For this reason, we must use the more general definition of equivalence that we already gave in Section 6.4: two propositions are *equivalent* if under all circumstances, they are either both true, or both false.

We give some examples in order to refresh memory:

- In Section 6.3 we showed that $\neg(P \Rightarrow Q)$ is equivalent to $P \wedge \neg Q$.

- From this it follows for example that, for any values of x and y, the proposition $\neg(x = 0 \Rightarrow y > 2)$ is equivalent to $x = 0 \wedge \neg(y > 2)$.

- Also, it follows that $\exists_{x,y}[(x,y) \in \mathbb{Z} \times \mathbb{Z} : \neg(x = 0 \Rightarrow y > 2)]$ is equivalent to $\exists_{x,y}[(x,y) \in \mathbb{Z} \times \mathbb{Z} : x = 0 \wedge \neg(y > 2)]$.

From the second example it seems that we must still generalize the concept of equivalence in order to deal with *predicates* (we have actually seen this already in Section 6.4). We give the definition for two-place predicates. For one- or three-place predicates, a similar definition holds.

Definition 9.1.1 *(Equivalence)*
The predicates $A(x,y)$ and $B(x,y)$ over $\mathbf{D_1} \times \mathbf{D_2}$ are equivalent if for every filling (or replacement) of x and y with values from $\mathbf{D_1}$ resp. $\mathbf{D_2}$, either they are both true, or both false.

For the equivalence of predicates we use the same symbol $\overset{val}{=\!=\!=}$ which we used earlier for propositions.

Example 9.1.2

- *The binary predicate $\neg(x = 0 \Rightarrow y > 2)$ (see above) is equivalent to the predicate $x = 0 \wedge \neg(y > 2)$. In fact, every filling of x and y is a concretization of the abstract equivalence $\neg(P \Rightarrow Q) \overset{val}{=\!=\!=} P \wedge \neg Q$.*

- *It also holds that: $x = 0 \wedge \neg(y > 2) \overset{val}{=\!=\!=} x = 0 \wedge y \leq 2$. This is because $\neg(y > 2) \overset{val}{=\!=\!=} y \leq 2$, which is true not on logical grounds, but because of the relation between $>$ and $\leq$ in mathematics.*

- *Be careful however: The domains are important for the equivalence of predicates. Example: the predicates $x > 0$ and $x \neq 0$ are equivalent over $\mathbb{N}$, but not over $\mathbb{Z}$. In fact, for $x = -1$ the first predicate is false, but the second is true.*

- *The predicates $x = x$ and `True` are equivalent, and so are $x \neq x$ and `False`.*

9.2   The renaming of bound variables

Just like for formulas with connectives (see Chapter 5), important *standard equivalences* exist for predicates, with or without the quantifiers $\forall$ and $\exists$. This chapter deals with these standard equivalences. We will try to make them as general as possible in order to apply them to as many situations as possible.

A one-place predicate $B(x)$ quantified over x, with domain description $A(x)$, is written as follows:

$\forall_x[A(x) : B(x)]$, respectively $\exists_x[A(x) : B(x)]$.

Note that the domain description $A(x)$ is itself *also* a one-place predicate!

In general, A and B can be *many-place* predicates, or zero-place predicates (propositions). We don't want to continuously distinguish A, $A(x)$, $A(x, y)$ etc. and hence we use in this chapter the letters P and Q, without x's and y's. These are the same letters P and Q used for abstract propositions (see Chapter 3), but here they mean *abstract predicates* instead of *abstract propositions*. Always keep in mind that object variables like x and y can occur in P, Q etc. (we just don't say which). We do not take into account whether such an abstract predicate P is one-, two-, many-, or even zero-place.

We give in this chapter the most important equivalences for formulas with quantifiers.

First, there is the rule which says that bound variables can take another name without any problems:

Bound Variable:

$\forall_x[P : Q] \stackrel{val}{=\!=\!=} \forall_y[P[y \text{ for } x] : Q[y \text{ for } x]],$

$\exists_x[P : Q] \stackrel{val}{=\!=\!=} \exists_y[P[y \text{ for } x] : Q[y \text{ for } x]].$

By $P[y \text{ for } x]$ we mean here the formula which corresponds to the predicate P where all the occurrences of the variable x are replaced by y.

With this rule, there is actually a snake under the grass. *You can only use this rule if no variables get in trouble.* We explain this with an example:

Look at the predicate $\forall_m[m \in \mathbb{Z} : m + n < 6]$. Here m is bound, but n is free (see Section 8.2). In fact, the formula expresses a one-place predicate in n. Only when you saturate this predicate (i.e., replace all occurrences of n by something concrete) do you get a proposition.

Now we can replace all occurrences of m by another letter, *but not by n*, because otherwise the difference between m and n gets lost. Therefore for example:

$\forall_m[m \in \mathbb{Z} : m + n < 6] \stackrel{val}{=\!=\!=} \forall_k[k \in \mathbb{Z} : k + n < 6],$

but *not*:

$\forall_m[m \in \mathbb{Z} : m + n < 6] \stackrel{val}{=\!=\!=} \forall_n[n \in \mathbb{Z} : n + n < 6].$

In the same way, you can in $\forall_m[m \in \mathbb{Z} : \exists_n[n \in \mathbb{N} : 3m + n > 3]]$ consistently replace all the occurrences of the bound variable m for example by k or l, but not by n. Similarly, you can choose for the bound variable n any other letter except m.

For example:

$$\forall_m[m \in \mathbb{Z} : \exists_n[n \in \mathbb{N} : 3m + n > 3]] \overset{val}{=\!=}$$
$$\forall_l[l \in \mathbb{Z} : \exists_k[k \in \mathbb{N} : 3l + k > 3]].$$

Note that the above exchange rule holds only for *bound* variables. It does not hold for *free* ones.

Example 9.2.1 *The formula $m+n < 6$ is really* different *from the formula $m + i < 6$. You can't change the free n into the free i, or vice versa, because these n and i can get different meaning outside these formulas. If for example we already had the declaration: 'Let $n = 1$ and $i = 3$', then the first formula would be equivalent to $m + 1 < 6$ and the second to $m + 3 < 6$, and these have evidently different content.*

9.3   Domain splitting

We will now go deeper in the domain description of quantified predicates. The domain description P in for example $\forall_x[P : Q]$ specifies the values that x can take. Therefore P *restricts* the values of x to a fixed set.

In computer science this domain is usually a subset of $\mathbb{Z}$, therefore integer numbers. For convenience, this information will sometimes be omitted.

We give two examples of the restrictive character of the domain description:

- The domain description in $\exists_m[0 \le m < 100 : m^2 < n]$ states that m is restricted to the domain $\{0, 1, 2, \ldots, 99\}$. Note: one is implicitly dealing here with *integer* numbers, and not with for example real numbers.

- In $\forall_x[x \le 1 \lor x \ge 7 : x^2 - 6x + 8 > 0]$ the domain of x is the set of all integer (!) numbers x for which it holds that $x \le 1$ *or* $x \ge 7$.

The following two standard equivalences say what happens to a quantified predicate if you split the domain in two parts:

> **Domain Splitting:**
> $$\forall_x[P \lor Q : R] \overset{val}{=\!=} \forall_x[P : R] \land \forall_x[Q : R],$$
> $$\exists_x[P \lor Q : R] \overset{val}{=\!=} \exists_x[P : R] \lor \exists_x[Q : R].$$

We give examples which illustrate this:

- Look again at the proposition $\forall_x[x \le 1 \lor x \ge 7 : x^2 - 6x + 8 > 0]$. The domain description here is of the form $P \lor Q$. More precisely: we consider x's such that $x \le 1$ *or* $x \ge 7$. The proposition says that the predicate $x^2 - 6x + 8 > 0$ holds for *all* these x's. In other words: it holds for x's ≤ 1 *and* for x's ≥ 7 and vice versa. Hence,

$$\forall_x[x \leq 1 \lor x \geq 7 : x^2 - 6x + 8 > 0] \overset{val}{=\!=\!=}$$
$$\forall_x[x \leq 1 : x^2 - 6x + 8 > 0] \land \forall_x[x \geq 7 : x^2 - 6x + 8 > 0].$$

- In $\exists_k[0 \leq k < n + 1 : f(k) > 3]$ the domain consists of the set $\{0, 1, \ldots, n\}$ (assume that $n > 0$). In computer science, the last element of the domain is often *singled out*: we especially want to consider the 'case' $k = n$. So we use: $\{0, 1, \ldots, n\} = \{0, 1, \ldots, n - 1\} \cup \{n\}$.

Following this, we replace the formula $0 \leq k < n + 1$ by the equivalent formula $(0 \leq k < n) \lor (k = n)$. Hence we obtain:

$$\exists_k[0 \leq k < n + 1 : f(k) > 3] \overset{val}{=\!=\!=}$$
$$\exists_k[(0 \leq k < n) \lor (k = n) : f(k) > 3].$$

Remark 9.3.1 *In addition to the* mathematical *fact that the formula* $0 \leq k < n + 1$ *is equivalent to the formula* $(0 \leq k < n) \lor (k = n)$, *we have also applied* Leibniz *here! The fact that the rule of Leibniz holds also for quantified predicates, will be made official in Section 9.7.*

Check now that the following equivalence, an application of the second Domain Splitting rule, matches your intuition:

$$\exists_k[(0 \leq k < n) \lor (k = n) : f(k) > 3] \overset{val}{=\!=\!=}$$
$$\exists_k[0 \leq k < n : f(k) > 3] \lor \exists_k[k = n : f(k) > 3].$$

The last part, $\exists_k[k = n : f(k) > 3]$, will be discussed in the following section.

Remark 9.3.2 *In computer science, domains are often split for operations that involve repetitions (or* loops*), especially when determining the invariant of such a repetition, which is a predicate that holds for* every *repetition step and describes hence a kind of an over-all property of the whole repetition.*

9.4 One- or zero-element domains

The domain description in $\exists_k[k = n : f(k) > 3]$ is so strict, that there is only *one* choice for k (namely n). In this case the following *one-element rule* is applicable:

One-element rule:

$\forall_x[x = n : Q] \overset{val}{=\!=\!=} Q[n \text{ for } x]$,

$\exists_x[x = n : Q] \overset{val}{=\!=\!=} Q[n \text{ for } x]$.

Because x can only be n, the use of the quantifiers $\forall$ and $\exists$ is superfluous. Therefore $\forall_x[x = n : Q]$ or $\exists_x[x = n : Q]$ can only be true if Q with n substituted for x is also true.

The last example from the previous section can now be expanded further:

$$\exists_k[0 \le k < n + 1 : f(k) > 3]$$
$$\stackrel{val}{=\!=\!=} \quad \{ \text{ Mathematics } \}$$
$$\exists_k[(0 \le k < n) \vee (k = n) : f(k) > 3]$$
$$\stackrel{val}{=\!=\!=} \quad \{ \text{ Domain Splitting } \}$$
$$\exists_k[0 \le k < n : f(k) > 3] \vee \exists_k[k = n : f(k) > 3]$$
$$\stackrel{val}{=\!=\!=} \quad \{ \text{ One-element rule } \}$$
$$\exists_k[0 \le k < n : f(k) > 3] \vee f(n) > 3$$

The next rules concern the case where the domain is so restricted that there is *nothing* left. The domain is empty, which we express by taking as domain description the predicate **False** which *no single* x can satisfy:

> **Empty Domain:**
>
> $\forall_x[\text{False} : Q] \stackrel{val}{=\!=\!=} \text{True},$
>
> $\exists_x[\text{False} : Q] \stackrel{val}{=\!=\!=} \text{False}.$

Of these, perhaps you did not expect the first. However, the equivalence of $\forall_x[\text{False} : Q]$ to **True** can be argued as follows: Does the (arbitrarily chosen) predicate Q hold for all x's in the empty domain (denoted $\emptyset$)? For this we must answer the question (see also the following section): does it always hold that $(x \in \emptyset) \Rightarrow Q$? Yes this holds, because $x \in \emptyset$ is equivalent to **False**, and **False** $\Rightarrow Q$ is a tautology (check this!), therefore the answer is indeed **True**!

Perhaps you don't find such an argument convincing. For this reason, we give another example where we split the domain $\mathbf{D}$ into $\mathbf{D}$ itself and $\emptyset$, the empty set. We use again Leibniz for quantified predicates (see Section 9.7):

$$\forall_x[x \in \mathbf{D} : R]$$
$$\stackrel{val}{=\!=\!=} \quad \{ \text{ True/False-elimination, using that } x \in \emptyset \stackrel{val}{=\!=\!=} \text{False} \}$$
$$\forall_x[x \in \mathbf{D} \vee x \in \emptyset : R]$$
$$\stackrel{val}{=\!=\!=} \quad \{ \text{ Domain Splitting } \}$$
$$\forall_x[x \in \mathbf{D} : R] \wedge \forall_x[x \in \emptyset : R]$$
$$\stackrel{val}{=\!=\!=} \quad \{ \text{ again because } x \in \emptyset \stackrel{val}{=\!=\!=} \text{False} \}$$
$$\forall_x[x \in \mathbf{D} : R] \wedge \forall_x[\text{False} : R]$$

Therefore $\forall_x[x \in \mathbf{D} : R] \stackrel{val}{=\!=\!=} \forall_x[x \in \mathbf{D} : R] \wedge \forall_x[\text{False} : R]$. This makes sense if $\forall_x[\text{False} : R] \stackrel{val}{=\!=\!=} \text{True}$, but not if $\forall_x[\text{False} : R] \stackrel{val}{=\!=\!=} \text{False}$.

(And for those who still think that this argument is vague, we ask them to take this rule as given: we bluntly *postulate* that the Empty Domain rules hold.)

9.5 Domain weakening

Quantifying a predicate $A(x)$ over a domain $\mathbf{D}$ can be done in two ways: via $\forall$ of via $\exists$. By so doing we get the propositions $\forall_x[x \in \mathbf{D} : A(x)]$ respectively $\exists_x[x \in \mathbf{D} : A(x)]$. However, there is an important difference in the *meaning* of the domain description $x \in \mathbf{D}$ in these two formulas. This can be seen as follows:

- ($\forall$) The proposition $\forall_x[x \in \mathbf{D} : A(x)]$ can be read as: 'For all x, *if* x is in $\mathbf{D}$, *then* $A(x)$ holds'. In other words: 'For all x it holds that: $x \in \mathbf{D} \Rightarrow A(x)$'.

  The domain description $x \in \mathbf{D}$ can hence be described as the left hand side of an *implication*.

- ($\exists$) For the proposition $\exists_x[x \in \mathbf{D} : A(x)]$ things are different. Here we have: 'There is an x for which it holds that x is in $\mathbf{D}$ *and* for which $A(x)$ holds'. In other words: 'There is an x for which it holds that: $x \in \mathbf{D} \wedge A(x)$'.

  Now one can treat $x \in \mathbf{D}$ as the left hand side of a *conjunction*.

Hence, if we want to get rid of the domain description $x \in \mathbf{D}$ by appending it to the predicate $A(x)$, we get the following difference:

- $\forall_x[x \in \mathbf{D} : A(x)]$ is equivalent to $\forall_x[x \in \mathbf{D} \Rightarrow A(x)]$,

- $\exists_x[x \in \mathbf{D} : A(x)]$ is equivalent to $\exists_x[x \in \mathbf{D} \wedge A(x)]$.

This also holds if we want to move a *part* of the domain description to the right. This occurs if the domain description is $P \wedge Q$, and we only want to keep P by moving Q 'over the colon'. This gives the following standard equivalences:

Domain Weakening:
$\forall_x[P \wedge Q : R] \overset{val}{=\!=\!=} \forall_x[P : Q \Rightarrow R]$,
$\exists_x[P \wedge Q : R] \overset{val}{=\!=\!=} \exists_x[P : Q \wedge R]$.

(This rule is also called *Trading* (exchanging) because the Q, is moved from the 'middle' to the 'right' (or vice versa).)

Example 9.5.1

- *The proposition $\forall_x[x \in \mathbb{R} \wedge x > -1 \wedge x \neq 1 : x^3 - x^2 - x + 1 > 0]$ is equivalent to $\forall_x[x \in \mathbb{R} \wedge x > -1 : x \neq 1 \Rightarrow x^3 - x^2 - x + 1 > 0]$.*

- *The predicate $\exists_k[0 \leq k : k < n \wedge k^2 > 5]$ is, again by Domain Weakening, now applied from right to left, equivalent to the predicate $\exists_k[0 \leq k < n : k^2 > 5]$.*

  (Remember here that $0 \leq k < n$ is a shorthand for $0 \leq k \wedge k < n$.)

9.6   De Morgan for $\forall$ and $\exists$

In Section 5.5 we described the 'laws' of De Morgan, which express what happens when a negation (with sign $\neg$) hits a conjunction ($\wedge$) or a disjunction ($\vee$). We repeat these rules here:

- $\neg(P \wedge Q) \stackrel{val}{=\!=\!=} \neg P \vee \neg Q,$

- $\neg(P \vee Q) \stackrel{val}{=\!=\!=} \neg P \wedge \neg Q.$

Note that $\wedge$ on the left changes to $\vee$ on the right and vice versa.

In Remark 8.3.3 at the end of Section 8.3 we saw, that $\forall$ is really a repeated $\wedge$, and $\exists$ is a repeated $\vee$. This we find again in the following standard equivalences for quantified predicates, which we call 'De Morgan' again, because they resemble the rules with this name in Section 5.5:

> **De Morgan:**
> $\neg\forall_x[P : Q] \stackrel{val}{=\!=\!=} \exists_x[P : \neg Q],$
> $\neg\exists_x[P : Q] \stackrel{val}{=\!=\!=} \forall_x[P : \neg Q].$

These standard equivalences say, read from left to right, what happens when we move a $\neg$ 'to the inside'. The $\neg$ sticks in this case to Q (*not to the domain description P!*) whereas the quantifier 'flips over': $\forall$ becomes $\exists$ and vice versa. This 'flipping over' of the quantifier looks a lot like the change of $\wedge$ to $\vee$ (and vice versa) in the 'old' case of De Morgan.

We give a description in words which expresses that these new rules of De Morgan are actually quite obvious:

- ($\neg\forall = \exists\neg$) If in a certain domain *not all* x's satisfy Q, then there must be x's in that domain such that $\neg Q$ holds, and vice versa. That is: 'not every = some not'.

- $(\neg\exists = \forall\neg)$ If in a certain domain there are *no* x's for which Q holds, then in that domain all x's must satisfy $\neg Q$. That is: 'not *one* = every not'.

A side remark: note that 'not every' is completely different from 'every not'. The same can be said for 'at least one not' (= 'some not') and 'not at least *one*' (= 'none').

Example 9.6.1

- $\neg\forall_n[n \in \mathbb{N} : n > p] \overset{val}{=\!=\!=} \exists_n[n \in \mathbb{N} : n \le p]$,
- $\neg\exists_n[n \in \mathbb{N} : n^2 = 3] \overset{val}{=\!=\!=} \forall_n[n \in \mathbb{N} : n^2 \ne 3]$.

(Here we implicitly use mathematical truths like $\neg(n > p) \overset{val}{=\!=\!=} n \le p$.*)*

With the help of the rules of De Morgan we can do the following calculation:

$$\neg\forall_x[x \in \mathbf{D} : \neg P]$$
$$\overset{val}{=\!=\!=}\qquad \{\text{ De Morgan}\}$$
$$\exists_x[x \in \mathbf{D} : \neg\neg P]$$
$$\overset{val}{=\!=\!=}\qquad \{\text{ Double Negation (and Leibniz) }\}$$
$$\exists_x[x \in \mathbf{D} : P]$$

The conclusion is:
$$\neg\forall_x[x \in \mathbf{D} : \neg P] \overset{val}{=\!=\!=} \exists_x[x \in \mathbf{D} : P],$$

In words: 'not every not = at least *one*'. This equivalence is sometimes written like $\neg\forall\neg = \exists$.

The 'mirror-image' calculation is:

$$\neg\exists_x[x \in \mathbf{D} : \neg P]$$
$$\overset{val}{=\!=\!=}\qquad \{\text{ De Morgan}\}$$
$$\forall_x[x \in \mathbf{D} : \neg\neg P]$$
$$\overset{val}{=\!=\!=}\qquad \{\text{ Double Negation (and Leibniz) }\}$$
$$\forall_x[x \in \mathbf{D} : P]$$

The conclusion is:
$$\neg\exists_x[x \in \mathbf{D} : \neg P] \overset{val}{=\!=\!=} \forall_x[x \in \mathbf{D} : P].$$

In words: 'not *one* not = every', also written as $\neg\exists\neg = \forall$.

Also in the last two conclusions the domain $\mathbf{D}$ does not actually take part; it remains unchanged.

9.7   Substitution and Leibniz for quantifications

The rules of Substitution and Leibniz (see Section 6.2) hold also for quantified predicates.

We give some examples, first for the Substitution rule:

- According to Domain Splitting we have:

  $$\forall_x[P \vee Q : R] \stackrel{val}{=\!=\!=} \forall_x[P : R] \wedge \forall_x[Q : R].$$

  And from this we can deduce with Substitution, to be precise (simultaneously): $[Q$ for P, $\neg P$ for Q, $R \Rightarrow S$ for $R]$, that

  $$\forall_x[Q \vee \neg P : R \Rightarrow S] \stackrel{val}{=\!=\!=} \forall_x[Q : R \Rightarrow S] \wedge \forall_x[\neg P : R \Rightarrow S].$$

- From the same Domain Splitting rule it follows also by Substitution, namely (simultaneously): $[x > y$ for P, $x < z$ for Q, Q for $R]$, that

  $$\forall_x[x > y \vee x < z : Q] \stackrel{val}{=\!=\!=} \forall_x[x > y : Q] \wedge \forall_x[x < z : Q].$$

You see that substitutions are allowed, both in the domain description on the left of the colon, and in the predicates on the right of the colon.

Something similar happens for the rule of Leibniz:

- The first rule for Domain Weakening says:

  $$\forall_x[P \wedge Q : R] \stackrel{val}{=\!=\!=} \forall_x[P : Q \Rightarrow R].$$

  Here we can replace with Leibniz the sub-formula $Q \Rightarrow R$ by the equivalent (see Section 5.6) $\neg Q \vee R$, so that we also have:

  $$\forall_x[P \wedge Q : R] \stackrel{val}{=\!=\!=} \forall_x[P : \neg Q \vee R].$$

- From De Morgan and Substitution we have:

  $$\neg \exists_x[x \in \mathbb{Z} \wedge 0 < x : P] \stackrel{val}{=\!=\!=} \forall_x[x \in \mathbb{Z} \wedge 0 < x : \neg P].$$

  Because (from mathematics) the formula $x \in \mathbb{Z} \wedge 0 < x$ is equivalent to the formula $x \in \mathbb{N} \wedge x \neq 0$, we can replace the domain description in the formula to the left of $\stackrel{val}{=\!=\!=}$, by applying Leibniz:

  $$\neg \exists_x[x \in \mathbb{N} \wedge x \neq 0 : P] \stackrel{val}{=\!=\!=} \forall_x[x \in \mathbb{Z} \wedge 0 < x : \neg P].$$

  (We can also change both domain descriptions – the one to the left *and* the one to the right of $\stackrel{val}{=\!=\!=}$ – by applying Leibniz twice.)

9.8   Other equivalences with ∀ and ∃

In this section we describe some more equivalences between quantified formulas which are often used. We don't make them into official *rules*, because we wish to keep our system of rules simple. Moreover, we are concerned in this book with the principles and techniques of logic, and only implicitly with computer science.

We also take the opportunity to give some more *examples* of calculations with quantified formulas.

We begin with two equivalences which illustrate an interesting '*exchange trick*':

$$\forall_x[P:Q] \overset{val}{=\!=\!=} \forall_x[\neg Q:\neg P],$$
$$\exists_x[P:Q] \overset{val}{=\!=\!=} \exists_x[Q:P]$$

Note that with a ∃-formula, the predicates P and Q can simply be exchanged around the colon, but that for a ∀-formula the ¬ sign appears twice.

The reason for this is actually that the Domain Weakening rule for ∃ returns a ∧, and $P \wedge Q \overset{val}{=\!=\!=} Q \wedge P$, but that Domain Weakening for ∀ returns a ⇒, for which we have: $P \Rightarrow Q \overset{val}{=\!=\!=} \neg Q \Rightarrow \neg P$. See the following two calculations, where this plays a role:

$$\forall_x[P:Q]$$
$\overset{val}{=\!=\!=}$ { True/False-elim. }
$$\forall_x[\text{True} \wedge P:Q]$$
$\overset{val}{=\!=\!=}$ { Domain Weakening }
$$\forall_x[\text{True}:P \Rightarrow Q]$$
$\overset{val}{=\!=\!=}$ { Contraposition }
$$\forall_x[\text{True}:\neg Q \Rightarrow \neg P]$$
$\overset{val}{=\!=\!=}$ { Domain Weakening }
$$\forall_x[\text{True} \wedge \neg Q:\neg P]$$
$\overset{val}{=\!=\!=}$ { True/False-elim. }
$$\forall_x[\neg Q:\neg P]$$

$$\exists_x[P:Q]$$
$\overset{val}{=\!=\!=}$ { True/False-elim. }
$$\exists_x[\text{True} \wedge P:Q]$$
$\overset{val}{=\!=\!=}$ { Domain Weakening }
$$\exists_x[\text{True}:P \wedge Q]$$
$\overset{val}{=\!=\!=}$ { Commutativity }
$$\exists_x[\text{True}:Q \wedge P]$$
$\overset{val}{=\!=\!=}$ { Domain Weakening }
$$\exists_x[\text{True} \wedge Q:P]$$
$\overset{val}{=\!=\!=}$ { True/False-elim. }
$$\exists_x[Q:P]$$

The following two equivalences are called *Term Splitting* in computer science:

$$\forall_x[P:Q \wedge R] \overset{val}{=\!=\!=} \forall_x[P:Q] \wedge \forall_x[P:R],$$
$$\exists_x[P:Q \vee R] \overset{val}{=\!=\!=} \exists_x[P:Q] \vee \exists_x[P:R]$$

The correctness of these equivalences is intuitively obvious and can be seen by realizing that $\forall$ is a generalized $\wedge$, and $\exists$ is a generalized $\vee$. (See also Remark 8.3.3 at the end of Section 8.3.)

For the first of these equivalences, we give a calculation where we use twice the above described 'exchange trick'. (Give a calculation yourself for the second equivalence.)

$$\forall_x[P:Q] \wedge \forall_x[P:R]$$
$$\overset{val}{=\!=\!=} \quad \{ \text{ 'exchange trick', twice } \}$$
$$\forall_x[\neg Q:\neg P] \wedge \forall_x[\neg R:\neg P]$$
$$\overset{val}{=\!=\!=} \quad \{ \text{ Domain Splitting } \}$$
$$\forall_x[\neg Q \vee \neg R:\neg P]$$
$$\overset{val}{=\!=\!=} \quad \{ \text{ De Morgan } \}$$
$$\forall_x[\neg(Q \wedge R):\neg P]$$
$$\overset{val}{=\!=\!=} \quad \{ \text{ 'exchange trick' } \}$$
$$\forall_x[P:Q \wedge R]$$

Note that we have started here with the *right-hand side* of the equivalence that we wanted to prove. This formula is the more complex of the two. In general, this is a good strategy for a calculation which aims at establishing the equivalence of two formulas: start with the most complex formula and rewrite it as much as necessary to obtain the other formula. (Another strategy is: rewrite *both* formulas and try to get a general 'result'. In other words: if you want to show that $P \overset{val}{=\!=} Q$, try to find an R such that P and Q can be *both* rewritten to R. Then it holds that both $P \overset{val}{=\!=} R$ and $Q \overset{val}{=\!=} R$, and hence also $P \overset{val}{=\!=} Q$.)

As an end to this section we give two equivalences which, again, are useful:

$$\forall_x[P:Q \Rightarrow R] \Rightarrow (\forall_x[P:Q] \Rightarrow \forall_x[P:R]) \overset{val}{=\!=\!=} \text{True},$$
$$\forall_x[P:Q \Rightarrow R] \Rightarrow (\exists_x[P:Q] \Rightarrow \exists_x[P:R]) \overset{val}{=\!=\!=} \text{True}$$

The formulas are respectively called *'Monotonicity of $\forall$'* and *'Monotonicity of $\exists$'* in computer science. The word 'monotonicity' is related to the following. Look at the left hand sides of the formulas above, the parts before the $\overset{val}{=\!=}$. In both left hand sides we find the implication '$Q \Rightarrow R$', whereas the same implication 'returns' after the main implication arrow, in a subformula of the form '... Q.. $\Rightarrow$ ... R..'. This reminds one of the formula used for the description of the *monotonicity of a function f*, namely: $x < y \Rightarrow f(x) < f(y)$. Here we find '$x < y$' before the implication arrow and '... x.. $< ... y$..' behind it.

Both rules assume as 'prerequisite' that $\forall_x[P : Q \Rightarrow R]$. This is a strong condition: *for all x*'s with domain description P it holds that $Q \Rightarrow R$.

The first formula now says that, if moreover *all* x's in that domain satisfy Q, then they all must also satisfy R. If you think this over a little bit, you will realize that it is obvious:

(1) *Assume* for the sake of argument that for all x's in the domain, $Q \Rightarrow R$ holds,

(2) assume also that for all these x's, Q holds,

(3) then for all x in that domain, R also holds.

The second formula starts with the same 'prerequisite' $\forall_x[P : Q \Rightarrow R]$. The formula expresses moreover that if furthermore *at least* one x in the domain satisfies Q, then at least *one* x satisfies R. This too is simple to see.

(1) Suppose that for all x's in the domain, $Q \Rightarrow R$ holds,

(2) and suppose that for at least *one* such x, Q also holds,

(3) then for the same x (or x's), R also holds.

Above, we argued for the correctness of the above two formulas via a *reasoning*. In Part II of this book we will see how we can reason in general. The above given reasonings are special examples of the general reasoning schemes which we will introduce in Part II. If you are still not convinced by the reasoning put forward so far, we give again a *calculation* according to the methods that we have developed in the previous chapters. We only give the calculation for the second formula. This calculation, given below, is more involved than the corresponding reasoning, and perhaps even more involved than you would like. (Which is another reason why you should take seriously the method of reasoning that we will present in Part II.)

$$\forall_x[P : Q \Rightarrow R] \Rightarrow (\exists_x[P : Q] \Rightarrow \exists_x[P : R])$$

$\overset{val}{=\!=}$ { Implication, twice }
$$\neg\forall_x[P : Q \Rightarrow R] \vee \neg\exists_x[P : Q] \vee \exists_x[P : R]$$

$\overset{val}{=\!=}$ { De Morgan }
$$\exists_x[P : \neg(Q \Rightarrow R)] \vee \neg\exists_x[P : Q] \vee \exists_x[P : R]$$

$\overset{val}{=\!=}$ { 'exchange trick', three times }
$$\exists_x[\neg(Q \Rightarrow R) : P] \vee \neg\exists_x[Q : P] \vee \exists_x[R : P]$$

$\overset{val}{=\!=}$ { Domain Splitting }
$$\exists_x[\neg(Q \Rightarrow R) \vee R : P] \vee \neg\exists_x[Q : P]$$

$\overset{val}{=\!=}$ { by $\neg(Q \Rightarrow R) \vee R \overset{val}{=\!=} Q \vee R$ }

$$\begin{aligned}
&\exists_x[Q \vee R : P] \vee \neg\exists_x[Q : P] \\
\overset{val}{=\!=}\quad &\{ \text{ Domain Splitting } \} \\
&\exists_x[Q : P] \vee \exists_x[R : P] \vee \neg\exists_x[Q : P] \\
\overset{val}{=\!=}\quad &\{ \text{ Excluded Middle } \} \\
&\exists_x[R : P] \vee \texttt{True} \\
\overset{val}{=\!=}\quad &\{ \text{ True/False-elimination } \} \\
&\texttt{True}
\end{aligned}$$

Midway, we used the equivalence $\neg(Q \Rightarrow R) \vee R \overset{val}{=\!=} Q \vee R$. We leave it to the reader to do the calculation which establishes this equivalence.

9.9 Tautologies and contradictions with quantifiers

Tautologies are abstract propositions which are *always* true, *contradictions* are *never* true. We have already described these two classes in Section 4.4, but then for propositions without quantifiers. The being-always-true respectively being-never-true could then be checked with truth-tables, which have in the corresponding columns only ones respectively zeros.

For abstract propositions where quantifiers are added, this must be done differently because the truth-tables don't work anymore. The best we can do is to give a new definition of 'tautology' and 'contradiction':

Definition 9.9.1 *(Tautology, contradiction)*
Tautologies are the propositions which are equivalent to `True`, contradictions are the propositions which are equivalent to `False`.

From the Empty Domain rule it follows therefore that $\forall_x[\texttt{False} : Q]$ is a tautology, and that $\exists_x[\texttt{False} : Q]$ is a contradiction.

We give more details here:

(1) Because the formula $\forall_x[\texttt{False} : Q]$ is a tautology *for every* Q, then also the formula $\forall_x[\texttt{False} : \neg Q]$ is a tautology, and hence so is $\forall_x[Q : \texttt{True}]$ (by the 'exchange trick' from the previous section). More specifically, the formulas $\forall_x[\texttt{True} : \texttt{True}]$ and $\forall_x[\texttt{False} : \texttt{True}]$ are both tautologies.

(2) The fact that the formula $\exists_x[\texttt{False} : Q]$ is a contradiction, implies also that the formula $\exists_x[Q : \texttt{False}]$ is a contradiction (again with the 'exchange trick'). More specifically therefore, both $\exists_x[\texttt{True} : \texttt{False}]$ and $\exists_x[\texttt{False} : \texttt{False}]$ are contradictions.

Note that if φ is a tautology, then $\neg\varphi$ is a contradiction. Moreover, the other way round holds: if φ is a contradiction, then $\neg\varphi$ is a tautology.

Therefore $\neg\forall_x[\text{False} : Q]$ is a contradiction and $\neg\exists_x[\text{False} : Q]$ is a tautology.

With the above definition of tautology, Lemma 6.1.3 remains valid:

if $P \overset{val}{=\!=} Q$, then $P \Leftrightarrow Q$ is a tautology, and vice versa.

Hence, the standard equivalences from the previous sections imply for example the following:

$\forall_x[P \wedge Q : R] \Leftrightarrow \forall_x[P : Q \Rightarrow R]$ is a tautology (see the first Domain Weakening rule).

$\neg\exists_x[P : Q] \Leftrightarrow \forall_x[P : \neg Q]$ is a tautology (see the second rule of De Morgan).

Also the concepts *'stronger'* and *'weaker'* can be generalized from abstract propositions without quantifiers to propositions *with* quantifiers:

Definition 9.9.2 *(Stronger, weaker)*
P is *stronger* than Q, if the truth of P entails the truth of Q; and conversely, P is *weaker* than Q, if the truth of Q entails the truth of P.

We shall also use for quantified formulas the notations $\overset{val}{\models\!=}$ and $\overset{val}{=\!\models}$ for 'stronger' and 'weaker'. We note that Lemma 7.3.4 is still valid:

If $P \overset{val}{\models\!=} Q$, then $P \Rightarrow Q$ is a tautology, and vice versa.

We end this section with some examples.
First we show the following:

Lemma 9.9.3 *If Q is stronger than R, then $\forall_x[P : Q]$ is stronger than $\forall_x[P : R]$.*

(This lemma does not need a lot of thinking to be believable: because if for all x's with domain description P it holds that Q, then surely R also holds; we are given that Q is stronger than R, therefore if Q holds for an x, then also R must hold.)

In order to be absolutely sure, we will also try to give a proof via a calculation. For this we assume that the formula $Q \Rightarrow R$ is a tautology (this is a translation of 'Q is stronger than R') and we show via a calculation that $\forall_x[P : Q] \Rightarrow \forall_x[P : R]$ is also a tautology (this is a translation of '$\forall_x[P : Q]$ is stronger than $\forall_x[P : R]$'). The calculation is not so simple, you will quickly get stuck. (Try this first on your own.)

The *idea* which will finally work is to use the fact that the following equivalence holds:

$$\forall_x[P : Q \Rightarrow R] \Rightarrow (\forall_x[P : Q] \Rightarrow \forall_x[P : R]) \stackrel{val}{=\!=} \text{True}$$

(We called this the 'monotonicity of $\forall$' at the end of the previous section.) Note that both $Q \Rightarrow R$ and $\forall_x[P : Q] \Rightarrow \forall_x[P : R]$ are *sub-formulas* of this long formula!

Here is now the calculation:

$$\text{True}$$
$$\stackrel{val}{=\!=} \qquad \{ \text{ 'Monotonicity of } \forall \text{' } \}$$
$$\forall_x[P : Q \Rightarrow R] \Rightarrow (\forall_x[P : Q] \Rightarrow \forall_x[P : R])$$
$$\stackrel{val}{=\!=} \qquad \{ \text{ Assumption that } Q \Rightarrow R \text{ is a tautology } \}$$
$$\forall_x[P : \text{True}] \Rightarrow (\forall_x[P : Q] \Rightarrow \forall_x[P : R])$$
$$\stackrel{val}{=\!=} \qquad \{ \forall_x[P : \text{True}] \text{ is a tautology, see above } \}$$
$$\text{True} \Rightarrow (\forall_x[P : Q] \Rightarrow \forall_x[P : R])$$
$$\stackrel{val}{=\!=} \qquad \{ \text{ Implication } \}$$
$$\text{False} \lor (\forall_x[P : Q] \Rightarrow \forall_x[P : R])$$
$$\stackrel{val}{=\!=} \qquad \{ \text{ True/False-elimination } \}$$
$$\forall_x[P : Q] \Rightarrow \forall_x[P : R]$$

From this it follows that $(\forall_x[P : Q] \Rightarrow \forall_x[P : R]) \stackrel{val}{=\!=} \text{True}$, therefore: the formula $\forall_x[P : Q] \Rightarrow \forall_x[P : R]$ is a tautology, but only *under the assumption that Q is stronger than R!*.

Finally, we show the following:

$$\forall_x[P : R] \Rightarrow \forall_x[P \land Q : R] \text{ is a tautology.}$$

Also here we have very few problems believing this intuitively. In fact, P is weaker than $P \land Q$. From this we get after a little reflection that the domain description P gives a domain which is *as big or maybe bigger than* the domain described by $P \land Q$. If hence, for all x's in that 'bigger' domain the predicate R holds, then in particular it holds for all x's in the 'smaller' domain.

But again, a calculation gives the desired certainty:

$$\forall_x[P : R] \Rightarrow \forall_x[P \land Q : R]$$
$$\stackrel{val}{=\!=} \qquad \{ \text{ Domain Weakening } \}$$
$$\forall_x[P : R] \Rightarrow \forall_x[P : Q \Rightarrow R]$$
$$\stackrel{val}{=\!=} \qquad \{ R \text{ is stronger than } Q \Rightarrow R; \text{ use now the above lemma } \}$$
$$\text{True}$$

(We leave to the reader the calculation which shows that R is stronger than $Q \Rightarrow R$.)

Remark 9.9.4 *The examples at the end of this section show that the method of calculation 'works' also for complex quantified formulas and for proofs about them. Exactly like at the end of the previous section, it is possibly the case that the result remains unsatisfactory, because calculations do not always fit our initial instincts. Also things that seem to be 'obvious' in these examples are not so easily 'proved'. This is the price one pays for 'absolute certainty'. Nevertheless, this certainty may still be achieved in a simpler manner: The reasoning method with the help of 'derivations' which we shall give in Part II, will in the above cases fit the intuition better and will give shorter 'proofs'.*

9.10   Exercises

9.1 Look at the following two predicates on $\mathbb{Z}^2$:

$$A(m, n) = m < n,$$

$$B(m, n) = \exists_x [x \in \mathbf{D} : m < x < n].$$

(a) Show that $A(m,n)$ and $B(m,n)$ are equivalent if $\mathbf{D} = \mathbb{R}$.

(b) Show that $A(m,n)$ and $B(m,n)$ are *not* equivalent if $\mathbf{D} = \mathbb{Z}$.

9.2 Check which of the following propositions are equivalent, independently of $\mathbf{D}$, where $\mathbf{D}$ is an arbitrary subset of $\mathbb{R}$.

(a) $\exists_x [x \in \mathbf{D} : \forall_y [y \in \mathbf{D} : y \leq x]]$

(b) $\exists_l [l \in \mathbf{D} : \forall_k [k \in \mathbf{D} : l \leq k]]$

(c) $\exists_k [k \in \mathbf{D} : \forall_m [m \in \mathbf{D} : \neg(k < m)]]$

(d) $\forall_y [y \in \mathbf{D} : \exists_x [x \in \mathbf{D} : y \leq x]]$

9.3 Rewrite via a calculation to a simpler formula:

(a) $\forall_x [P : \mathtt{True}]$

(b) $\forall_x [P : \mathtt{False}]$

(c) $\exists_x [P : \mathtt{True}]$

(d) $\exists_x [P : \mathtt{False}]$

9.4 As Exercise 9.3:

    (a) $\forall_x[P \vee Q : \neg P]$

    (b) $\forall_x[P \wedge Q : \neg P]$

    (c) $\exists_x[P \vee Q : \neg P]$

    (d) $\exists_x[P \wedge Q : \neg P]$

9.5 Show via a calculation that:

    (a) $\exists_k[P : Q] \overset{val}{=\!=} \neg\forall_k[Q : \neg P]$

    (b) $\forall_k[P : Q \vee R] \overset{val}{=\!=} \forall_k[P \wedge \neg Q : R]$

9.6 Show with a counterexample that:

    (a) $\forall_k[P : Q] \overset{val}{\neq} \forall_k[Q : P]$

    (b) $\exists_k[P : Q] \wedge \exists_k[P : R] \overset{val}{\neq} \exists_k[P : Q \wedge R]$

Chapter 10

Other binders of variables

Within the bounds of reason

10.1 Predicates versus abstract function values

We have already seen how a predicate can be quantified with a quantifier, that is, with $\forall$ or $\exists$. With such quantification, *free* variables can become *bound*. We revisit the concept of quantification with an example (see also Sections 8.3 and 8.4):

- Look at the predicate $6m + 9n > 2$ over $\mathbb{Z} \times \mathbb{N}$. One sees that m and n are free variables, where m belongs to $\mathbb{Z}$ and n belongs to $\mathbb{N}$. This formula is a two-place predicate. We can only say something about its truth/falsity *after* we fill the values for m and n (but then it becomes another formula).

- In the formula $\exists_n[n \in \mathbb{N} : 6m + 9n > 2]$, m is still free, but n is bound. Because there is only *one* free variable in the formula, it is a one-place predicate (in m). If m comes from domain $\mathbb{Z}$, then the formula is a *predicate over* $\mathbb{Z}$. Again, nothing can be said about the truth/falsity of the formula.

- In $\forall_m[m \in \mathbb{Z} : \exists_n[n \in \mathbb{N} : 6m + 9n > 2]]$ there are no more free variables. It is a zero-place predicate, or said differently, a proposition (the formula is true or false; to be precise: in this case it is true). Both m and n are bound variables in the formula.

In short, quantified predicates are *again* predicates. In special cases (if there are no more free variables) they are propositions.

Free variables can become bound in different ways than simply via the use of the quantifiers $\forall$ and $\exists$. In this chapter we give three examples of such phenomena. We will no longer be dealing only with *predicates*, but also with *abstract function-values*, which are formulas which after saturation return an *object*. We give the following example in order to clarify the distinction between predicates and abstract function-values:

- The formula $6m + 9n$ is an *abstract function-value* with free variables m and n. If we fill values for all free variables, for example $m = 5$ and $n = 2$, we get an *object*, namely the concrete function-value $6 \cdot 5 + 9 \cdot 2$ (the number 48). An object can never be true or false.

- The formula $6m + 9n > 2$ is a *predicate* with free variables m and n. If we fill all free variables by a value, for example again $m = 5$ and $n = 2$, we get a *proposition*, namely $6 \cdot 5 + 9 \cdot 2 > 2$. Such a proposition is always true or false.

10.2   The set binder

In this section we look at the way in which *sets* can be described.

Finite sets are often *listed* ('enumerated') between two braces. This means that all their elements are written between the braces. Sometimes this takes place with the help of three dots $(\ldots)$, where the reader can fill what has been omitted.

Example 10.2.1

- *The finite set which consists of the numbers 0, 1, 2 and 3 is written as* $\{0, 1, 2, 3\}$. *The order does not matter:* $\{3, 1, 0, 2\}$ *is the same set. Every element counts but only once: also* $\{3, 1, 1, 1, 0, 0, 2\}$ *is the same as* $\{0, 1, 2, 3\}$. *(Sometimes this is not assumed and e.g.* $\{3, 1, 1, 1, 0, 0, 2\}$ *is taken to be* different *from* $\{0, 1, 2, 3\}$; *in that case we don't speak of 'sets', but of* multi-sets. *These are also called* bags *in computer science.)*

- *A set with* one *element, like* $\{6\}$, *is a* one-element set *or* singleton. *Note that* $\{6\}$ *is a set, which is different from 6, a number.*

- *The (finite) set without* elements *is called the* empty set. *Notation:* $\emptyset$.

- $\{5, 6, \ldots, 20\}$ *is the set of all integer numbers from* 5 *to* 20 *inclusive.*

- $\{0, 1, \ldots, n\}$ *is the set of the integer numbers from* 0 *to* n *inclusive.*
  For $n = 2$, 1 *and* 0, *one gets* $\{0, 1, 2\}$, $\{0, 1\}$ *resp.* $\{0\}$. *For* $n < 0$ *the set is empty.*

For bigger sets, possibly infinite, there are again other notations. Standard sets have their own names, for example: $\mathbb{N}$ (the natural numbers) and $\mathbb{Z}$ (the integer numbers).

Also, a set can be written with a *predicate*, which the elements must satisfy. Braces are also used for such sets.

If we for example want to write the set of the integer numbers m which satisfy the predicate $-3 \le m \le 1 \vee m > 5$, we can use the *standard mathematical notation*:

$\{m \in \mathbb{Z} \mid -3 \le m \le 1 \vee m > 5\}$.

This way of forming sets is called *comprehension*. This word comes from the logic of the seventeenth century and means something like 'concept': with the help of the braces one expresses a new set concept.

The comprehension-notation has *bindings of variables*, exactly like quantified formulas. The m, which was free in the predicate $-3 \le m \le 1 \vee m > 5$, is *bound* in the above expression for the corresponding set. We can see this for example, because the rule of the Bound Variable is also valid here. We can describe this set just as well with k instead of m:

$\{k \in \mathbb{Z} \mid -3 \le k \le 1 \vee k > 5\}$.

It is important to note that the *result* of the set binding is different from the quantifier binding:

- Binding a variable with a *quantifier* returns as a result a *predicate* (or, if there are no more free variables, a *proposition*). See the examples at the beginning of this chapter.

- Binding a variable with the *set binder* $\{\ldots \mid \ldots\}$ on the other hand, gives (the word says it already) a *set*. A set is an 'object', that can never become **True** or **False**, even after filling values for free variables.

The standard mathematical notation for set formation looks in general as follows:

$\{m \in \mathbf{D} \mid P\}$.

Here P is the predicate which describes what m must satisfy (given that m also belongs to the domain $\mathbf{D}$). Note that the naming of m directly after the opening brace takes care of two things at the same time: it states that (1) m is the *bound variable* and,

(2) m's in **D** are those things that get *collected* (as long as they satisfy the predicate P).

In computer science, another notation which separates these two roles of m, is sometimes used for the description of a set. The name of the bound variable stays in front, but the things which get collected are put at the *end*. With this separation, the notation of computer science gives some flexibility, as we will see.

If for example, exactly like above, we want to collect integer numbers m, then things look as follows:

(Set $\ldots : \ldots : m$).

The above example becomes in this *computer science notation* (where we implicitly assume that $m \in \mathbb{Z}$, so $\mathbb{Z}$ is the domain of m):

(Set $m : -3 \le m \le 1 \vee m > 5 : m$).

The word Set points to the fact that this is a set in computer science notation. The variable which becomes bound (in this case m) will be placed at the *first* sequence of dots, exactly like for quantifier binding. The *second* sequence of dots, is reserved for the predicate which the numbers m must satisfy to be in the set. And *what* is collected is put in the *third* sequence of dots. In this case, we simply have m, which means that we are precisely collecting these numbers m which are in the domain *and* satisfy the predicate. Hence, the set which we get is *equal* to the subdomain, consisting of all domain elements that satisfy the predicate.

This notation expresses also that we can collect other things than m's (and this is a great advantage), for example m^2's:

(Set $m : -3 \le m \le 1 \vee m > 5 : m^2$).

Here we get the set of all *m-squares* where m comes from a subdomain which can be written as $\{-3, -2, -1, 0, 1, 5, 6, 7, \ldots\}$. Now the set that we get is *different* from that subdomain: in the set there is now 4 (because $4 = (-2)^2$), but not 16 (because neither -4, nor 4 is in the domain).

Note that after the last colon and hence in general, we can have an *abstract function-value* which describes what the objects collected in general look like. They can be m, but also m^2 or $|m - 5| + 3$.

Such a set formula in computer science notation has therefore the following form:

(Set $x : P : F$).

Remark 10.2.2 *There is also a mathematical notation for the more general case where function-values are collected. The last example becomes in this notation:*

$\{m^2 | -3 \leq m \leq 1 \lor m > 5\}$.
Here we get the collected objects again in the first place. The name of the bound variable (m) does not specifically get declared.

Just like in the previous section, we give an example to illustrate the different concepts, but this time with the abstract function-value $6m + 9n$, instead of the predicate $6m + 9n > 2$ (we assume that m has domain $\mathbb{Z}$ and n has domain $\mathbb{N}$):

- The formula $6m+9n$ is an abstract function-value over $\mathbb{Z} \times \mathbb{N}$, with free variables m and n. If we fill m by the number 5, we get the abstract function-value $30 + 9n$ (over $\mathbb{N}$!). If we take $m = 5$ and $n = 2$, we get the object 48.

- In the formula (Set $m : m \in \mathbb{Z} : 6m + 9n$), m is bound and n is free. It is a set *which depends on n*. For example: 6 is in this set if n is equal to 0, but not if $n = 1$.

- The formula (Set $m, n : (m, n) \in \mathbb{Z} \times \mathbb{N} : 6m + 9n$) is a set of numbers. (It can be easily seen that this is precisely the set of all integer multiples of three.)

10.3   The sum binder

A *sequence* of numbers is something different from a *set*: a sequence always has an *order*. A sequence is usually described by its elements presented one after another (in a certain order), and separated by comma's: $2, 5, 1, 2, 2, 6$ is such a sequence, with 2 as first element and 6 as last element. The element 2 appears three times in this sequence, but you can't remove two of these occurrences as you could do with the *set* $\{2, 5, 1, 2, 2, 6\}$.

In order to describe sequences in abstract terms, *one* letter is usually used (for example x) which is indexed: $x_0, x_1, x_2, x_3, x_4, x_5$ is such a general sequence of length 6, with first element x_0 and last element x_5.

In mathematics and computer science one is often interested in the *sum* of the elements of such a sequence. For such a sum, one uses the Greek letter Σ (capital letter 'sigma', the 'S' of 'Sum'). In mathematics a sum is expressed as in the following example:

$$\sum_{k=0}^{5} x_k,$$

or also:

$$\sum_{k \in \{0, \ldots, 5\}} x_k.$$

This is therefore a short notation for $x_0 + x_1 + x_2 + x_3 + x_4 + x_5$.

Note that the k in the 'entry' x_k is still free, but in $\sum_{k=0}^{5} x_k$ it is bound.

Again, in computer science one sometimes uses a variant notation: instead of the above one writes
$$(\Sigma k : 0 \leq k < 6 : x_k).$$

In order to *calculate* with the sum of a sequence, one uses the available rules. For example, if n is positive, then the *Split rule* is valid:
$$(\Sigma k : 0 \leq k < n + 1 : x_k) = (\Sigma k : 0 \leq k < n : x_k) + x_n.$$
In order to ensure that this rule also holds for $n - 0$, one agrees on the *Empty-sum convention*:
$$(\Sigma k : \texttt{False} : x_k) = 0.$$
With this convention, the following calculation 'makes sense' (of course this is a rather strange detour, because $(\Sigma k : 0 \leq k < 1 : x_k)$ is already directly equal to x_0, *by definition*):

$$
\begin{aligned}
& (\Sigma k : 0 \leq k < 1 : x_k) \\
= \quad & \{ \text{ Split rule } \} \\
& (\Sigma k : 0 \leq k < 0 : x_k) + x_0 \\
= \quad & \{ \text{ Mathematics } \} \\
& (\Sigma k : \texttt{False} : x_k) + x_0 \\
= \quad & \{ \text{ Empty-sum convention } \} \\
& 0 + x_0 \\
= \quad & \{ \text{ Mathematics } \} \\
& x_0
\end{aligned}
$$

Similarly, there is a notation for the *product* of the elements in a sequence. For this, one uses the Greek letter Π (capital letter 'pi', the 'P' of 'Product').

Also here some simple rules hold, such as:
$$(\Pi k : 0 \leq k < n + 1 : x_k) = (\Pi k : 0 \leq k < n : x_k) \cdot x_n.$$
Comparable with the above, the *Empty-product convention* is valid:
$$(\Pi k : \texttt{False} : x_k) = 1.$$

10.4   The symbol

If a set is *finite*, then one describes its *number* of elements with the symbol #. (This sign is pronounced in the Anglo-American world as 'number', here with the meaning 'quantity'.)

Example: $\#\{0, 1, 2, 3\} = 4$ expresses that $\{0, 1, 2, 3\}$ has four elements.

The sign # is also used in order to give the number of elements of a set which is described by a predicate.

Example 10.4.1 $\{k \in \mathbb{Z} | 0 < k < 20\}$ *is the mathematical notation for the set of numbers between 0 and 20. The (finite) quantity (or number of elements) of these numbers is given by* $\#\{k \in \mathbb{Z} | 0 < k < 20\}$, *therefore* $\#\{k \in \mathbb{Z} | 0 < k < 20\} = 19$.

There is also a variant *computer science notation* for the number of elements of a finite set. We give an example:

$(\#i : 0 < i \leq 100 : i^2 < 90)$.

This gives 'the number (quantity) of integer numbers greater than 0 and smaller or equal to 100 for which the square is smaller than 90'. (The number required is therefore nine.) Note here again that the *binding* changes: the variable i is free in both the predicates $0 < i \leq 100$ and $i^2 < 90$, but is bound in $(\#i : 0 < i \leq 100 : i^2 < 90)$.

The general form in this case is hence:

$(\# \, x : P : Q)$,

with P and Q as predicates. The meaning is: the number of x's for which P and (also) Q hold.

10.5 Scopes of binders

As we saw before, each binder has a variable linked to it, the *bound variable* of that binder. This variable may come back in the remainder of the expression, but the question arises: how far does the 'influence' of the binder range? This range is called the *scope* of the binder. For example, in the formula

$\forall_x [x \in \mathbb{N} : x^2 \geq 0] \wedge \exists_y [y \in \mathbb{Z} : y < 0 \wedge y^2 = 49]$,

there are *two* bound variables involved: the first one is the x 'under' the $\forall$, and the second one is the y 'under' the $\exists$. The corresponding binders have different scopes, the $\forall_x$ ranges over the part $[x \in \mathbb{N} : x^2 \geq 0]$ and the $\exists_y$ over $[y \in \mathbb{Z} : y < 0 \wedge y^2 = 49]$. So all x's in $[x \in \mathbb{N} : x^2 \geq 0]$ are bound to the x in $\forall_x$, and a similar observation holds for the y's.

Clearly, the scopes of $\forall_x$ and $\exists_y$ are *disjoint*: they do not overlap. Therefore it is in this case acceptable to use *the same name* for both bound variables. For example, we can write the above formula as

$\forall_x [x \in \mathbb{N} : x^2 \geq 0] \wedge \exists_x [x \in \mathbb{Z} : x < 0 \wedge x^2 = 49]$,

using the name x twice for the bound variables, without this leading to confusion.

However, in the formula

$\forall_x [x \in \mathbb{N} : \exists_y [y \in \mathbb{Z} : y < x]]$

the scope of the $\forall_x$ is everything behind it, up to the end of the formula, hence *including* the subformula starting with the $\exists$-binder. So the scopes of $\forall_x$ and $\exists_y$ *overlap*.

It will be obvious that in this case it is not allowed to use the bound variable name x for both bound variables, since then the subformula $y < x$ would become $x < x$. Then we are in trouble, since it is no longer obvious that the first x in $x < x$ is linked to the $\exists$-binder, and the second to the $\forall$-binder.

In general, each binder occurring in a formula has a well-defined scope, which can be found as follows. First determine the subformula with that binder as its main symbol (which is the subformula which *begins with* the binder). Then, the *scope of the binder* is the part of that subformula *after* the binder. One alternatively calls this *the scope of the bound variable* belonging to the binder.

10.6   Exercises

10.1 Write the following as a set of the form $\{\ldots|\ldots\}$ and also with the set binder (Set $\ldots:\ldots:\ldots$):

(a) The set of all real numbers between -10 and 10, but not equal to 0.

(b) The set of natural numbers which are not even.

(c) The set of all integer numbers that are multiples of six.

(d) The set of all natural numbers which are the sum of two squares of natural numbers.

10.2 Show that (Set $m, n : (m, n) \in \mathbb{Z} \times \mathbb{N} : 6m + 9n$) is the set of all integer multiples of three.

10.3 Calculate:

(a) $\sum_{k=0}^{99} k$

(b) $\prod_{k=0}^{99} (-1)^k$

(c) $(\sum k : -10 \leq k \leq 10 : k^{33})$

(d) $(\#k : -10 \leq k \leq 10 : k^2 > 9)$

10.4 Describe the scopes of all binders occurring in

(a) the formula in Figure 8.4,

(b) the formulas occurring in Exercise 8.9.

Part II

Logical Derivations

Chapter 11

Reasoning

Let's get this right

11.1 The strength and weakness of calculations

In the earlier chapters we saw how to reach certain conclusions via 'calculations':

- In Section 6.3 we gave the following example of a calculation, which was meant to show that $\neg(P \Rightarrow Q)$ is equivalent to $P \wedge \neg Q$:

  $$
  \begin{aligned}
  &(1) \quad \neg(P \Rightarrow Q) \\
  &\overset{val}{=\!=} \quad \{ \text{ Implication } \} \\
  &(2) \quad \neg(\neg P \vee Q) \\
  &\overset{val}{=\!=} \quad \{ \text{ De Morgan } \} \\
  &(3) \quad \neg\neg P \wedge \neg Q \\
  &\overset{val}{=\!=} \quad \{ \text{ Double Negation } \} \\
  &(4) \quad P \wedge \neg Q
  \end{aligned}
  $$

  (In order to easily be able to talk about such calculations, we use here the numbers (1) to (4) to refer to the lines.)

  Note that $\neg(P \Rightarrow Q)$ is not a tautology and neither is $P \wedge \neg Q$. The calculation only shows that they are *equivalent*. But by Lemma 6.1.3 one can derive from the above calculation a second conclusion, namely

113

that the following formula is a tautology:

$$\neg(P \Rightarrow Q) \Leftrightarrow P \wedge \neg Q.$$

- We have also seen calculations where now and then the symbols $\stackrel{val}{\Longleftarrow}$ or $\stackrel{val}{\Longrightarrow}$ instead of $\stackrel{val}{=\!=}$ appeared in the margin. In Section 7.4 we saw for example:

(1) $\neg P$
$\stackrel{val}{\Longleftarrow}$ { $\wedge$-$\vee$-weakening }
(2) $\neg P \wedge \neg Q$
$\stackrel{val}{=\!=}$ { De Morgan }
(3) $\neg(P \vee Q)$

From this calculation we get the end conclusion:

$$\neg P \stackrel{val}{\Longleftarrow} \neg(P \vee Q),$$

which expresses that the proposition $\neg P$ is weaker than the proposition $\neg(P \vee Q)$.

Again: neither $\neg P$, nor $\neg(P \vee Q)$ is a tautology. But by Lemma 7.3.4 there is also here a second end conclusion to be derived, namely that the following formula is *definitely* a tautology:

$$\neg(P \vee Q) \Rightarrow \neg P.$$

This rewriting via a calculation, as in the above two examples, is a powerful way of being able to derive correct conclusions. The *advantages* are:

- It is a *well structured* method where correct application of the rules will definitely deliver correct conclusions.

- The *arguments* or *reasons* are also present (between the braces), and we mention the name of the applied rules.

- The method works with *small steps*, which enables a good overview.

- A calculation can be built *from top to bottom*, but also *from bottom to top*. Sometimes it is even useful to work 'from both directions' and to try and complete the reasoning in the middle. This method allows all this.

In many cases the method works quickly and smoothly. We must however realize that there are nevertheless *disadvantages* associated with this method:

- *The method is successive.* This means that you make a *chain* of propositions which always appear in pairs related by some reason. In the first example above, this happens as follows: (1) is paired with (2), then (2) is paired with (3), and finally (3) is paired with (4). Only the end conclusion bridges a bigger distance than from (k) to $(k+1)$; it relates the beginning and the end of the chain: (1) with (4).

  This leads to the disadvantage that one can only derive the conclusion on the grounds of the *last* result. The proposition which occurs in line $(k+1)$ in the calculation, is 'reached' with the help of the proposition which *immediately precedes* it, i.e., in line (k). You can *not* therefore use as a reason for proposition $(k+1)$ the proposition of line $(k-5)$ for example, or the propositions of lines $(k-5)$ and (k) *together*.

- *The method uses a fixed collection of standard equivalences without clarifying what actually is meant by 'standard'.* See Chapter 5 and Chapter 9. There we saw a number of useful equivalences (Associativity, De Morgan, ...). But one was never told why these rules and no others are taken as basic. The listed standard equivalences were chosen because of their *practical applications*, but this is a rather vague criterion. The *logical* background is only indirectly visible.

  For example: $P \Rightarrow Q$ can be rewritten with Implication or with Contraposition delivering 'via this rewriting' $\neg P \lor Q$, respectively $\neg Q \Rightarrow \neg P$. But as regards content, the fact that $P \Rightarrow Q$ is a logical *implication*, is not used. In other words: we know: 'P implies Q' (or: 'If P, then Q'), but our intuition about 'if...' and 'then...' is not used (or at best it is used via a detour).

- *The method gives little guidance during the calculation process.* In the worst case, one can endlessly apply standard equivalences hoping it will lead to the desired result. This is obviously neither efficient nor desirable and in practice it rarely happens, because one will gradually develop a feel for such kind of calculations. But the fact remains that one always has this undesirable feeling of uncertainty during the calculation. One is always asking: 'Which standard equivalence should I now actually use?'

- *The method forces you sometimes to take a path that you don't really wish to take.* Especially for proofs in both mathematics and computer science, there are other, more satisfying tools available than just the rewriting of formulas via standard equivalences. We show this in the following two sections.

11.2   'Calculating' against 'reasoning'

The above mentioned disadvantages of the method of 'calculations' sometimes have unpleasant consequences. Look for example at the tautology

$$((P \Rightarrow Q) \land (Q \Rightarrow R)) \Rightarrow (P \Rightarrow R).$$

We can see that this is a tautology via a calculation:

(1) $(P \Rightarrow Q) \land (Q \Rightarrow R)$
$\stackrel{val}{=\!=}$ { Implication, twice }
(2) $(\neg P \lor Q) \land (\neg Q \lor R)$
$\stackrel{val}{=\!=}$ { Distributivity, repeated }
(3) $(\neg P \land \neg Q) \lor (\neg P \land R) \lor (Q \land \neg Q) \lor (Q \land R)$
$\stackrel{val}{=\!=}$ { Contradiction, False-elimination }
(4) $(\neg P \land \neg Q) \lor (\neg P \land R) \lor (Q \land R)$
$\stackrel{val}{\models\!=}$ { $\land$-weakening, three times, plus Monotonicity }
(5) $\neg P \lor \neg P \lor R$
$\stackrel{val}{=\!=}$ { Idempotence }
(6) $\neg P \lor R$
$\stackrel{val}{=\!=}$ { Implication }
(7) $P \Rightarrow R$

We are however not satisfied with this, because it appears to be a complex calculation for something that can *intuitively*, immediately be seen to be a tautology. Whenever we know: 'P implies Q' *and* 'Q implies R', it follows naturally that 'P implies R'. We see this 'immediately', but we can also give reasons as follows, via what we call a *reasoning*:

* *Assume:* we know (i) 'If P then Q', and (ii) 'If Q then R'.

* Now *we must show:* 'If P then R'.

* We show the last proposition as follows: we *assume* (iii) that 'P' holds, and we try to show that also R holds. (If we are successful, then we have shown that 'If P then R'.)

   So far, we have set the stage and we can now start the play.

> *We start by summarizing what we have and what we need: we must give a reasoning which*
> *– assuming* (i) *'If P then Q' and* (ii) *'If Q then R',*
> *– and moreover, assuming* (iii) *'P',*
> *– leads to 'R'.*
>
> *We do this as follows:*
>
> ∗ *From* (iii) *'P' and* (i) *'If P then Q' it follows that* (iv) *'Q'.*
>
> ∗ *From* (iv) *'Q' and* (ii) *'If Q then R' it follows that 'R'.*

And we are done.

Note that we have now *indeed* used the meaning and the content (the 'if-then-behavior') of the implication. For example: the fact that we had available to us both *'P'* and the *implication* 'If *P* then *Q*' leads us to the *conclusion* *'Q'*.

In the above reasoning, there are a couple of notable issues that we did not come across earlier:

- We use *assumptions* or *hypotheses*:

  Assume: (i) 'If *P* then *Q*' and (ii) 'If *Q* then *R*';

  Assume: (iii) *'P'*.

- We use *inferences*, that is: we draw conclusions. Moreover, a conclusion may now be derived from *everything that we 'know' at a certain moment*, hence not only from the very last proposition at hand. We can even derive conclusions from *more than one* proposition, as in:

  ∗ *From* (iii) *'P' and* (i) *'If P then Q' it follows that* (iv) *'Q'.*

Yet, this is all quite normal and resembles how we usually reason. In order to show this, we give in the following section an example of a reasoning in mathematics. This example is not very simple, and hence, you should do your best to follow what is happening. It is however worth the effort because it illustrates important aspects of abstract reasoning.

11.3 An example from mathematics

Our example deals with infinite sequences of real numbers. An example of such a sequence is $1, 2, 4, 8, \ldots$ or $0, \frac{1}{2}, \frac{2}{3}, \frac{3}{4}, \ldots$. In a general format, such a sequence looks like $a_0, a_1, a_2, \ldots$, also written as $(a_n)_{n \in \mathbb{N}}$. (The symbol $\mathbb{N}$ represents the set of all natural numbers, see also Part III, Section 19.1.)

In case we have, next to $(a_n)_{n\in\mathbb{N}}$, a second sequence: $(b_n)_{n\in\mathbb{N}}$, we may construct the *sum-sequence* of the two: $(a_n + b_n)_{n\in\mathbb{N}}$, which is the following sequence: $a_0 + b_0, a_1 + b_1, a_2 + b_2, \ldots$.

A sequence $(a_n)_{n\in\mathbb{N}}$ is called *convergent*, if the sequence has a limit. For example, the sequence $0, \frac{1}{2}, \frac{2}{3}, \frac{3}{4}, \ldots$ is convergent, with limit 1, but the sequence $1, 2, 4, 8, \ldots$ is *not* convergent.

Now the following theorem holds:

Lemma 11.3.1 *The sum-sequence of two convergent sequences of real numbers is also convergent.*

Proof:

* Let $(a_n)_{n\in\mathbb{N}}$ and $(b_n)_{n\in\mathbb{N}}$ be two convergent sequences of real numbers.

* Assume that (i) $\lim_{n\to\infty} a_n = A$ and (ii) $\lim_{n\to\infty} b_n = B$.

  Now first a short remark.

  We can also say the last phrase differently: $a_n \to A$ and $b_n \to B$ when n goes towards ∞. Or: $|a_n - A| \to 0$ and $|b_n - B| \to 0$.

  We need to show now that the sum-sequence converges too. This sum-sequence is the sequence $(a_n + b_n)_{n\in\mathbb{N}}$. A reasonable conjecture is that $a_n + b_n \to A + B$, which we can prove by showing, for $n \to \infty$, that $|(a_n + b_n) - (A + B)| \to 0$.

  We have now set up the stage and we will start the play:

* Take a natural number n.

* Then $|(a_n + b_n) - (A + B)| = |(a_n - A) + (b_n - B)| \le |a_n - A| + |b_n - B|$. (We give the name (iii) to this inequality.)

  Comment: This is an example of an intelligent mathematical calculation, in which we apply the triangle inequality: for all numbers x and y it holds that $|x + y| \le |x| + |y|$.

* Now we set free the n that we had chosen above and we assume that it is going towards ∞.

* Then obviously by (i) and (ii), both $|a_n - A|$ and $|b_n - B|$ will go towards 0.

* Hence, their sum, $|a_n - A| + |b_n - B|$, will also go towards 0 if n goes towards ∞.

* Because, according to (iii), $|(a_n + b_n) - (A + B)| \leq |a_n - A| + |b_n - B|$, then also $|(a_n + b_n) - (A + B)|$ will go towards 0 if n goes towards ∞.

* Hence $a_n + b_n$ goes towards $A + B$ and in this way, we have shown that the sum-sequence converges.[1]

In this reasoning one finds the already mentioned elements of hypotheses and inferences:

- *Hypotheses* of different sort, for example:

  - The hypothesis that we have the sequences $(a_n)_{n\in\mathbb{N}}$ and $(b_n)_{n\in\mathbb{N}}$.
  - The hypothesis that both sequences converge.
  - The hypothesis that A is the limit of the first sequence and B is the limit of the second.
  - The *temporary* hypothesis that we have a fixed number n in $\mathbb{N}$. (Later we remove this hypothesis, and we let n move towards ∞.)

- *Inferences* of different nature, for example:

  - The inference, wrapped in a mathematical calculation, with as conclusion

    $$\text{(iii)} \quad |(a_n + b_n) - (A + B)| \leq |a_n - A| + |b_n - B|.$$

  - The inference that if $|a_n - A|$ goes towards 0 and $|b_n - B|$ goes towards 0, then also the sum $|a_n - A| + |b_n - B|$ goes towards 0.

---

[1] This mathematical style of reasoning often has a deceptive appearance. A proof, after completion, is usually written down from the beginning to the end, without explanation of how the writer actually reached this proof. An inexperienced reader gets the impression that everything was conceived *in the given order*.

Don't be intimidated by this style of mathematical proofs. What you see is only the *end result*. During the building process of a difficult proof, usually a large pile of paper is used (most of which ends up in the wastebasket). During this proof process, progress is achieved by working sometimes forwards and sometimes backwards. Before the completion of the proof, many failed attempts may have taken place and a lot of creativity was probably needed.

It is the habit, when writing the proof in the end, of not showing much if any of this creative process. What matters in the end is that the proof is correct and convincing.

This style of proofs, which is actually quite beautiful (and does not lose any of that beauty by the above remarks), was actually started by Euclid, who wrote thirteen very famous books (*'The Elements'*) on geometry (see T.L. Heath: *The Thirteen Books of Euclid's Elements*, Dover Publications, 1956). These books are full of beautiful mathematical proofs. Euclid wrote them in Alexandria in Egypt, around 325 B.C.!

The conclusions of an inference are derived from *everything* that is available, this means

– all previously assumed and (still) valid hypotheses,

– all (still) valid, earlier conclusions,

– the results of a correct calculation,

– even an 'old' Proposition which we recall in memory: the 'triangle inequality'.

In the following sections we show that those two items: hypotheses and inferences, fit well together. We begin with inferences.

11.4   Inference

An inference in a reasoning is always of the kind:
From one or more propositions (the so-called *premisses*)
follows a new proposition (the *conclusion*).

The premisses must be *valid*, if they are to be 'of service'. We will later explain precisely what this means. In what follows think of valid propositions as things like:

- Hypotheses that are assumed but are not yet 'retracted' or 'withdrawn'.

- All proven theorems and the like.

- Tautologies, which are actually 'always true'.

From valid premisses we can derive conclusions. When is such a conclusion 'correct'? If the premisses *imply* indeed that this conclusion holds, hence if these premisses together *are stronger* than the conclusion. This can be specified formally as follows:

$$
\boxed{
\begin{array}{l}
Q \text{ is a correct conclusion from the premisses } P_1, \ldots, P_n \text{ if} \\
\qquad P_1 \wedge \ldots \wedge P_n \models^{val} Q
\end{array}
}
$$

Remark 11.4.1 *In case $n = 0$, when there are* zero *premisses, you must read this as follows:*

Q is a correct conclusion from zero premisses if $\text{True} \models^{val} Q$,

because a conjunction of zero propositions is by definition equivalent to True.

In that case $Q \overset{val}{=\!=} \texttt{True}$ should hence be valid, and so, Q too must 'hold'. This is the case if Q is a tautology, or is itself a valid hypothesis, or a proven theorem or something like that.

A 'correct' inference from valid propositions ensures that the *conclusion* is valid. Hence via an inference you can extend the set of valid propositions. These inferences may enlarge that set even more, giving you more opportunities to continue.

When deriving conclusions, you obviously don't want to work arbitrarily. In every reasoning step, you have a *goal* in mind which you would like to reach eventually. When making inferences you are (almost always) keeping that goal in sight because this is where you eventually want to get. All taken together:

A reasoning enables you to expand the set of valid expressions so that you can reach your goal.

Said differently: You want to 'direct' the reasoning so that the goal is finally *valid* itself; in this case you have achieved your goal, you are done.

You make therefore *deliberately* the one inference after the other. With every such inference, you get a conclusion which you derive from zero or more premisses:

- *Zero premisses.* A conclusion with zero premisses is a proposition that you 'simply' know to hold. A typical example is every *tautology*. Also an *already proven theorem* can act as a conclusion without premisses.[2]

- *One premiss.* Conclusions with *one* premiss occur regularly in the logical calculations of Part I. Example:

$$
\begin{aligned}
&\quad\quad \cdots \\
(m-1) &\quad \neg(\neg P \vee Q) \\
\overset{val}{=\!=} &\quad \{ \text{ De Morgan } \} \\
(m) &\quad \neg\neg P \wedge \neg Q \\
&\quad\quad \cdots
\end{aligned}
$$

This is a correct conclusion, because $\neg(\neg P \vee Q) \overset{val}{\models} \neg\neg P \wedge \neg Q$ (even $\overset{val}{=\!=}$ holds here).

---

[2]A *tautology* is an 'always valid' proposition from *logic*, for example: $P \vee \neg P$, $P \Leftrightarrow \neg\neg P$ or $\forall_x[P : Q] \Leftrightarrow \neg\exists_x[P : \neg Q]$. A *theorem* is a *mathematical* truth, for example: $1 + 2 = 3$, or the triangle inequality $\forall_{x,y}[x, y \in \mathbb{R} : |x + y| \leq |x| + |y|]$. Note that there is actually a *logical quantifier* ($\forall$) in this triangle inequality, but that the content is *mathematical*, because of the following symbols occurring in the formula: $\mathbb{R}$ for the set of all real numbers, $+$ for addition, $\leq$ for smaller-than-or-equal-to and $|\ldots|$ for absolute value.

With this sort of logical calculations, the premiss appears *just above* the conclusion. In general, this is not necessary when reasoning: The following situation is just as acceptable, as long as $l < m$ (and as long as the formula in line (l) holds, which we will come back to later):

$$\cdots$$
(l) $\quad \neg(\neg P \vee Q)$
$$\cdots$$
$\qquad \{$ De Morgan on (l): $\}$
(m) $\quad \neg\neg P \wedge \neg Q$
$$\cdots$$

Note that the justification '$\{$ De Morgan on (l): $\}$' does not serve now to connect lines $(m-1)$ and (m), but is exclusively meant to express why you are allowed to add the line with number (m).

Another example of a conclusion from *one* premiss:

$$\cdots$$
(l) $\quad \neg P \wedge \neg Q$
$$\cdots$$
$\qquad \{$ From (l) it follows that: $\}$
(m) $\quad \neg Q$
$$\cdots$$

The correctness of the justification '$\{$ From (l) it follows that: $\}$' is here a consequence of the standard weakening

$$\neg P \wedge \neg Q \models^{val} \neg Q.$$

- *Two premisses.* We give again an example:

$$\cdots$$
(k) $\quad P \vee Q$
$$\cdots$$
(l) $\quad \neg P$
$$\cdots$$
$\qquad \{$ By (k) and (l): $\}$
(m) $\quad Q$
$$\cdots$$

Here the conclusion in line (m) is derived from the propositions in lines (k) and (l). That this conclusion is correct, follows from the correctness of:

$$(P \vee Q) \wedge \neg P \models^{val} Q.$$

Note that in the above scheme, k and l must both be smaller than m, but that the order of the lines (k) and (l) does not matter: the line with number (l) can also occur *under* the line with number (k).

- *Three premisses.* Example:

$$
\begin{array}{ll}
& \cdots \\
(k) & P \vee Q \\
& \cdots \\
(l_1) & P \Rightarrow R \\
& \cdots \\
(l_2) & Q \Rightarrow R \\
& \cdots \\
& \{ \text{ By } (k), (l_1) \text{ and } (l_2) \text{: } \} \\
(m) & R \\
& \cdots
\end{array}
$$

This reasoning is a bit involved. We will see in Section 14.5 that it is intuitively correct. Technically speaking however, the correctness of the conclusion in line number (m) follows from:

$$(P \vee Q) \wedge (P \Rightarrow R) \wedge (Q \Rightarrow R) \models^{val} R.$$

The statement of the above line can be verified without any difficulty using truth-tables.

A variant of the above example is:

$$
\begin{array}{ll}
& \{ \text{ Tautology: } \} \\
(k) & P \vee \neg P \\
& \cdots \\
(l_1) & P \Rightarrow R \\
& \cdots \\
(l_2) & \neg P \Rightarrow R \\
& \cdots \\
& \{ \text{ By } (k), (l_1) \text{ and } (l_2) \text{: } \} \\
(m) & R \\
& \cdots
\end{array}
$$

The *tautology* $P \vee \neg P$ is used as one of the three premisses for line (m). This tautology has zero premisses and hence there are no dots above it. The reasoning which leads to line (k) is actually already done with the comment just above it, viz. { Tautology: }.

An *inference* hence always looks as follows:

$$\text{From } P_1, \ldots, P_n \text{ follows } Q,$$

with n a natural number that gives the number of premisses : 0, 1 or more.

The inference as a whole is *correct* if Q is a correct conclusion from P_1 to P_n (see the beginning of this section), hence if

$$(P_1 \wedge \ldots \wedge P_n) \overset{val}{\models} Q.$$

Hence, if we come across a reasoning where P_1 to P_n occur at the lines numbered (k_1) to (k_n) respectively, we may draw the conclusion Q at line number (m), provided that:

- All these P_i are *valid* (see Section 13.1, where also an exception to this rule is discussed) and

- $k_i < m$ for all i such that $1 \leq i \leq n$.

(The order of k_1 to k_n is not important.)

11.5   Hypotheses

There are three kinds of hypotheses, which we must distinguish:

(1) *The pure hypothesis.* This is a (temporary) proposition which is assumed, without side-effects. We give some examples:

  − 'Assume: $P \wedge \neg Q$.'

  − 'Assume: $\forall_x [x \in \mathbb{N} : P]$.'

  − 'Assume: the sequence converges.' (If we know which sequence is referred to.)

  − 'Assume: n is greater than 10.' (If it is a 'known' n.)

  − 'Assume: the function f is continuous.' (If f has already been introduced or defined and is still 'known'.)

  − 'Assume: $\sqrt{2}$ is a rational number.' (For example in order to show that this hypothesis is 'impossible', and that $\sqrt{2}$ *cannot* hence be a rational number.)

(2) *The generating hypothesis.* This introduces a *new* name (it is 'generated'). This name is used for an 'arbitrary' variable from a certain domain. This domain is given beforehand and will (in general) have

more than *one* element. From these elements we choose one, but we don't say which.

You should not take it literally that this name is 'new'. Usually it will be a letter which has been used thousands of times before, but which happens to be 'available' at the moment.

The *hypothesis* in question here is the hypothesis that the element with the 'new' name belongs to the given domain.

Examples:

- 'Assume that: n is a natural number greater than 10.' (In case this n is 'new', i.e. if there are no other 'active' n's, earlier n's are all 'out of service'.)

  The arbitrary natural number that we have in mind, has now received a name. The corresponding hypothesis is that n belongs to the domain $\{x \in \mathbb{N} | x > 10\}$.[3]

- 'Assume that: f is a continuous function from $\mathbb{R}$ to $\mathbb{R}$.' (If f is new.)

  Here we want to take an arbitrary element from the domain **D**, where **D** is the set of all continuous functions from $\mathbb{R}$ to $\mathbb{R}$. We call that arbitrary element f. The hypothesis is that $f \in$ **D**.

- 'Assume: (a, b) is a pair of integer numbers with $a < b$.' (Both a and b are new.)

  The hypothesis is that $(a, b) \in \{(x, y) \in \mathbb{Z}^2 | x < y\}$. We give the name (a, b) to an arbitrary pair of integer numbers from that domain.

(3) *The identifying hypothesis.* This is nothing else than a *definition*, which is a shorthand which makes it easy to talk about some object or some concept. The difference with the earlier, generating hypothesis is that with the identifying hypothesis one never names an 'arbitrary' element from a domain, but *one well-described object*. That one thing gets a name. You can choose this *name* yourself. However, it must still be relatively 'new', which means: there must not be any confusion with a name that is still 'active'.

You better avoid the identifying hypotheses, but you will often come across them in the literature. It is preferable in this case to be explicit and to use the word 'definition' or 'define', as we do in the following examples:

---

[3] We use here the *mathematical* notation for sets. See Section 10.2.

- 'Assume that n is the root of 533.' (The n is new.)

  There is however only *one* root of 533, hence n is used as a name for this unique root.

  You can better formulate this as: 'Define $n = \sqrt{533}$.'

  Note: If the name n is not new, but is *already known*, then the sentence 'Assume that n is the root of 533' expresses a *pure hypothesis*, namely the hypothesis that this known n is equal to $\sqrt{533}$.

- 'Let k be the average value of m and n.' (The k is new, m and n are already known.)

  There is precisely *one* average value of the (known) m and n, hence this too is a definition. Better: 'Define k as the average value of m and n.'

We will only rarely consider the third kind of hypotheses, the *identifying* ones, in this book. This third kind is concerned with *definitions* which we treat only on the side in this book.

The first two kinds of hypotheses, on the other hand, the *pure* and the *generating* hypotheses, play a big role in reasoning. Therefore, we will come back to them in more details.

11.6   The use of hypotheses

We will check in this section, under which circumstances hypotheses can be used in reasoning.

There are two kinds of usage that must be distinguished:

- The hypotheses which *precede* the 'real' reasoning, are used to specify the *situation* in which the reasoning takes place. These hypotheses are fixed at the beginning and *stay in use till the end*.

  See the mathematical example from Section 11.3. There, the situation is first described in the announcement of the proposition and thereafter, for completeness, it is specified explicitly by the following hypotheses:

  - *hypothesis 1:* 'Let $(a_n)_{n \in \mathbb{N}}$ and $(b_n)_{n \in \mathbb{N}}$ be two convergent sequences of real numbers'.

    This can actually be seen as *four* hypotheses given at the same time:

– The *generating* hypotheses that we take two 'arbitrary' sequences of real numbers, which we give the new names $(a_n)_{n \in \mathbb{N}}$ and $(b_n)_{n \in \mathbb{N}}$ in order to be able to talk about them,

– the *pure* hypotheses that both sequences are *convergent*.

– *hypothesis 2:* 'Assume that $\lim a_n = A$ and $\lim b_n = B$'.

These are two *identifying* hypotheses, or *definitions*. Namely: we give the 'one and only' $\lim a_n$ the name A, and similarly we give $\lim b_n$ the name B. Note that A is not an arbitrary element from a domain, but is instead exactly this unique $\lim a_n$.

- The pure and generating hypotheses which are assumed *during* the reasoning process, usually serve a specific goal:

  – A *pure* hypothesis leads in a natural way to an *implication*.

  – A *generating* hypothesis leads in a natural way to a conclusion with a ∀-quantifier as a main symbol.

We will not explain here how these last two claims actually work. We postpone this explanation to Chapters 12 and 15.

11.7 Exercises

11.1 Assume that the following is true:
'If the weather is good, then Charles will go to the lake and not to his aunt. If Charles goes to the lake or if he goes to the sea, then he will be fishing.'

(a) Formulate the above in the form of abstract propositions.

(b) Give *reasonings* which show that the following is also true:
  (1) If the weather is good, then Charles will not go to his aunt.
  (2) If the weather is good, then Charles will be fishing.

11.2 Take a circle C with centre M. Take further a triangle D where the three corner points occur on C, whereas one side of D goes through M.

Give a reasoning which shows that D is a rectangular triangle.

11.3 Give reasonings which show the following:

(a) The product of two odd numbers is odd.

(b) If n^2 is even, then n is also even (n is an integer number).

(c) Every multiple of six is also a multiple of three.

11.4 Check whether the following propositions are true. If so, give a reasoning which shows this. If not so, give a counterexample.

(a) All prime numbers are odd, except the number 2.

(b) Every sum of three prime numbers is also a prime number.

(c) There is a prime number which is 1 plus a multiple of seven.

11.5 Give a reasoning which shows the following (x is a real number):

(a) If $x^3 + x^2 - 2 = 0$ then $x = 1$, and vice versa (i.e. the other way round).

(b) If $x = 1$, then $x^3 + x^2 - x - 1 = 0$, but not vice versa.

11.6 Look at the following proposition:
'A square of an odd integer number is 1 plus a multiple of eight.'
Give a reasoning which proves it.

11.7 A sequence $(a_n)_{n \in \mathbb{N}}$ of real numbers is called *bounded* if there is a real number M such that $|a_n| < M$ for all $n \in \mathbb{N}$.

(a) Prove the following lemma:
'If two sequences of real numbers are bounded, then the sum-sequence is also bounded.'

(b) Point out which hypotheses you use in your proof of (a). Say which of these hypotheses are pure, generating or identifying.

Chapter 12

Reasoning with ∧ and ⇒

Bring it to the proof

12.1 'Flags'

Implication is not popular when 'calculating with formulas': We have already seen that a formula of the form $P \Rightarrow Q$ is often directly rewritten to $\neg P \vee Q$ with the help of a standard equivalence called (indeed) 'Implication'.

When *reasoning* however, implication plays a major role. Based on this, we concentrate in this chapter on implication. We do this in combination with conjunction which is itself also of extreme importance during reasoning. (The conjunction is by the way *always* important, *also* when *calculating* with logical formulas.)

Hypotheses are fundamental in many reasonings. In particular, the pure hypotheses are important especially in connection with implication and the generating hypotheses are especially important for universal (∀-) propositions (for the latter: see Chapter 15). Therefore we *mark* these two sorts of hypotheses in the rest of this book in a special way: we put them in a rectangle (a 'flag').

On the left hand side, and below this rectangle, we attach a vertical line (the 'flag-pole') which expresses the life duration of the hypothesis, i.e., the duration for which this hypothesis is valid.

For a pure hypothesis like 'Assume: $P \vee (Q \Leftrightarrow R)$' this will hence look as follows:

{ Assume: }

(1) $\boxed{P \vee (Q \Leftrightarrow R)}$

$\vdots$

(l) $\dots$

$\vdots$

(m) $\dots$

The hypothesis occurs here in line number (1) and stretches to line (l). Its validity is hence assumed up to and including line (l). In the lines below (l), including line number (m), the hypothesis is no longer valid.

We can also assume hypotheses *inside* other hypotheses, as we shall see in the first example of the following section. Also we can, as we shall see later, make a new hypothesis *after* a previous one has been closed (we also say *withdrawn* or *retracted*).

12.2   Introduction and elimination rules

As an example of a proof in flag style we take again the reasoning which shows that the formula

$$((P \Rightarrow Q) \wedge (Q \Rightarrow R)) \Rightarrow (P \Rightarrow R)$$

is a tautology (see Section 11.2). In the 'flag notation' the complete reasoning looks as shown on the following page.

In that flag proof, we see that before every line, there is an argument given between braces, either '{ Assume: }', or '{ By ...: }'.

For arguments of this last kind – of the form '{ By ...: }' – we can even be more specific, since 'By' is actually a bit vague.

Let us look in more details at such arguments.

We see '{ By (1) }' just before the line with number (3). In this case, the reason is that the *conjunction* $(P \Rightarrow Q) \wedge (Q \Rightarrow R)$ has as a consequence that its left hand side holds: $P \Rightarrow Q$. This is justified by the standard $\wedge$-$\vee$-weakening rule

$$P \wedge Q \models^{val} P \; (*),$$

which gives via Substitution that: $(P \Rightarrow Q) \wedge (Q \Rightarrow R) \models^{val} P \Rightarrow Q$.

A similar thing holds for the right hand side (see Section 7.2):

$$P \wedge Q \stackrel{val}{\models} Q \quad (**),$$

from which, again by Substitution, we get $(P \Rightarrow Q) \wedge (Q \Rightarrow R) \stackrel{val}{\models} Q \Rightarrow R$. This is used – again with a 'by'-argument – in line number (4).

Here is the full reasoning in flag style. Please compare it carefully with the reasoning 'in words', as given in Section 11.2:

	{ Assume: }
(1)	$(P \Rightarrow Q) \wedge (Q \Rightarrow R)$
	{ Assume: }
(2)	P
	{ By (1): }
(3)	$P \Rightarrow Q$
	{ Once again by (1): }
(4)	$Q \Rightarrow R$
	{ By (3) and (2): }
(5)	Q
	{ By (4) and (5): }
(6)	R
	{ By (2) and (6): }
(7)	$P \Rightarrow R$
	{ By (1) and (7): }
(8)	$((P \Rightarrow Q) \wedge (Q \Rightarrow R)) \Rightarrow (P \Rightarrow R)$

The two weakening rules $(*)$ and $(**)$ actually say what you can do if you come across a *conjunction* when reasoning from top to bottom. Because this is very natural (and also very obvious), we shall make a separate *reasoning rule*, which we call $\wedge$-*elimination*. The rule says how the conjunction sign $\wedge$ can be 'gotten rid of', or *eliminated*.

For clarity, we write this rule as a scheme (the four vertical dashes ‖‖ mean that anything can appear there, we are in the middle of a reasoning):

$\wedge$-elimination:

$$\|\|\|$$
$$(k) \qquad P \wedge Q$$
$$\|\|\|$$
$$\{ \wedge\text{-elim on } (k) \colon \ \}$$
$$(m) \qquad P$$

This rule is *general*, in the sense that Substitution is allowed. If for example on line number (k) one does not have $P \wedge Q$, but another $\wedge$-formula, e.g. $(P \Rightarrow Q) \wedge (Q \Rightarrow R)$, then one can conclude with $\wedge$-elim that $P \Rightarrow Q$.

Obviously, the $\wedge$-elim rule has the following variant:

$\wedge$-elimination:

$$\|\|\|$$
$$(k) \qquad P \wedge Q$$
$$\|\|\|$$
$$\{ \wedge\text{-elim on } (k) \colon \ \}$$
$$(n) \qquad Q$$

In both cases we reason in a *forward* manner, starting from an $\wedge$-formula: if we 'know' $P \wedge Q$, then we may conclude both P (the first case) and Q (the second case). But be careful: *first* we must know $P \wedge Q$, and only *afterwards* can we conclude P respectively Q. Hence $k < m$, respectively $k < n$. We reason *from top to bottom*.

This *forward* reasoning can also take place if we come across an $\Rightarrow$-formula. Look for example at the lines with numbers (5) and (6) in the example in the beginning of the present section. The arguments that we gave there (of the form '{ By ... }') can also be made more specific. The first case deals with the fact that the *implication* $P \Rightarrow Q$, together with P, leads to the conclusion Q. This is the case because

$$(P \Rightarrow Q) \wedge P \models^{val} Q$$

is a valid weakening (check this!). In the second case something similar takes place.

This so-called weakening rule actually tells you what you can do if you 'know' an implication $P \Rightarrow Q$. On its own this does not yet lead anywhere, but *together* with P it allows you to conclude Q. This is actually a natural application of an implication: when you know 'If P then Q', then this means that: *as soon as* you (also) know P, then you may conclude Q.

Also here we make an elimination rule, the $\Rightarrow$-*elimination*, which says how you can use $\Rightarrow$ (and immediately get rid of, or eliminate it: in the end result Q, the original $\Rightarrow$ can no longer be found). This rule looks as follows:

$\Rightarrow$-elimination:

$$
\begin{array}{ll}
& \|\|\| \\
(k) & P \Rightarrow Q \\
& \|\|\| \\
(l) & P \\
& \|\|\| \\
& \{ \Rightarrow\text{-elim on } (k) \text{ and } (l): \ \} \\
(m) & Q
\end{array}
$$

The order of the lines with numbers (k) and (l) does not have any effect here. However it must be that $k < m$ and $l < m$. Note also here that we are doing *forward* reasoning (*from top to bottom*): we start first with the fact that we already 'know' $P \Rightarrow Q$. If we then also get to 'know' P, then we can *use it to* derive the conclusion Q.

Be careful: We have not at all said that we will be *successful* in deriving P if we know $P \Rightarrow Q$. If we can't derive P then the application of the rule $\Rightarrow$-elimination is not possible. This risk will always be present with an $\Rightarrow$-formula: perhaps you 'know it', but you *can't* do anything with it.

Also with $\Rightarrow$-elimination, Substitution is permitted.

Finally we look closer at the arguments before the lines with numbers (7) and (8), in the example given in the beginning of this section. In both cases one sees that a flag-pole ends. This flag-pole corresponds to a hypothesis. In the first case, for example, the hypothesis P from line number (2), which led to the conclusion R in line number (6), is retracted. This *whole reasoning* from line number (2) to line number (6) is summarized in the conclusion which appears in line (7): $P \Rightarrow R$. (Everything *between* (2) and (6) is forgotten, it was only necessary in order to reach (6) from (2) in a correct way, in this case also using (1).)

In short, this is an application of a *general method* in order to obtain an implication of the form '... $\Rightarrow$ ...' as a *conclusion*. This method is a form of *backward* reasoning: we want to reach $P \Rightarrow Q$ and so we investigate how a reasoning *above* $P \Rightarrow Q$ must look like. Hence, we work here *from bottom to top*.

This general rule of 'getting' (*'introducing'*) an implication is summarized in the following ⇒-*introduction rule* (instead of the vertical strips we use a 'hole' $\vdots$, which still has to be filled).

⇒-introduction:

$$\{ \text{ Assume: } \}$$

(k) $\boxed{P}$

$\vdots$

$(m-1)$ $\quad Q$

$$\{ \Rightarrow\text{-intro on } (k) \text{ and } (m-1)\text{: } \}$$

(m) $\quad P \Rightarrow Q$

Note that, when applying an ⇒-intro, a hypothesis gets always *retracted* (a flag-pole ends) *immediately before* the place where the implication gets introduced. In the above scheme you see that, just after line number $(m-1)$ the flag-pole disappears, whereas on line number (m) (hence immediately after) the conclusion is derived. In this conclusion $(P \Rightarrow Q)$ the retracted hypothesis (P) appears on the *left* of the implication arrow, and the *last* conclusion which is made under the hypothesis P (namely Q) appears on the *right* of this implication arrow. It looks very simple and it is actually so, as long as you apply the rule '⇒-intro' precisely 'according to the recipe'.

It is also important to note that the ⇒-introduction rule really differs from the ⇒-elimination rule. This is because, as we have seen above, the *situation* where you use each of these rules is very different.

We summarize below the differences between the introduction and the elimination rules, not only for ⇒, but in general:

- An *elimination*-rule serves for reasoning *from top to bottom* (forward). You start with something that you already 'know' and from which you try to reach a conclusion. If this succeeds, you can write this conclusion *below* what you know at the top.

- An *introduction*-rule on the other hand serves for reasoning *from bottom to top* (backwards). You look at the goal (that you still have to reach, you still *don't yet* 'know' it) and you check how you can reach it. You do this by starting a reasoning *above* this goal.

To summarize, we repeat the reasoning given in the beginning of this section, but now with the more precise arguments ($\land$-introduction, $\Rightarrow$-introduction and -elimination) that we have introduced in this section. See the derivation below.

Note that we repeatedly apply Substitution when using the introduction and elimination rules.

$\{$ Assume: $\}$

(1) $\quad \boxed{(P \Rightarrow Q) \land (Q \Rightarrow R)}$

        $\{$ Assume: $\}$

(2) $\qquad \boxed{P}$

          $\{$ $\land$-elim on (1): $\}$

(3) $\qquad P \Rightarrow Q$

          $\{$ $\land$-elim on (1): $\}$

(4) $\qquad Q \Rightarrow R$

          $\{$ $\Rightarrow$-elim on (3) and (2): $\}$

(5) $\qquad Q$

          $\{$ $\Rightarrow$-elim on (4) and (5): $\}$

(6) $\qquad R$

       $\{$ $\Rightarrow$-intro on (2) and (6): $\}$

(7) $\quad P \Rightarrow R$

     $\{$ $\Rightarrow$-intro on (1) and (7): $\}$

(8) $\quad ((P \Rightarrow Q) \land (Q \Rightarrow R)) \Rightarrow (P \Rightarrow R)$

We have so far discussed:

– The $\land$-elimination rule,

– The $\Rightarrow$-elimination rule and

– The $\Rightarrow$-introduction rule.

In this list, an $\land$-*introduction rule* is missing. Such a rule, which should be a 'natural' method to *form* a conjunction, is easy to devise.

We give the general form of the $\land$-introduction rule, which is a *backward* method:

$\wedge$-introduction:

$$\vdots$$

$(k) \qquad P$

$$\vdots$$

$(l) \qquad Q$

$\qquad\qquad \{\ \wedge\text{-intro on } (k) \text{ and } (l).\ \}$

$(m) \qquad P \wedge Q$

Hence, in order to reach the conclusion $P \wedge Q$ in line (m), we must first derive both the conclusion P and the conclusion Q. Hence $k < m$ and $l < m$. (This can also take place in the opposite order, hence both $k < l$ and $k > l$ are possible.) This is so simple, that you almost don't see that it is a fundamental property of conjunction.

When applying this method, you have *two* 'holes': *one* above P and *one* above Q. These holes must still be filled.

You can say that $\wedge$-intro and $\wedge$-elim set up the natural meaning of $\wedge$, exactly like $\Rightarrow$-intro and $\Rightarrow$-elim do for $\Rightarrow$. In all these rules, Substitution is allowed.

Remark 12.2.1 *We have now consecutively defined* four *new derivation rules:* $\wedge$-elim, $\Rightarrow$-elim, $\Rightarrow$-intro *and* $\wedge$-intro. *Three of these are a direct consequence of valid weakening rules:*

- $\wedge$-elim *is based on* $P \wedge Q \models^{val} P$ *respectively on* $P \wedge Q \models^{val} Q$.
- $\Rightarrow$-elim *is based on* $(P \Rightarrow Q) \wedge P \models^{val} Q$.
- $\wedge$-intro *is actually an application of* $P \wedge Q \models^{val} P \wedge Q$: *from* P *and* Q we conclude $P \wedge Q$.

The only rule which is really new and is necessary in order to be able to use this new style of reasoning (with flags), is the $\Rightarrow$-intro. *This rule, which describes when a flag gets 'retracted', is essential for reasoning with hypotheses.*

12.3   The construction of an abstract reasoning

The reasoning that we have just set up, with use of introduction and elimination rules (but also with conclusions based on different arguments, for example as the result of an 'intermediate' calculation), is called an *abstract reasoning*. We note that the introduction and elimination rules are very general, they *also* work after Substitution (see Section 6.2).

In this section we give another example of such reasoning, where we devote particular attention to how reasoning can be built or *constructed* in a natural way. (This is the reason that the name *natural deduction* is usually given to the system of logical reasoning as exposed in the present Part II.)

We take again a formula with only $\wedge$ and $\Rightarrow$ as connectives:

$$(P \Rightarrow (Q \wedge R)) \Rightarrow ((P \Rightarrow Q) \wedge (Q \Rightarrow (P \Rightarrow R))).$$

Our goal is to show that this is a tautology, via a natural reasoning. This formula is hence our *goal*, which we write at the bottom of the page. (We don't know how long the reasoning will be, and hence we reserve some space *above* our goal.)

We begin hence as follows:

$$\vdots$$

$(m) \quad (P \Rightarrow (Q \wedge R)) \Rightarrow ((P \Rightarrow Q) \wedge (Q \Rightarrow (P \Rightarrow R)))$

The 'hole' is where the dots occur. There we must add the reasoning which *from top to bottom* will lead to the goal. But in order to succeed, it makes sense to keep looking *at the bottom* as long as possible. Hence, we start with reasoning in the 'wrong' direction, *from bottom to top*, by trying to replace our goal by another, preferably simpler goal.

This can be done here because the goal formula in line number (m) is an *implication*. The standard way to derive an implication, is via the rule $\Rightarrow$-intro. The corresponding abstract reasoning must hence look as follows:

$$\{ \text{ Assume: } \}$$

$(1) \quad \boxed{P \Rightarrow (Q \wedge R)}$

$$\vdots$$

$(m-1) \quad \bigg| \quad (P \Rightarrow Q) \wedge (Q \Rightarrow (P \Rightarrow R))$

$\{ \Rightarrow\text{-intro on } (1) \text{ and } (m-1): \}$

$(m) \quad (P \Rightarrow (Q \wedge R)) \Rightarrow ((P \Rightarrow Q) \wedge (Q \Rightarrow (P \Rightarrow R)))$

The *left hand side* of the implication in line number (m), namely the formula $P \Rightarrow (Q \wedge R)$, now occurs on top of the reasoning-under-construction, in a flag (this means, it is added as a hypothesis). The *right-hand side* of this implication is the new goal at line number $(m-1)$. Note that this new goal is located 'under' the hypothesis, and so in order to derive it, we *can use* the hypothesis in (1).

We keep trying to solve the goal. The new goal, which replaces the old one is: $(P \Rightarrow Q) \wedge (Q \Rightarrow (P \Rightarrow R))$. This is a conjunction. Therefore, it makes sense to try solving this goal with ∧-intro:

$$
\begin{array}{rl}
& \{ \text{ Assume: } \} \\
(1) & \boxed{P \Rightarrow (Q \wedge R)} \\
& \quad \vdots \\
(l) & P \Rightarrow Q \\
& \quad \vdots \\
(m-2) & Q \Rightarrow (P \Rightarrow R) \\
& \{ \wedge\text{-intro on } (l) \text{ and } (m-2) \text{: } \} \\
(m-1) & (P \Rightarrow Q) \wedge (Q \Rightarrow (P \Rightarrow R)) \\
& \{ \Rightarrow\text{-intro on } (1) \text{ and } (m-1) \text{: } \} \\
(m) & (P \Rightarrow (Q \wedge R)) \Rightarrow ((P \Rightarrow Q) \wedge (Q \Rightarrow (P \Rightarrow R)))
\end{array}
$$

Note that we apply ∧-intro *'under'* the flag in line (1): the flag pole of the flag in line (1) extends over lines (l) and $(m-2)$, until it ends after line $(m-1)$. So, although the assumption in line (1) does not play any role in the application of the ∧-introduction rule, it doesn't prevent this application either (as long as the flag structure remains unchanged).

We now obtained *two* new goals from the old one: $P \Rightarrow Q$ in line number (l) and $Q \Rightarrow (P \Rightarrow R)$ in line number $(m-2)$. Both can still be made smaller by trying ⇒-intro. Hence, when applying the standard scheme for ⇒-introduction twice, we may extend the derivation as shown on the following page.

The reasoning obtained, still has two *holes*: *one* between lines (2) and $(l-1)$ and another one between $(l+1)$ and $(m-3)$. Both have to be filled, although the *order* in which this is done is irrelevant: one may start filling either the first or the second hole.

$\{$ Assume: $\}$

(1) $\boxed{P \Rightarrow (Q \wedge R)}$

$\quad\{$ Assume: $\}$

(2) $\quad\boxed{P}$

$\quad\quad\vdots$

$(l-1)$ $\quad Q$

$\quad\{ \Rightarrow$-intro on (2) and $(l-1)$: $\}$

(l) $\quad P \Rightarrow Q$

$\quad\{$ Assume: $\}$

$(l+1)$ $\quad\boxed{Q}$

$\quad\quad\vdots$

$(m-3)$ $\quad P \Rightarrow R$

$\quad\{ \Rightarrow$-intro on $(l+1)$ and $(m-3)$: $\}$

$(m-2)$ $\quad Q \Rightarrow (P \Rightarrow R)$

$\quad\{ \wedge$-intro on (l) and $(m-2)$: $\}$

$(m-1)$ $\quad (P \Rightarrow Q) \wedge (Q \Rightarrow (P \Rightarrow R))$

$\{ \Rightarrow$-intro on (1) and $(m-1)$: $\}$

(m) $\quad (P \Rightarrow (Q \wedge R)) \Rightarrow ((P \Rightarrow Q) \wedge (Q \Rightarrow (P \Rightarrow R)))$

Let us start with the first hole. For this, we temporarily isolate the first part of the reasoning, from line (1) up to line $(l-1)$. So we only consider:

$\{$ Assume: $\}$

(1) $\boxed{P \Rightarrow (Q \wedge R)}$

$\quad\{$ Assume: $\}$

(2) $\quad\boxed{P}$

$\quad\quad\vdots$

$(l-1)$ $\quad Q$ (Here below we imagine the rest of the reasoning.)

The goal Q in line number $(l-1)$ cannot be simplified any further. But in the 'hole', both line number (1): $P \Rightarrow (Q \wedge R)$, and line number (2): P, are 'available' (or 'valid'). Note that $\Rightarrow$-elim is applicable on these two!

Applying $\Rightarrow$-elimination, we obtain the conclusion $Q \wedge R$, which can be written as line number (3) – 'under' the flags in lines number (1) and (2).

{ Assume: }

(1) $\boxed{P \Rightarrow (Q \wedge R)}$

      { Assume: }

(2) $\boxed{P}$

        { $\Rightarrow$-elim on (1) and (2): }

(3) $Q \wedge R$

        $\vdots$

$(l-1)$ Q (etc.)

This hole can now simply be closed with $\wedge$-elim:

{ Assume: }

(1) $\boxed{P \Rightarrow (Q \wedge R)}$

      { Assume: }

(2) $\boxed{P}$

        { $\Rightarrow$-elim on (1) and (2): }

(3) $Q \wedge R$

        { $\wedge$-elim on (3): }

(4) Q (etc.)

So the first hole has been successfully dealt with. What is left, is the second hole.

But it is not difficult to also close this second hole, following the same principles that we have just used for the first hole:

– firstly, apply another time the $\Rightarrow$-introduction rule (because of the $\Rightarrow$ in line $(m-3)$, becoming line (10) below): this gives the flag in line number (7), and the new goal R in line number (9) below;

– and secondly, use another $\Rightarrow$-elim followed by an $\wedge$-elim to close the last gap.

The end result is the reasoning that is written here below.

{ Assume: }

(1) $\boxed{P \Rightarrow (Q \wedge R)}$

    { Assume: }

(2) $\boxed{P}$

      { $\Rightarrow$-elim on (1) and (2): }

(3) $Q \wedge R$

      { $\wedge$-elim on (3): }

(4) Q

    { $\Rightarrow$-intro on (2) and (4): }

(5) $P \Rightarrow Q$

    { Assume: }

(6) $\boxed{Q}$

      { Assume: }

(7) $\boxed{P}$

        { $\Rightarrow$-elim on (1) and (7): }

(8) $Q \wedge R$

        { $\wedge$-elim on (8): }

(9) R

      { $\Rightarrow$-intro on (7) and (9): }

(10) $P \Rightarrow R$

    { $\Rightarrow$-intro on (6) and (10): }

(11) $Q \Rightarrow (P \Rightarrow R)$

    { $\wedge$-intro on (5) and (11): }

(12) $(P \Rightarrow Q) \wedge (Q \Rightarrow (P \Rightarrow R))$

  { $\Rightarrow$-intro on (1) and (12): }

(13) $(P \Rightarrow (Q \wedge R)) \Rightarrow ((P \Rightarrow Q) \wedge (Q \Rightarrow (P \Rightarrow R)))$

What may attract attention in this reasoning is that the hypothesis P is made *twice*: in line number (2) and in line number (7). This is less strange than it seems. Because, in both cases, there were good reasons to make hypothesis P:

– the hypothesis of P in line (2) was meant to be the beginning of a reasoning which should lead to Q (line (4)), with the intention that via $\Rightarrow$-intro one reaches $P \Rightarrow Q$ (line (5)),

– the hypothesis of P in line (7) was meant to lead to R (line (9)), in order to obtain $P \Rightarrow R$ via $\Rightarrow$-intro.

Hence, on a second reflection, there is nothing strange in this double hypothesis of P. Even stronger, you can in principle make a hypothesis from *everything*, when and where you like. It is even allowed to assume P and immediately next, assume $\neg P$. Or you can even take `False` as a hypothesis!

Of course there is nothing for free: a hypothesis that you assume during a reasoning must be retracted again, otherwise, you don't reach your goal (at best you may reach a version of the goal 'with conditions', i.e., with some 'open' hypotheses; but this is not the goal that you had in mind).

You can only retract a hypothesis by making it the left hand side of an implication (see the $\Rightarrow$-rule). So, if you wildly start making hypotheses and then later retract them, you will get these hypotheses on 'the left-hand side' of your conclusion.

Hence, the wisdom is, make hypotheses only *if there is a good motivation to do so*. In the above example, every hypothesis is accountable: the motivation is always a goal of the form $S \Rightarrow T$, an implication, that you try to get via $\Rightarrow$-intro; this always leads to a hypothesis of the form 'Assume S'.

12.4   The setting up of a reasoning

The example in the previous section shows that in order to set up a correct reasoning, there exist *strategic proof principles* which help attain a goal by means of the system of natural deduction.

What you want is to get in the end a final demonstration of this form:

- The demonstration consists of a list of propositions.

- Every proposition is either a *hypothesis*, or a *conclusion* from earlier propositions.

- The *last* proposition consists of the desired result (the original *goal*).

In order to get this, you need to work as follows:

(1) It makes sense to start with the goal, hence begin at the *bottom*. Try to replace this goal by one or more subgoals, preferably simpler ones, and repeat this process until you can't do so any more. (This takes place by applying *introduction* rules.)

(2) Now you have a reasoning with one or more 'holes'. Try to fill each of these holes from top to bottom by deriving conclusions. Try to 'direct' this reasoning towards the goal which occurs under such a hole. (This simply takes place by applying *elimination* rules.)

Often (but not always) this process can be completed using this general strategy. In some more complex cases however (see for example Section 14.1), it is necessary in the course of step (2) to devise *new goals*, which can hence lead you to return again to step (1). We will not go into these details further. You will learn it yourself by doing exercises.

Step (1) is important indeed, but not that problematic. If you know what to do in order to simplify a goal, this step can be done smoothly. This is also the case if you are reasoning with more connectives than just $\Rightarrow$ and $\wedge$ (as in the previous section), or with quantifiers. Also for a mathematical reasoning, step (1) is often an excellent preparation.

The advantage of step (1) is that it helps you to get started and it enables you to get a clear picture of the overall structure.

Usually, step (2) is the most difficult. There, creativity is really needed, whether one is dealing with a purely logical reasoning as in the previous section, or with a difficult mathematical theorem.

Hence, although you know well what a 'correct reasoning' precisely is, the real problems will remain. But the *thinking* about these problems is made *much* simpler, thanks to the flag-structured representation of a derivation-to-be, which gives you a pictorial overview of the state of affairs. Your eyes may dwell over the formulas, in order to decide which new step is possible to continue your proof attempt in order to fill the hole(s).

Regrettably, it is possible that you choose the wrong direction, but in that case you can always withdraw to plan a new attack. 'Reculer pour mieux sauter': step back for a better jump – as the Frenchman says.

Remark 12.4.1 *As we tried to clarify in this chapter, it is very important that you make a clear distinction between what you* know *and what you* do not (yet) know. *In the flag representation, this distinction coincides to a great extent with the difference between what's* above *the hole and what's* below *it.*

So you can see directly, from the lay-out alone:

- *what you 'know' and hence what you can use (this occurs* above *the 'hole',*

- *and where you want to go (the goal; which occurs* under *the hole).*

12.5   Exercises

12.1 Give the justifications (arguments) for the following derivations:

(a)

        $\{ \dots \}$

(1) $\boxed{P \wedge P}$

        $\{ \dots \}$

(2) P

        $\{ \dots \}$

(3) $(P \wedge P) \Rightarrow P$

(b)

        $\{ \dots \}$

(1) $\boxed{P}$

        $\{ \dots \}$

(2) $\boxed{Q}$

        $\{ \dots \}$

(3) $P \wedge Q$

        $\{ \dots \}$

(4) $Q \Rightarrow (P \wedge Q)$

        $\{ \dots \}$

(5) $P \Rightarrow (Q \Rightarrow (P \wedge Q))$

(c)

        $\{ \dots \}$

(1) $\boxed{P}$

        $\{ \dots \}$

(2) $\boxed{P \Rightarrow Q}$

        $\{ \dots \}$

(3) Q

        $\{ \dots \}$

(1) $(P \Rightarrow Q) \Rightarrow Q$

        $\{ \dots \}$

(2) $P \Rightarrow ((P \Rightarrow Q) \Rightarrow Q)$

12.2 Fill the dots in the following derivations:

(a)
                { Assume: }

    (1) $\boxed{P \Rightarrow (P \Rightarrow Q)}$

                { Assume: }

    (2) $\boxed{P}$

                   { $\Rightarrow$-elim on (1) and (2): }

    (3)   . . .

                   { $\Rightarrow$-elim on (3) and (2): }

    (4)   . . .

                { ... }

    (5)   . . .

             { ... }

    (6)   . . .

(b)
                { Assume: }

    (1) $\boxed{(P \Rightarrow Q) \wedge P}$

                 { $\wedge$-elim on (1): }

    (2)   . . .

                 { $\wedge$-elim on (1): }

    (3)   . . .

                 { $\Rightarrow$-elim on (2) and (3): }

    (4)   . . .

               { ... }

    (5)   . . .

12.3 Show via an *abstract reasoning* that the following formulas are tautologies:

(a) $((P \Rightarrow Q) \Rightarrow P) \Rightarrow ((P \Rightarrow Q) \Rightarrow Q)$

(b) $P \Rightarrow ((P \wedge Q) \Rightarrow Q)$

(c) $(P \Rightarrow Q) \Rightarrow ((P \wedge R) \Rightarrow (Q \wedge R))$

(d) $((P \wedge Q) \Rightarrow R) \Rightarrow (P \Rightarrow (Q \Rightarrow R))$

12.4 As Exercise 12.3:

(a) $(P \Rightarrow (Q \Rightarrow R)) \Rightarrow ((P \Rightarrow Q) \Rightarrow (P \Rightarrow R))$

(b) $(P \Rightarrow Q) \Rightarrow (P \Rightarrow (P \wedge Q))$

(c) $((P \Rightarrow Q) \wedge (R \Rightarrow S)) \Rightarrow ((P \wedge R) \Rightarrow (Q \wedge S))$

(d) $(P \Rightarrow Q) \Rightarrow ((R \Rightarrow (P \Rightarrow Q)) \wedge ((P \wedge R) \Rightarrow Q))$

12.5 Show via a *calculation* that the following formulas are tautologies:

(a) The formula of Exercise 12.3 (a).

(b) The formula of Exercise 12.4 (c).

Chapter 13

The structure of the context

Keep the flag flying

13.1 Validity

Abstract reasonings in the system of natural deduction, as were given in the previous chapter, are also called *derivations*. They deal purely with logic and not with mathematics. All justifications are also only of a logical nature, like for example '∧-intro' and '⇒-elim'. Also if we add ' $\overset{val}{=\!=}$ ' or ' $\overset{val}{\models}$ ', we can still speak of 'derivations' (see the following chapter).

In derivations, one mostly finds hypotheses which fit a certain pattern. This chapter will deal with such patterns. We will explain both the consequences which these patterns have on the *validity* of propositions (this section), and the *general form* of these patterns: the *structure of the context* (see the following section).

A hypothesis has only a finite life. In the previous chapter, we gave the exact life cycle of a hypothesis inside a flag by drawing a 'flag-pole' on the left hand side.

If a hypothesis is withdrawn (the flag-pole ends), then you cannot use it anymore. It will then turn up as *the left hand side* of the conclusion (an implication) which immediately follows it, but the hypothesis *as such* is no longer available.

In addition, everything that was derived as a conclusion 'under' this hypothesis (hence everything that occurs *next to* the corresponding flag-pole), also loses its validity after the withdrawal of the hypothesis. The reason is, that for these conclusions the hypothesis might have been (directly or indirectly) needed, so that these conclusions *depend* on the hypothesis. Hence, as soon as the hypothesis is declared non-active, the same will also hold for the conclusions that depend on it.

This means that, by deriving conclusions in a reasoning you must precisely know what is still 'valid', and what is not. In order to make this precise, we repeat the last example from the previous chapter, however without the justifications.

$$
\begin{array}{ll}
(1) & P \Rightarrow (Q \wedge R) \\
(2) & \quad P \\
(3) & \quad Q \wedge R \\
(4) & \quad Q \\
(5) & \quad P \Rightarrow Q \\
(6) & \quad Q \\
(7) & \quad\quad P \\
(8) & \quad\quad Q \wedge R \\
(9) & \quad\quad R \\
(10) & \quad P \Rightarrow R \\
(11) & \quad Q \Rightarrow (P \Rightarrow R) \\
(12) & \quad (P \Rightarrow Q) \wedge (Q \Rightarrow (P \Rightarrow R)) \\
(13) & (P \Rightarrow (Q \wedge R)) \Rightarrow ((P \Rightarrow Q) \wedge (Q \Rightarrow (P \Rightarrow R)))
\end{array}
$$

From the above, we can easily read what is valid and where it is valid.

- the hypothesis in (1) is valid up to (and including) line (12), but not in (13),

- the hypothesis in (2) is valid up to (and including) line (4), but not further,

- the conclusions in the lines (3) and (4) are also valid up to (and not further than) line (4),

- the conclusion in line (5) is valid up to (and including) line (12) (and indeed, we also use it in line (12)),

- the hypothesis in line (6) is valid up to (and including) line (10) (we use it in line (8)),

- and so on. Finally:

- the conclusion in line (13) is henceforth *always* valid (it is a tautology).

'Validity' is important for all introduction- and elimination rules:

Validity condition. You can at a certain place in a reasoning only derive conclusions from propositions that are valid in that place.

An *exception* is the $\Rightarrow$-intro-rule, which when applied makes an end to validity. We repeat this rule again below:

$\Rightarrow$-introduction:

$$\{ \text{ Assume: } \}$$

$$(k) \qquad \boxed{P}$$

$$\vdots$$

$$(m-1) \qquad Q$$

$$\{ \Rightarrow\text{-intro on } (k) \text{ and } (m-1)\colon \}$$

$$(m) \qquad P \Rightarrow Q$$

Here you see that the conclusion $P \Rightarrow Q$ in line number (m) is derived from the hypothesis in line number (k) and the conclusion from this hypothesis in line number $(m-1)$, *but that both line (k) and line $(m-1)$ (and everything in between) are no longer valid in line number (m)*. This one specific case deviates from the Validity condition.

Check it out yourself that in the example of Section 12.3, the validity condition is always respected, except when applying $\Rightarrow$-intro.

13.2 Nested contexts

The hypotheses from a derivation together constitute the so-called *context structure*: at a certain point in a derivation, the *context* consists of all the hypotheses which are valid at that point.

Hence, in line (3) of the previous example, the context consists of the hypotheses in (1) and (2), whereas the context in line (9) consists of the hypotheses in (1), (6) and (7).

If we simply look at the context structure of that example, we see the following:

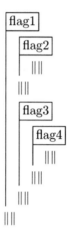

We clearly see here that every pair of flag-poles is *nested* in the following way:

- The one *contains* the other, *or*

- each stands completely independently of the other, without overlap.

In the first case, the first flag-pole starts before, and ends after the other. See for example the poles of flag 1 and flag 2, or of flag 1 and flag 4. In the second case, the first flag-pole ends *before* the second begins. For example: the flag-poles of flag 2 and flag 3 (or flag 4).

Hence, it can never happen that one flag-pole begins after another and *also* ends after it. In this case these two poles are not 'nested'.

13.3   Other notations

In this book, we deal with the flag notation. This however is not used in general. You will probably not see it anywhere else.[1]

---

[1] A notation which strongly resembles the flag notation was first given by F.B. Fitch in his book *Symbolic Logic, an Introduction*, New York, The Ronald Press Co., 1952. This notation is also used by R. Thomason in his book *Symbolic Logic, an Introduction*, MacMillan, 1970.

The notation is purely meant to clearly show what is *really* involved in a reasoning. If you have completely set up the flag notation for a certain reasoning, then you have learnt what you need to learn and you can forget about the flags. This means, you can omit these flags and flag-poles. But of course you must keep the words 'Assume:' because otherwise, you will not know which are your hypotheses.

By removing the flags and the flag-poles, you get a notation which looks a lot like the notation used in mathematics (and computer science). There is a big disadvantage to this traditional notation however: you always see where a hypothesis is assumed, but never where it is retracted (the flag-poles are missing!). You must guess yourself where a hypothesis has been retracted.

In computer science, there is a notation which looks like the flag notation for presenting contexts. This notation uses the open square brackets '|[' when assuming a hypothesis. The retraction of this hypothesis is shown with the corresponding closing square brackets ']|'. The hypothesis itself becomes closed with the sign '▷'. See the following example where the simple tautology

$$P \Rightarrow (Q \Rightarrow P)$$

is derived, first in the flag notation, and then in computer science notation.

In flag notation we obtain:

     { Assume: }

(1) $\boxed{P}$

       { Assume: }

(2) $\boxed{Q}$

         { Still   valid: (1): }

(3) P

      { ⇒-intro on (2) and (3): }

(4) $Q \Rightarrow P$

    { ⇒-intro on (1) and (4): }

(5) $P \Rightarrow (Q \Rightarrow P)$

Whereas, in computer science notation, the above becomes:

$$\begin{array}{l} \|[\quad P \\ \triangleright \\ \qquad \|[\quad Q \\ \qquad \triangleright \\ \qquad\qquad P \\ \qquad \|| \\ \qquad Q \Rightarrow P \\ \|| \\ P \Rightarrow (Q \Rightarrow P) \end{array}$$

(Two remarks about the flag derivation:
(1) In line number (3) the P from line (1) is repeated. This is acceptable because P is still *valid*.
(2) The hypothesis of Q in line (2) is not used in line (3). Still, this hypothesis is needed, in order to be able to derive $Q \Rightarrow P$ in line (4) via $\Rightarrow$-elim.)

The above derivations can also be given in a *shorter form* (A reader can still see how things fit together). The short flag derivation looks as follows:

(1) $\boxed{P}$

(2) $\quad\boxed{Q}$

(3) $\quad\quad P$

And the short computer science version can take the following form:

$$\begin{array}{l} \|[\quad P \\ \triangleright \\ \qquad \|[\quad Q \\ \qquad \triangleright \\ \qquad\qquad P \\ \qquad \|| \\ \|| \end{array}$$

The advantages of the short notation are:

- Pretty clear.
- Gives a good overview.

But there are also disadvantages:

- The accounting of the uses of (intro- and elim-) rules is missing.

- It is not clear what the original goal was. For instance, there are three possibilities in the above example:

  - 'Assume P. Assume Q. Prove P.' or:

  - 'Assume P. Prove $Q \Rightarrow P$.' or:

  - 'Prove $P \Rightarrow (Q \Rightarrow P)$.'

By the way, for the real die-hards, we always have the following 'turbo-proof', as an experienced mathematician (or computer scientist) will give it:

'Assume P, assume Q. Then P.'

And we are done. It looks so simple, this reasoning, doesn't it!?

13.4 Exercises

13.1 (a) For each of the line numbers of your solution to Exercise 12.4 (c), say where the proposition which occurs on that line is valid (i.e. allowed to be used).

(b) Do the same for your solution to Exercise 12.4 (d).

13.2 (a) For each of the line numbers of your solution to Exercise 12.4 (c), say which is the context.

(b) Do the same for your solution to Exercise 12.4 (d).

Chapter 14

Reasoning with other connectives

Draw your own conclusions

14.1 Reasoning with ¬

In Chapter 12 we have seen how, in the system of natural deduction , we could do reasoning in a standard way when it concerns formulas with $\Rightarrow$ and $\wedge$. There, we gave the introduction and elimination rules for $\Rightarrow$ and $\wedge$ and illustrated with examples how these rules are used in abstract reasonings.

In this chapter we see how one can reason with the other three connectives: $\neg$, $\vee$ and $\Leftrightarrow$.

We begin with negation, with sign $\neg$. A proposition with $\neg$ as a main symbol, can always be rewritten via the standard equivalence *Negation* to a proposition with $\Rightarrow$ as a main symbol. This is because:

$$\neg P \stackrel{val}{=\!=\!=} P \Rightarrow \texttt{False}.$$

For this reason, we don't need any separate introduction- and elimination rules for the connective $\neg$:

(I) ¬-*intro via Negation*

If we are in a situation where the *goal* is $\neg P$ (and hence $\neg P$ occurs *under* the hole):

$$\vdots$$

(m) $\neg P$

then we replace $\neg P$ *backwards* by $P \Rightarrow$ False:

$$\vdots$$

$(m-1)$ $P \Rightarrow$ False

{ Negation on $(m-1)$: }

(m) $\neg P$

after which we can apply $\Rightarrow$-intro:

{ Assume: }

(l) $\boxed{P}$

$$\vdots$$

$(m-2)$ False

{ $\Rightarrow$-intro on (l) and $(m-2)$: }

$(m-1)$ $P \Rightarrow$ False

{ Negation on $(m-1)$: }

(m) $\neg P$

Sometimes, we shall write this in a somewhat shorter form:

{ Assume: }

(l) $\boxed{P}$

$$\vdots$$

$(m-1)$ False

{ $\Rightarrow$-intro on (l) and $(m-1)$, and Negation: }

(m) $\neg P$

(II) $\neg$-*elim via Negation*

If on the other hand we want to derive a *conclusion* from $\neg P$ (which hence occurs *above* the hole):

$$\overset{\|\|\|}{\underset{\|\|\|}{(l) \quad \neg P}}$$

then we replace ¬*P forward* by $P \Rightarrow$ `False` (note that anything can occur *between* line number (l) and line number (m), hence the dashes $\|\|\|$):

$$(l) \qquad \neg P$$
$$\|\|\|$$
$$\{ \text{ Negation on } (l) \colon \ \}$$
$$(m) \qquad P \Rightarrow \texttt{False}$$

After this we are ready for $\Rightarrow$-elim:

$$\|\|\|$$
$$(l) \qquad \neg P$$
$$\|\|\|$$
$$\{ \text{ Negation on } (l) \colon \ \}$$
$$(m) \qquad P \Rightarrow \texttt{False}$$
$$\vdots$$
$$(n) \qquad P$$
$$\{ \Rightarrow\text{-elim on } (m) \text{ and } (n) \colon \ \}$$
$$(n+1) \qquad \texttt{False}$$

From the last scheme you see how ¬*P* can be used (in forward direction): if you can also derive P, then you have `False`. (And this can be very useful, see Section 14.2.)

Remark 14.1.1 *We shall* not *in what follows use the names '¬-intro' and '¬-elim', because as we saw above, they are redundant.*

As an example we give a derivation of

$$\neg(P \Rightarrow Q) \Rightarrow \neg Q.$$

We do this in phases. The first is easy. Very quickly, we get the following :

{ Assume: }

(1) $\boxed{\neg(P \Rightarrow Q)}$

$\vdots$

$(m-1)$ $\neg Q$

{ $\Rightarrow$-intro on (1) and $(m-1)$: }

(m) $\neg(P \Rightarrow Q) \Rightarrow \neg Q$

The goal is now '$\neg Q$', in line $(m-1)$. We change it into '$Q \Rightarrow$ False':

{ Assume: }

(1) $\boxed{\neg(P \Rightarrow Q)}$

$\vdots$

$(m-2)$ $Q \Rightarrow$ False

{ Negation on $(m-2)$: }

$(m-1)$ $\neg Q$

{ $\Rightarrow$-intro on (1) and $(m-1)$: }

(m) $\neg(P \Rightarrow Q) \Rightarrow \neg Q$

The new goal '$Q \Rightarrow$ False' asks for the $\Rightarrow$-intro-rule:

{ Assume: }

(1) $\boxed{\neg(P \Rightarrow Q)}$

{ Assume: }

(2) $\boxed{Q}$

$\vdots$

$(m-3)$ False

{ $\Rightarrow$-intro on (2) and $(m-3)$: }

$(m-2)$ $Q \Rightarrow$ False

{ Negation on $(m-2)$: }

$(m-1)$ $\neg Q$

{ $\Rightarrow$-intro on (1) and $(m-1)$: }

(m) $\neg(P \Rightarrow Q) \Rightarrow \neg Q$

Now things become a bit difficult. The goal 'False' can no longer be made smaller. How can we now get 'False'? It makes sense to realize that '¬$(P \Rightarrow Q)$' in line (1) is equivalent to '$(P \Rightarrow Q) \Rightarrow$ False', and from the latter we can get False with $\Rightarrow$-elim, *if* we can derive '$P \Rightarrow Q$'. We therefore consider $P \Rightarrow Q$ as a new *goal*, see below.

It is important to see why we add $P \Rightarrow Q$ as a *goal*, and not – for example – as an *assumption*:

– Adding it as a *goal* (so *below* the hole) corresponds to the fact that we do not yet 'know' $P \Rightarrow Q$ to hold: *if* we knew it, then we were ready, by combining line number (3) with it. But we're not yet so far. So it still has to be derived.

– Adding it as an *assumption* is tempting, but useless, since addition of an assumption does certainly not mean that we *proved* it: we just *assumed* it to be true. Moreover, we then so to say work 'on the wrong end' (*above* the hole). It only *appears* to be helpful: adding $P \Rightarrow Q$ as an assumption, also allows us to derive False by combining it with line number (3), *but one flag pole too high*, viz. *under* that assumption. We never get it 'down' to the level of line $(m - 3)$. Try it for yourself!

	{ Assume: }
(1)	$\boxed{\neg(P \Rightarrow Q)}$
	{ Assume: }
(2)	$\boxed{Q}$
	{ Negation on (1): }
(3)	$(P \Rightarrow Q) \Rightarrow$ False
	$\vdots$
$(m-4)$	$P \Rightarrow Q$
	{ $\Rightarrow$-elim on (3) and $(m-4)$: }
$(m-3)$	False
	{ $\Rightarrow$-intro on (2) and $(m-3)$: }
$(m-2)$	$Q \Rightarrow$ False
	{ Negation on $(m-2)$: }
$(m-1)$	$\neg Q$
	{ $\Rightarrow$-intro on (1) and $(m-1)$: }
(m)	$\neg(P \Rightarrow Q) \Rightarrow \neg Q$

Remark 14.1.2 *Adding $P \Rightarrow Q$ 'below' the hole, is an example of what we meant in Section 12.4, where we discussed introducing a new goal 'along the way'!*

The new goal '$P \Rightarrow Q$' 'requires' again $\Rightarrow$-intro, and the rest is not difficult any more. So we get the following complete derivation as our result:

$\quad\quad$ { Assume: }

(1) $\quad$ $\boxed{\neg(P \Rightarrow Q)}$

$\quad\quad\quad$ { Assume: }

(2) $\quad\quad$ $\boxed{Q}$

$\quad\quad\quad\quad$ { Negation on (1): }

(3) $\quad\quad\quad$ $(P \Rightarrow Q) \Rightarrow \text{False}$

$\quad\quad\quad\quad$ { Assume: }

(4) $\quad\quad\quad$ $\boxed{P}$

$\quad\quad\quad\quad\quad$ { Still valid: (2): }

(5) $\quad\quad\quad\quad$ Q

$\quad\quad\quad\quad$ { $\Rightarrow$-intro on (4) and (5): }

(6) $\quad\quad\quad$ $P \Rightarrow Q$

$\quad\quad\quad\quad$ { $\Rightarrow$-elim on (3) and (6): }

(7) $\quad\quad\quad$ False

$\quad\quad\quad$ { $\Rightarrow$-intro on (2) and (7): }

(8) $\quad\quad$ $Q \Rightarrow \text{False}$

$\quad\quad\quad$ { Negation on (8): }

(9) $\quad\quad$ $\neg Q$

$\quad\quad$ { $\Rightarrow$-intro on (1) and (9): }

(10) $\quad$ $\neg(P \Rightarrow Q) \Rightarrow \neg Q$

Note that the lines numbered (2), (4), (5) and (6) of this reasoning look a lot like the lines numbered (1) to (4) from the reasoning of $P \Rightarrow (Q \Rightarrow P)$ of Section 13.3! The only difference is that the letters P and Q have been interchanged.

14.2 Reasoning with False

In the previous section we saw that we don't need any separate ¬-intro- of ¬-elim-rules in the system of natural deduction, because we can use ⇒-intro and ⇒-elim instead.

We repeat below once again the scheme for '¬-*elim via Negation*':

$$
\begin{array}{ll}
& |||| \\
(l) & \neg P \\
& |||| \\
& \{ \text{ Negation on } (l) \colon \ \} \\
(m) & P \Rightarrow \textsf{False} \\
\\
& \vdots \\
(n) & P \\
& \{ \Rightarrow\text{-elim on } (m) \text{ and } (n) \colon \ \} \\
(n+1) & \textsf{False}
\end{array}
$$

You see from this example how you can 'use' ¬P: try to also conclude P and then you get False.

You can also turn this round: If you want to get False, you can try in the derivation to first derive a formula ¬P and afterwards to derive P, or the other way round! (This appears to be simpler than it actually is, because this P can in principle be 'anything'.) You must look for the suitable P on your own, the derivation does not 'direct' you in any way. See also the example from Section 14.1, where we had False as a midway goal. There we reached that goal by combining $\neg(P \Rightarrow Q)$ with $P \Rightarrow Q$.

(I) False-*intro via Contradiction:*

In the previous scheme we have found a way of *introducing* False:

If we are in a situation where False occurs *under* the hole:

$$
\begin{array}{ll}
& \vdots \\
(m) & \textsf{False}
\end{array}
$$

we try to find a P such that both P and ¬P hold. You can also write this (a bit shorter than above) as follows:

$$\vdots$$

(l) $\neg P$

$$\vdots$$

$(m-1)$ P

{ Contradiction on $(m-1)$ and (l): }

(m) False

(The standard equivalence Contradiction: $P \wedge \neg P \overset{val}{=\!=\!=}$ False, gives in particular that $\neg P \wedge P \overset{val}{\models}$ False, hence the above inference is *correct*.)

Remark 14.2.1 *The above inference is also usable as a possible shortening of $\neg$-elim. In Section 14.1, (II), we first replaced the formula $\neg P$, via Negation, by $P \Rightarrow$ False and in the case that P was derivable as well, the rule $\Rightarrow$-elim led to the conclusion* False. *This can be shorter: from $\neg P$ and P we may directly draw the conclusion* False, *by means of Contradiction. Check yourself that this enables us to omit line number (3) in the last example of Section 14.1.*

(II) False-*elim via Extremes:*

There is also a way to *eliminate* False. If the situation is such that False occurs *above* the hole:

|||

(l) False

|||

then we are lucky, as *anything* follows from False, because False is stronger than every P. (See the rule 'Extremes': False $\overset{val}{\models} P$, from Section 7.2.) Hence no matter which goal P we had, we are done:

|||

(l) False

|||

{ Extremes on (l): }

(m) P

This rule is also called the *falsum-rule*.

Remark 14.2.2 *In the sections below, we shall not use anymore the* names *'False-intro', 'False-elim' or 'falsum-rule', because they are not needed. Instead, we will apply the* methods *described above.*

14.3 Reasoning with ¬¬

From the equivalence rule 'Double Negation',

$$\neg\neg P \overset{val}{=\!=\!=} P,$$

it follows that we can replace P by $\neg\neg P$, and vice versa.
    We can use this if we come across a double negation:

(I) ¬¬-*intro via Double Negation:*

If we want to derive $\neg\neg P$:

$$\vdots$$

$$(m) \qquad \neg\neg P$$

it is enough to derive P:

$$\vdots$$

$(m-1) \qquad P$

$\qquad\qquad$ { Double Negation on $(m-1)$: }

$(m) \qquad \neg\neg P$

(II) ¬¬-*elim via Double Negation:*

And if we have already derived $\neg\neg P$:

$$\|\|\|$$

$$(l) \qquad \neg\neg P$$

$$\|\|\|$$

we can immediately conclude P:

$$||\,||$$

(l) $\neg\neg P$

$$||\,||$$

{ Double Negation on (l): }

(m) P

Remark 14.3.1 *Again, we shall not use the* names $\neg\neg$-*intro and* $\neg\neg$-*elim in what follows, only the corresponding* methods.

14.4   Reasoning 'by contradiction'

In contrast with the introduction of $\neg P$, as described in Section 14.1, there is a proof method which looks similar, but is in fact different: it is the *proof by contradiction*.

We compare these methods below.

(1) introduction of $\neg P$:

The introduction of $\neg P$ goes as follows (we repeat the scheme from Section 14.1, in the shortened version):

{ Assume: }

(l) $\boxed{P}$

        $\vdots$

$(m-1)$ | False

{ $\Rightarrow$-intro on (l) and $(m-1)$, and Negation: }

(m) $\neg P$

This method is based on the following: in order to *get* $\neg P$, we replace it 'backwards') by $P \Rightarrow$ False, via Negation. As this latter is an $\Rightarrow$-formula, it seems a natural step (by $\Rightarrow$-intro) to assume P and thereafter to try 'under' this hypothesis to give a derivation of False.

This is an almost obvious way of doing things, as soon as we get used to the idea of treating $\neg P$ as $P \Rightarrow$ False. The hypothesis of P is not an arbitrary choice, it follows directly from the application of $\Rightarrow$-intro.

(2) proof by contradiction:

The method of 'proof by contradiction' is almost a mirror image of the above method, but it is *not* as obviously natural as the method described just now. Yet, proving by contradiction is a current technique, which is often useful and practical.

The method goes as follows. We have an *arbitrary* formula as a goal, say *P*. It does not matter what its main symbol is. It can be anything. (It can even have no logical symbols at all.) So the state of affairs is:

$$\vdots$$

(n) P

Now things go further as follows: *Assume ¬P and try under this hypothesis to get* False. If we do this we get:

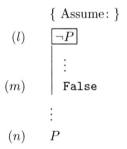

This does actually not look very convincing. In order to derive *P*, one introduces 'out of the blue' a flag with ¬*P*. The proposition *P* didn't give any motivation for doing this.

(This 'assumption of ¬*P*' is the *contradiction*, the 'peculiar', 'illogical' thing: you must prove *P*, hence you may well conjecture that *P* is 'true' in the given context, but you assume precisely ¬*P*; you assume hence something which is very likely to be 'false'!)

Why does this method actually work? Because immediately under line number (*m*), with ⇒-intro we can conclude ¬*P* ⇒ False which is equivalent to ¬¬*P*, which in turn is equivalent to *P* ...! We get hence the 'proof by contradiction' scheme as displayed on the following page.

Apparently, the method does make sense. If you succeed in closing the hole between line number (*l*) and line number (*n* − 2), then you have completed the derivation.

$$
\begin{array}{ll}
 & \{ \text{Assume:} \} \\
(l) & \boxed{\neg P} \\[2pt]
 & \quad\vdots \\
(n-2) & \;\; \texttt{False} \\
 & \{ \Rightarrow\text{-intro on } (l) \text{ and } (n-2), \text{ and Negation:} \} \\
(n-1) & \;\; \neg\neg P \\
 & \{ \text{Double Negation on } (n-1): \} \\
(n) & \;\; P
\end{array}
$$

Why should you *still* be careful with such a 'proof by contradiction'? Because it can easily lead you to an unnecessary and 'illogical' path.

Often one comes across a reasoning where the hypothesis $\neg P$ in rule number (l) *is not used at all*, whereas the reasoning 'under' this hypothesis nevertheless leads to the conclusion P just above **False**. (This **False** is hence a consequence of P and $\neg P$.) But in such a case you could have also derived P *directly*. Hence, the lines with number (l), $(n-2)$ and $(n-1)$, including the flag and the justification, are redundant.

In summary, 'proving by contradiction' can be very useful, *but only if you have exhausted all other possibilities.* If you don't have any other choice, then you can try 'proving by contradiction'.

By the way, it is good to know that *with* 'proofs by contradiction' you can do more than without them: some derivations can *only* be completed via a proof by contradiction or something similar. (That this is the case can be *proven*, but this is far from obvious.) Hence it is useful to remember this method for those times when nothing else 'seems' to work.

14.5   Reasoning with $\vee$

When 'calculating' with propositions, as was done in for example Chapter 6, we saw that the $\Rightarrow$ is less 'usable' than $\wedge$, $\vee$ and the $\neg$. Therefore we often applied there the implication-rule:

$$
P \Rightarrow Q \overset{val}{=\!=\!=} \neg P \vee Q
$$

in order to replace a formula whose main connective is $\Rightarrow$ by a formula *without* $\Rightarrow$.

In the more general method of *reasoning* that we follow from Chapter 11, the ⇒ is, however, of great importance. Because, when working with contexts, we heavily lean on the ⇒-intro and ⇒-elim rules.

We have already seen how we could turn ¬-formulas into ⇒-formulas, via

$$\neg P \overset{val}{=\joinrel=} P \Rightarrow \text{False}.$$

We shall also turn a ∨-formula into a ⇒-formula. We do this by using one of the Implication-rules (see Section 5.6):

$$P \vee Q \overset{val}{=\joinrel=} \neg P \Rightarrow Q. \tag{14.1}$$

Because ∨ is commutative, it immediately follows that:

$$Q \vee P \overset{val}{=\joinrel=} \neg P \Rightarrow Q,$$

hence with Substitution [P for Q and Q for P]:

$$P \vee Q \overset{val}{=\joinrel=} \neg Q \Rightarrow P. \tag{14.2}$$

We have thus obtained *two* ways of rewriting $P \vee Q$ (you may choose):

- to $\neg P \Rightarrow Q$, or

- to $\neg Q \Rightarrow P$.

From now on, we give the name *Implication* not only to formula (14.1), but also to formula (14.2).

The above can be summarized as follows:

(I) ∨-*intro via Implication:*

If the goal is $P \vee Q$:

$$\vdots$$

$$(m) \qquad P \vee Q$$

we can pursue it, either on the basis of (14.1), with

$$\vdots$$

$$(m-1) \qquad \neg P \Rightarrow Q$$
$$\{ \text{ Implication on } (m-1) \text{: } \}$$
$$(m) \qquad P \vee Q$$

or on the basis of (14.2), with

$$\vdots$$

$(m-1)$ $\neg Q \Rightarrow P$

{ Implication on $(m-1)$: }

(m) $P \vee Q$

In both cases we can try to go further ('backwards') by $\Rightarrow$-intro. In the first case things look as follows:

{ Assume: }

(l) $\boxed{\neg P}$

$$\vdots$$

$(m-2)$ Q

{ $\Rightarrow$-intro on (l) and $(m-2)$: }

$(m-1)$ $\neg P \Rightarrow Q$

{ Implication on $(m-1)$: }

(m) $P \vee Q$

The other case is similar.

Remark 14.5.1 *It is good to know that there is sometimes a nice and easy solution to attain a goal of the form $P \vee Q$, by using the second $\wedge$-$\vee$-weakening rule:*

$$P \models^{val} P \vee Q .$$

That is to say: if you are in the lucky position that P has already been derived, then $P \vee Q$ may immediately be concluded, with as argumentation: '$\wedge$-$\vee$-weakening'. (Of course, this is also possible when Q has been derived, since $Q \models^{val} P \vee Q$ also holds. The latter is an easy consequence of the same weakening rule, by applying Substitution and Commutativity.)

This process could be called '$\vee$-intro via Weakening'. However, be aware of the fact that this approach leads only now and then to the desired goal $P \vee Q$, since it is often the case that $P \vee Q$ is indeed derivable, whereas this holds for neither P, nor Q alone. So usually we need the general strategy '$\vee$-intro via Implication' as given above.

(II) ∨-*elim via Implication:*

If $P \vee Q$ occurs *above* the hole:

$$\|\|\|$$
$$(l) \qquad P \vee Q$$
$$\|\|\|$$

we can replace $P \vee Q$ *forward* by for example $\neg P \Rightarrow Q$:

$$\|\|\|$$
$$(l) \qquad P \vee Q$$
$$\|\|\|$$
$$\{ \text{ Implication on } (l): \}$$
$$(m) \qquad \neg P \Rightarrow Q$$

From here we can apply $\Rightarrow$-elim if we succeed in deriving $\neg P$:

$$\|\|\|$$
$$(l) \qquad P \vee Q$$
$$\|\|\|$$
$$\{ \text{ Implication on } (l): \}$$
$$(m) \qquad \neg P \Rightarrow Q$$
$$\vdots$$
$$(n) \qquad \neg P$$
$$\{ \Rightarrow\text{-elim on } (m) \text{ and } (n): \}$$
$$(n+1) \qquad Q$$

From the last scheme you see how $P \vee Q$ can be used (in forward direction): if you can also derive $\neg P$ (be aware of the $\neg$-symbol!), then you can derive Q.

Also here a second version can be given, where we replace $P \vee Q$ by the formula $\neg Q \Rightarrow P$. This says over the same situation, namely when $P \vee Q$ is 'available', that: if you can also derive $\neg Q$, then you have P.

Remark 14.5.2 *It is clear that in what follows we don't need to use the names '∨-intro' and '∨-elim': we can deal with ∨ by using Implication.*

As an example we show that the following proposition is a tautology. (This proposition was chosen because it will be discussed in the following section. We have also seen it in Section 11.4.)

$$((P \vee Q) \wedge (P \Rightarrow R) \wedge (Q \Rightarrow R)) \Rightarrow R.$$

The beginning is obvious: we write this formula as a goal at the bottom and because it is an $\Rightarrow$-formula, we try to complete the derivation with $\Rightarrow$-intro:

$$
\begin{array}{ll}
 & \{ \text{ Assume: } \} \\
(1) & \boxed{(P \vee Q) \wedge (P \Rightarrow R) \wedge (Q \Rightarrow R)} \\
 & \quad \vdots \\
(n-1) & \mid R \\
 & \{ \Rightarrow\text{-intro on (1) and } (n-1)\text{: } \} \\
(n) & ((P \vee Q) \wedge (P \Rightarrow R) \wedge (Q \Rightarrow R)) \Rightarrow R
\end{array}
$$

The new goal R can no longer be split up. Hence we proceed on the upper side, where $\wedge$-elim leads to three consequences. (To simplify things, we also apply $\wedge$-elim to a conjunction of *three* formulas.)

$$
\begin{array}{ll}
 & \{ \text{ Assume: } \} \\
(1) & \boxed{(P \vee Q) \wedge (P \Rightarrow R) \wedge (Q \Rightarrow R)} \\
 & \quad \{ \wedge\text{-elim on (1): } \} \\
(2) & P \vee Q \\
 & \quad \{ \wedge\text{-elim on (1): } \} \\
(3) & P \Rightarrow R \\
 & \quad \{ \wedge\text{-elim on (1): } \} \\
(4) & Q \Rightarrow R \\
 & \quad \vdots \\
(n-1) & R \\
 & \{ \Rightarrow\text{-intro on (1) and } (n-1)\text{: } \} \\
(n) & ((P \vee Q) \wedge (P \Rightarrow R) \wedge (Q \Rightarrow R)) \Rightarrow R
\end{array}
$$

But now it is not clear how we can proceed further. The replacement of $P \vee Q$ by $\neg P \Rightarrow Q$ or $\neg Q \Rightarrow P$ does not seem to bring any benefits either.

Therefore, this is an excellent opportunity to try the 'proof by contradiction' method!

{ Assume: }

(1) $\boxed{(P \vee Q) \wedge (P \Rightarrow R) \wedge (Q \Rightarrow R)}$

{ ∧-elim on (1): }

(2) $P \vee Q$

{ ∧-elim on (1): }

(3) $P \Rightarrow R$

{ ∧-elim on (1): }

(4) $Q \Rightarrow R$

{ Assume: }

(5) $\boxed{\neg R}$

$\vdots$

$(n-3)$ False

{ ⇒-intro on (5) and $(n-3)$, and Negation: }

$(n-2)$ $\neg\neg R$

{ Double Negation on $(n-2)$: }

$(n-1)$ R

{ ⇒-intro on (1) and $(n-1)$: }

(n) $((P \vee Q) \wedge (P \Rightarrow R) \wedge (Q \Rightarrow R)) \Rightarrow R$

We use here the equivalence of $\neg R \Rightarrow$ False to $\neg\neg R$, and hence to R
itself.

Now we have obtained $\neg R$ above the 'hole'. With this we can proceed
further if we recall that the $Q \Rightarrow R$ in line number (4) is equivalent to
$\neg R \Rightarrow \neg Q$ ('Contraposition'). This would give $\neg Q$ by ⇒-elim, which can
be used (as we shall show) as a first step to derive False.

However, the rule 'Contraposition' is not included in the set of rewrite-
rules permitted in this Part II: up till now, we only 'legalized' the rules
Negation (for ¬), Contradiction and Extremes (for False), Double Negation
(for ¬¬) and Implication (for ∨). So we try to avoid 'Contraposition' in
deriving $\neg Q$. This is, fortunately, not hard: in order to derive $\neg Q$, the
natural thing to do is '¬-intro' via Negation (see Section 14.1). And indeed,

assuming Q leads almost directly to `False`.

Finally, we use $\neg Q$ in combination with $P \vee Q$ (which is $\neg Q \Rightarrow P$ by Implication), and the rest follows easily. See Figure 14.1.

14.6   Case distinction

The tautology that we came across at the end of the previous section, is used in practice if there are different *'cases'*, which must be considered one by one. This is called *case distinction*.

We give an example from mathematics. We construct a proof of the mathematical inequality $(*)$:
$$|x - 1| \geq \tfrac{1}{2}x - \tfrac{1}{2},$$
with x an arbitrary real number.

Because $(*)$ deals with the absolute value $|x-1|$, we will divide the proof into two cases (this is called *case distinction*):
– *case 1:* $x \geq 1$,
– *case 2:* $x \leq 1$.

In the first case, $|x-1|$ is actually equal to $x-1$, in the second it is equal to $-(x-1)$.

Remark 14.6.1 *The two cases* overlap *for* $x = 1$. *We could of course avoid this, but it does not cause any problems. The most important thing is that* all *the possibilities for* x *must be considered, which is obviously the case here. It does not matter if some x's are considered twice.*

The proof by case distinction now proceeds as follows:

In *case 1* we have to prove $x - 1 \geq \tfrac{1}{2}x - \tfrac{1}{2}$, which holds since from $x \geq 1$ follows $\tfrac{1}{2}x \geq \tfrac{1}{2}$, hence $x - 1 \geq \tfrac{1}{2}x - \tfrac{1}{2}$.

In *case 2* we have to prove $1 - x \geq \tfrac{1}{2}x - \tfrac{1}{2}$, which holds since from $x \leq 1$ follows $-\tfrac{3}{2}x \geq -\tfrac{3}{2}$, hence $1 - x \geq \tfrac{1}{2}x - \tfrac{1}{2}$.

Hence in *both* cases, $|x-1| \geq \tfrac{1}{2}x-\tfrac{1}{2}$. Both cases cover *all* the possibilities. Hence inequality $(*)$ *always* holds.

What is now the connection with the tautology
$$((P \vee Q) \wedge (P \Rightarrow R) \wedge (Q \Rightarrow R)) \Rightarrow R?$$

Take $x \geq 1$ for P; $x \leq 1$ for Q; and $(*)$ for R.

- Then $P \vee Q$ is $(x \geq 1) \vee (x \leq 1)$. This proposition is obviously *true* on mathematical grounds. *(Continuation on page 174.)*

	{ Assume: }
(1)	$(P \vee Q) \wedge (P \Rightarrow R) \wedge (Q \Rightarrow R)$
	{ $\wedge$-elim on (1): }
(2)	$P \vee Q$
	{ $\wedge$-elim on (1): }
(3)	$P \Rightarrow R$
	{ $\wedge$-elim on (1): }
(4)	$Q \Rightarrow R$
	{ Assume: }
(5)	$\neg R$
	{ Assume: }
(6)	Q
	{ $\Rightarrow$-elim on (4) and (6): }
(7)	R
	{ Contradiction on (7) and (5): }
(8)	**False**
	{ $\Rightarrow$-intro on (6) and (8), and Negation: }
(9)	$\neg Q$
	{ Implication on (2): }
(10)	$\neg Q \Rightarrow P$
	{ $\Rightarrow$-elim on (10) and (9): }
(11)	P
	{ $\Rightarrow$-elim on (3) and (11): }
(12)	R
	{ Contradiction on (12) and (5): }
(13)	**False**
	{ $\Rightarrow$-intro on (5) and (13), and Negation: }
(14)	$\neg\neg R$
	{ Double Negation on (14): }
(15)	R
	{ $\Rightarrow$-intro on (1) and (15): }
(16)	$((P \vee Q) \wedge (P \Rightarrow R) \wedge (Q \Rightarrow R)) \Rightarrow R$

Figure 14.1: A reasoning to derive $((P \vee Q) \wedge (P \Rightarrow R) \wedge (Q \Rightarrow R)) \Rightarrow R$.

- The proposition $P \Rightarrow R$ now reads: $(x \geq 1) \Rightarrow (*)$. This is proven above using mathematical phrases, namely 'In *case 1* $(x \geq 1)$ we have to prove $x - 1 \geq \frac{1}{2}x - \frac{1}{2}$'. This succeeds, so: $(x \geq 1)$ leads to $(*)$.

- The proposition $Q \Rightarrow R$ reads: $(x \leq 1) \Rightarrow (*)$. This is proven above as 'In *case 2* $(x \leq 1)$ we have to prove $1 - x \geq \frac{1}{2}x - \frac{1}{2}$'. This succeeds, again, hence also: $(x \leq 1)$ leads to $(*)$.

- Hence for these special P, Q and R we have proved:
  – $P \vee Q$ (there are two possible 'cases', which together cover all possibilities),
  – $P \Rightarrow R$ (case 1 leads to R) and
  – $Q \Rightarrow R$ (case 2 leads to R).

- The *final conclusion* on the grounds of the above tautology is hence R, which is nothing else than the proposition $(*)$.

The tautology given above can also be considered as an alternative rule for $\vee$-*elimination* (without calling it so). Namely, if the disjunction $P \vee Q$ is available to you and if your goal is R, then it is enough to prove $P \Rightarrow R$ and $Q \Rightarrow R$.

In derivations this is usually a smooth and elegant method. The reason for this is that you don't 'disturb' the symmetry of $P \vee Q$, whereas this *does* happen if you replace $P \vee Q$ by either $\neg P \Rightarrow Q$, or $\neg Q \Rightarrow P$.

14.7   Reasoning with $\Leftrightarrow$

If a formula has $\Leftrightarrow$ as a main symbol, then the standard equivalence 'Biimplication' will be useful:

$$P \Leftrightarrow Q \stackrel{val}{=\!=\!=} (P \Rightarrow Q) \wedge (Q \Rightarrow P).$$

This leads to the following:

(I) $\Leftrightarrow$-*intro via* $\wedge$-*intro:*

If the *goal* is $P \Leftrightarrow Q$:

$$\vdots$$

$$(m) \qquad P \Leftrightarrow Q$$

then this $\Leftrightarrow$-formula is normally rewritten to:

$$\vdots$$

$(m-1)$ $(P \Rightarrow Q) \wedge (Q \Rightarrow P)$

               $\{$ Bi-implication on $(m-1)$ $\}$

    (m) $P \Leftrightarrow Q$

after which the goal in line number $(m-1)$ can be replaced by the *two* goals $P \Rightarrow Q$ and $Q \Rightarrow P$ (think of $\wedge$-intro). Each of these goals is an $\Rightarrow$-formula, which can be reached in a natural way via $\Rightarrow$-intro ('Assume P, prove Q', respectively 'Assume Q, prove P').

(II) $\Leftrightarrow$-*elim via* $\wedge$-*elim:*

Also when an $\Leftrightarrow$-formula occurs *above* the 'hole' and hence can be used, the standard equivalence 'Bi-implication' is useful. With this equivalence, $P \Leftrightarrow Q$ can be replaced by $(P \Rightarrow Q) \wedge (Q \Rightarrow P)$, which with $\wedge$-elim returns both $P \Rightarrow Q$ and $Q \Rightarrow P$. With these new results we can proceed in the usual way: we can (for example) use $P \Rightarrow Q$ by trying to derive P and to apply $\Rightarrow$-elim, and we can do something similar with $Q \Rightarrow P$.

As before, we don't use the names '$\Leftrightarrow$-intro' and '$\Leftrightarrow$-elim': if we come across an $\Leftrightarrow$, it is enough (see above) to use Bi-implication, and the intro and elim rules for $\wedge$ and $\Rightarrow$.

14.8 Exercises

14.1 Give derivations for the following tautologies. Use only methods described in Chapters 12 and 14.

    (a) $\neg Q \Rightarrow \neg(P \wedge Q)$

    (b) $\neg(P \wedge Q) \Rightarrow (P \Rightarrow \neg Q)$

    (c) $(P \wedge \neg Q) \Rightarrow \neg(P \Rightarrow Q)$

14.2 As Exercise 14.1:

    (a) $(P \Rightarrow \neg Q) \Rightarrow ((P \Rightarrow Q) \Rightarrow \neg P)$

    (b) $((P \Rightarrow Q) \Rightarrow \neg P) \Rightarrow (P \Rightarrow \neg Q)$

14.3 As Exercise 14.1:

    (a) $(P \wedge Q) \Rightarrow (\neg P \Rightarrow R)$

(b) $\neg P \Rightarrow \neg((P \Rightarrow Q) \Rightarrow P)$

14.4 Show with *calculations* that the formulas of Exercise 14.3 are tautologies.

14.5 Give logical derivations for the following tautologies, only using the methods of Chapters 12 and 14:

(a) $(\neg P \Rightarrow P) \Rightarrow P$

(b) $\neg(P \Rightarrow Q) \Rightarrow P$

14.6 As Exercise 14.5:

(a) $(P \Rightarrow Q) \vee P$

(b) $(P \Rightarrow Q) \vee \neg Q$

14.7 Investigate whether the following formulas are tautologies. If so, give a logical derivation to prove this; if not so, give a counterexample.

(a) $(P \vee Q) \Rightarrow (P \vee (\neg P \wedge Q))$

(b) $(P \Rightarrow Q) \Rightarrow (P \vee (Q \Rightarrow R))$

(c) $(P \Rightarrow Q) \Rightarrow (Q \vee (P \Rightarrow R))$

14.8 Give proofs of the truth of the following propositions with the help of *case distinction* (x and y are real numbers). Say precisely how you use the tautology

$$((P \vee Q) \wedge (P \Rightarrow R) \wedge (Q \Rightarrow R)) \Rightarrow R.$$

(a) $|x + 4| \geq \frac{1}{2}x + 2$

(b) $(x \geq 2 \vee x = -1) \Rightarrow x^3 - 3x - 2 \geq 0$

(c) $x^2 = y^2 \Leftrightarrow (x = y) \vee (x = -y)$

14.9 Prove the following tautologies via a logical derivation (you can omit the justifications):

(a) $(P \Leftrightarrow Q) \Rightarrow ((P \wedge Q) \vee (\neg P \wedge \neg Q))$

(b) $(P \Leftrightarrow Q) \Rightarrow (\neg P \Leftrightarrow \neg Q))$

(c) $(P \wedge (Q \Rightarrow R)) \Leftrightarrow ((P \Rightarrow Q) \Rightarrow (P \wedge R))$

14.10 Show with *calculations* that the formulas of Exercise 14.9 are tautologies.

Chapter 15

Reasoning with quantifiers

Beyond all doubt

15.1   Reasoning with $\forall$

In the previous chapter we have seen how to *reason*, in the system of natural deduction, with the connectives $\wedge$, $\Rightarrow$, $\neg$, $\vee$ and $\Leftrightarrow$. Contexts played there an important role. Moreover, apart from a couple of old equivalences and weakenings, only the rules $\Rightarrow$-intro, $\Rightarrow$-elim, $\wedge$-intro and $\wedge$-elim were needed!

How does all this now fit if we add the quantifiers $\forall$ and $\exists$? In this chapter we will show that actually only two extra rules are needed: the $\forall$-intro and the $\forall$-elim. (In Section 15.3 we will see that it is very useful – though not necessary – to also add two extra rules for $\exists$.)

Before we begin with $\forall$-intro and $\forall$-elim, and for simplicity, we will change a little bit the notation from Chapters 8 and 9: for quantified formulas, we will from now on write the free variables which play a role in the predicates between parentheses. Hence if the variable x occurs free in P, we write $P(x)$ instead of P.

In what follows we write hence:

- $\forall_x[P(x) : Q(x)]$ instead of $\forall_x[P : Q]$, and

- $\exists_x[P(x) : Q(x)]$ instead of $\exists_x[P : Q]$.

The advantage of this is that a *filling of a value* for such an x can be expressed in a simpler manner: if a is to be used instead of x in P, we simply write now $P(a)$ instead of $P[a$ for $x]$.

177

Something similar can be done for many-place predicates. If for example R is binary, with variables x and y, then we write it as $R(x, y)$.

Example 15.1.1 *Let R be the binary predicate $x + y > 5$. Then:*

- $R(x, y)$ *is the same as R, and hence it is $x + y > 5$,*

- $R(2, y)$ *is the one-place predicate $2 + y > 5$, a predicate in y,*

- $R(x, 1)$ *is the one-place predicate $x + 1 > 5$, a predicate in x, and*

- $R(2, 1)$ *is the proposition $2 + 1 > 5$.*

(I) ∀-*intro*:

We begin with the ∀-quantifier and we consider the situation where the ∀-formula $\forall_x[P(x) : Q(x)]$ occurs *under* the 'hole'. In other words: we are looking at how a ∀-formula can be *introduced* by means of natural deduction.

Let us deliver as an example a *proof* that

$$\forall_x[x \in \mathbb{R} \wedge x > 4 : x^2 - 2x > 8].$$

Which is in words: 'For all real numbers x greater than 4, $x^2 - 2x$ is greater than 8'. A proof will approximately look as follows:

'Take a real x which is greater than 4. Then

$$x^2 - 2x - 8 = (x + 2)(x - 4) > 0,$$

this last holds because both $x + 2$ and $x - 4$ are greater than 0 (since x itself is greater than 4).

Hence, $x^2 - 2x > 8$.'

An important step in this proof is 'Take a real x greater than 4'. In order to give a proof of $x^2 - 2x > 8$ for *all* real numbers greater than 4, it is enough to take an *arbitrary* real number greater than 4 and to deliver *for this arbitrary number* the requested proof.

This first step has actually two parts:

– Take a real number greater than 4,

– call it x.

We can also exchange these two steps:

– Declare a variable x,

– assume that $x \in \mathbb{R}$ and $x > 4$.

Both this declaration of x and the corresponding hypothesis about x, viz. $x \in \mathbb{R} \wedge x > 4$ have only a *temporary* validity. They serve for reaching the conclusion $x^2 - 2x > 8$, but as soon as we have reached that conclusion, we won't need them anymore. In short, this is exactly the behaviour that we came across earlier with *contexts*. The difference is that here the context consists not only of a *hypothesis*, but also of a *declaration*. We shall write these together in *one* flag in the following manner:

$\{$ Assume: $\}$

(1) $\boxed{\text{var } x;\ x \in \mathbb{R} \land x > 4}$

    $\vdots$

The whole reasoning will hence look as follows:

$\{$ Assume: $\}$

(1) $\boxed{\text{var } x;\ x \in \mathbb{R} \land x > 4}$

(2)   Then $x^2 - 2x - 8 = (x+2)(x-4) > 0$,

(3)   hence $x^2 - 2x > 8$

(4)   Conclusion : $\forall_x [x \in \mathbb{R} \land x > 4 : x^2 - 2x > 8]$

Remark 15.1.2 *The hypothesis that we have placed in a flag here is a generating hypothesis (see Section 11.5), because a 'new' name (x) is given to a variable.*

Now it is obvious what the general rule looks like:

∀-introduction

$\{$ Assume: $\}$

(k) $\boxed{\text{var } x;\ P(x)}$

    $\vdots$

$(m-1)$ $Q(x)$

$\{$ ∀-intro on (k) and $(m-1)$: $\}$

(m) $\forall_x [P(x) : Q(x)]$

Note that ∀-introduction looks in a certain sense like ⇒-introduction :

- In order to derive $P \Rightarrow Q$, we *assume* P, and then we derive Q *under this hypothesis*.

- In order to derive $\forall_x[P(x) : Q(x)]$, we *declare* x and we *assume* $P(x)$, and then we derive $Q(x)$ *under this hypothesis* (and with the *use* of the declared x).

This resemblance is not surprising if we observe (see Section 9.5) that a $\forall$-formula like $\forall_x[P(x) : Q(x)]$ is a kind of *generalized implication*. According to the rule Domain Weakening we have:

$$\forall_x[P(x) : Q(x)] \overset{val}{=\!=} \forall_x[\text{True} : P(x) \Rightarrow Q(x)],$$

hence such a $\forall$-formula means something like: '$P(x) \Rightarrow Q(x)$ holds for all values of the variable x'.

Hence in order to derive $\forall_x[P(x) : Q(x)]$, we must show that the implication $P(x) \Rightarrow Q(x)$ holds *for every possible* x. For this, we consider an 'arbitrary' x, denoted by '<u>var</u> x', we assume at the same time that $P(x)$ holds and we try to reach $Q(x)$. The latter is done completely according to the pattern of $\Rightarrow$-intro.

Remark 15.1.3 *In case the goal has the form $\forall_x[\text{True} : Q(x)]$ (also written as $\forall_x[Q(x)]$), so with an 'invisible' domain description, then it is supposed that at that place a* well-known *domain description $P(x)$ is omitted for convenience's sake. One possibility is that the domain description is actually* **True** *(see Remark 8.4.1 in Section 8.4). When we use $\forall$-introduction according to the above rule, the flag should contain the omitted $P(x)$ as an assumption, so the flag text should look like '<u>var</u> x; $P(x)$'. In the case that $P(x)$ is* **True**, *we may simply write '<u>var</u> x' in the flag.*

(II) $\forall$-*elim*:

What can we do with a $\forall$-formula which occurs above the 'hole' and is therefore usable? If we for example know that the following holds:

$$\forall_x[-1 < x < 2 : x^3 - 3x - 2 < 0],$$

how can we use this? With the formula on its own, we cannot do much, but as soon as we have a number between -1 and 2, then we *can* use it. For example: 0 is such a number, hence $0^3 - 3 \cdot 0 - 2 < 0$. This is indeed true, because here we have that -2 is smaller than 0. It gets more interesting when we take $\frac{1}{2}\sqrt{2}$. This also occurs between -1 and 2, hence we can in a similar way conclude that: $(\frac{1}{2}\sqrt{2})^3 - 3.\frac{1}{2}\sqrt{2} - 2 < 0$. This is already more exciting.

A third example: assume that we observe in an experiment that an arbitrary measure value t is in absolute value always smaller than 1. Then it follows from the ∀-formula that at every moment $t^3 - 3t - 2$ is smaller than 0.

Let us write $P(x)$ for the first predicate: $-1 < x < 2$, and $Q(x)$ for the second predicate: $x^3 - 3x - 2 < 0$.

The fact that $\forall_x[P(x) : Q(x)]$ holds, implies that: '*as soon as* $P(a)$ holds for a certain a, then also $Q(a)$ holds (for the same a)'.

In our case:

- ($a = 0$): Because $P(0)$ holds (namely $-1 < 0 < 2$), it follows that $Q(0)$ holds (which is: $0^3 - 3 \cdot 0 - 2 < 0$),

- ($a = \frac{1}{2}\sqrt{2}$): Moreover, because $P(\frac{1}{2}\sqrt{2})$ holds, then $Q(\frac{1}{2}\sqrt{2})$ follows.

- ($a = t$): If we know for sure that $P(t)$ holds, then $Q(t)$ follows.

Now we make a general rule of the above:

∀-elimination

$$
\begin{array}{ll}
 & |\,|\,|\,| \\
(k) & \forall_x[P(x) : Q(x)] \\
 & |\,|\,|\,| \\
(l) & P(a) \\
 & |\,|\,|\,| \\
 & \{ \text{∀-elim on } (k) \text{ and } (l): \ \} \\
(m) & Q(a)
\end{array}
$$

Here, a is an 'object' which must be available. It can be a number (0 or $\frac{1}{2}$), but also a declared variable which still 'lives' (for example y or t), or even a combination: $y + \frac{1}{2}$. As long as a 'makes sense' and satisfies P, then this same a also satisfies Q, by the ∀-formula in line number (k); this is what the above ∀-elimination rule says.

Again it is clear that ∀ and ⇒ are related to each other, ∀-elimination looks like ⇒-elimination:

- If we 'know' $P \Rightarrow Q$, this is not enough to derive a conclusion. Only if we also 'know' P, can we with ⇒-elim reach the conclusion Q.

- Also if we 'know' $\forall_x[P(x) : Q(x)]$, this is not on its own enough to derive a conclusion. Only if we also 'know' $P(a)$ for a certain a, can we conclude $Q(a)$.

Also in this case, the similarities can be explained by the equivalence:

$$\forall_x[P(x) : Q(x)] \stackrel{val}{=\!=\!=} \forall_x[\text{True} : P(x) \Rightarrow Q(x)].$$

The latter formula says that $P(x) \Rightarrow Q(x)$ holds for every x. Especially if we fill x by a then the following holds:

$$P(a) \Rightarrow Q(a).$$

Therefore, as soon as $P(a)$ holds, then so does $Q(a)$ (see above).

Remark 15.1.4 *In the case that the domain description is* True, *so if we 'know' that* $\forall_x[\text{True} : Q(x)]$ *(also written as:* $\forall_x[Q(x)]$*), then of course there is no need for the derivation of line number (l) in the above scheme:* True *always holds.*

We conclude this section with an example in which both $\forall$-intro and $\forall$-elim are used. For this purpose we give a derivation of

$$\forall_x[P(x) : Q(x) \wedge R(x)] \Rightarrow \forall_y[\neg Q(y) : \neg P(y)] .$$

(The fact that this is a tautology follows easily from a logical *calculation*, see Part I. But here we want to show that it is also easy to *reason* with $\forall$.)

The start of the derivation is simple, the main symbol $\Rightarrow$ requires the rule $\Rightarrow$-intro:

$$
\begin{array}{ll}
& \{ \text{ Assume: } \} \\
(1) & \boxed{\forall_x[P(x) : Q(x) \wedge R(x)]} \\
& \quad \vdots \\
(n-1) & \quad \forall_y[\neg Q(y) : \neg P(y)] \\
& \{ \Rightarrow\text{-intro on (1) and } (n-1)\text{: } \} \\
(n) & \forall_x[P(x) : Q(x) \wedge R(x)] \Rightarrow \forall_y[\neg Q(y) : \neg P(y)]
\end{array}
$$

The new goal is $\forall_y[\neg Q(y) : \neg P(y)]$, a formula with main symbol $\forall$. It is obvious that we try to continue with $\forall$-intro:

{ Assume: }

(1) $\boxed{\forall_x[P(x) : Q(x) \wedge R(x)]}$

     { Assume: }

(2) $\boxed{\underline{\text{var }} y;\ \neg Q(y)}$

       $\vdots$

$(n-2)$ $\neg P(y)$

     { ∀-intro on (2) and $(n-2)$: }

$(n-1)$ $\forall_y[\neg Q(y) : \neg P(y)]$

     { ⇒-intro on (1) and $(n-1)$: }

(n) $\forall_x[P(x) : Q(x) \wedge R(x)] \Rightarrow \forall_y[\neg Q(y) : \neg P(y)]$

The goal is now $\neg P(y)$, which can be achieved in a standard fashion by assuming $P(y)$ and then deriving **False**:

{ Assume: }

(1) $\boxed{\forall_x[P(x) : Q(x) \wedge R(x)]}$

     { Assume: }

(2) $\boxed{\underline{\text{var }} y;\ \neg Q(y)}$

       { Assume: }

(3) $\boxed{P(y)}$

         $\vdots$

$(n-3)$ **False**

       { ⇒-intro and Negation on (3) and $(n-3)$: }

$(n-2)$ $\neg P(y)$

     { ∀-intro on (2) and $(n-2)$: }

$(n-1)$ $\forall_y[\neg Q(y) : \neg P(y)]$

     { ⇒-intro on (1) and $(n-1)$: }

(n) $\forall_x[P(x) : Q(x) \wedge R(x)] \Rightarrow \forall_y[\neg Q(y) : \neg P(y)]$

Now the goal, **False**, cannot be further simplified. Let's see what we *know*: that's everything written in lines number (1) up to (3). The formula $\forall_x[P(x) : Q(x) \wedge R(x)]$ from line number (1) is only able to 'operate', via $\forall$-elim, if we have an object a for which $P(a)$ holds. However, such an a exists, namely the y occurring in line number (2)! Indeed, $P(y)$ holds, as is assumed in line number (3). This leads to the conclusion $Q(y) \wedge R(y)$, see line number (4) on the following page.

The rest is straightforward. From $Q(y) \wedge R(y)$ we get $Q(y)$ and this contradicts the right hand side of line number (2), the assumption $\neg Q(y)$. Hence we obtain `False`. The full reasoning is given below.

$\qquad$ { Assume: }

(1) $\quad \boxed{\forall_x[P(x) : Q(x) \wedge R(x)]}$

$\qquad$ { Assume: }

(2) $\qquad \boxed{\text{var } y; \ \neg Q(y)}$

$\qquad\qquad$ { Assume: }

(3) $\qquad\qquad \boxed{P(y)}$

$\qquad\qquad$ { $\forall$-elim on (1) and (3): }

(4) $\qquad\qquad Q(y) \wedge R(y)$

$\qquad\qquad$ { $\wedge$-elim on (4): }

(5) $\qquad\qquad Q(y)$

$\qquad\qquad$ { Contradiction on (2) and (5): }

(6) $\qquad\qquad$ `False`

$\qquad\qquad$ { $\Rightarrow$-intro and Negation on (3) and (6): }

(7) $\qquad\qquad \neg P(y)$

$\qquad$ { $\forall$-intro on (2) and (7): }

(8) $\qquad \forall_y[\neg Q(y) : \neg P(y)]$

$\qquad$ { $\Rightarrow$-intro on (1) and (8): }

(9) $\quad \forall_x[P(x) : Q(x) \wedge R(x)] \Rightarrow \forall_y[\neg Q(y) : \neg P(y)]$

15.2   Reasoning with $\exists$

In Section 9.6 we gave a calculation which only needs to be slightly changed in order to show that:

$$\exists_x[P(x):Q(x)] \stackrel{val}{=\!=} \neg\forall_x[P(x):\neg Q(x)].$$

In this way, an $\exists$-formula can always be written to a formula with two $\neg$'s and a $\forall$ in between. This can take place both when the $\exists$-formula occurs *under* the 'hole' and when it occurs *above* it.

(I) $\exists$-*intro via De Morgan:*

If the goal is $\exists_x[P(x):Q(x)]$:

$$\vdots$$

$(n) \qquad \exists_x[P(x):Q(x)]$

then we can replace it 'backwards' by $\neg\forall_x[P(x):\neg Q(x)]$ (see Section 9.6) obtaining:

$$\vdots$$

$(n-1) \qquad \neg\forall_x[P(x):\neg Q(x)]$
$\qquad\qquad\quad$ { De Morgan and Double Negation on $(n-1)$: }
$(n) \qquad\quad \exists_x[P(x):Q(x)]$

after which the new goal, the $\neg$-formula $\neg\forall_x[P(x):\neg Q(x)]$, can be replaced backwards by $\forall_x[P(x):\neg Q(x)] \Rightarrow$ False, which in turn requires $\Rightarrow$-intro:

$\qquad\qquad\quad$ { Assume: }

$(1) \qquad \boxed{\forall_x[P(x):\neg Q(x)]}$

$$\qquad\qquad\qquad \vdots$$

$(n-2) \qquad \big|\ $ False
$\qquad\qquad\quad$ { $\Rightarrow$-intro on (1) and $(n-2)$, and Negation: }
$(n-1) \qquad \neg\forall_x[P(x):\neg Q(x)]$
$\qquad\qquad\quad$ { De Morgan and Double Negation on $(n-1)$: }
$(n) \qquad\quad \exists_x[P(x):Q(x)]$

An example of how this can all take place, can be seen in the following section.

(II) ∃-*elim via De Morgan:*

If on the other hand we 'know' that $\exists_x[P(x) : Q(x)]$ (which occurs *above* the hole):

$$\text{||||}$$

(l) $\exists_x[P(x) : Q(x)]$

$$\text{||||}$$

then we can again replace $\exists_x[P(x) : Q(x)]$ by $\neg\forall_x[P(x) : \neg Q(x)]$, but now 'forward':

$$\text{||||}$$

(l) $\exists_x[P(x) : Q(x)]$

$$\text{||||}$$

        { Double Negation and De Morgan on (l): }

(m) $\neg\forall_x[P(x) : \neg Q(x)]$

This latter formula is a ¬-formula, and hence we can for example try to derive the 'complementary' formula $\forall_x[P(x) : \neg Q(x)]$ with the intention of reaching **False**:

$$\text{||||}$$

(l) $\exists_x[P(x) : Q(x)]$

$$\text{||||}$$

        { Double Negation and De Morgan on (l): }

(m) $\neg\forall_x[P(x) : \neg Q(x)]$

$$\vdots$$

(n) $\forall_x[P(x) : \neg Q(x)]$

        { Contradiction on (n) and (m): }

$(n+1)$ **False**

Filling the hole between the lines numbered (m) and (n) can now begin by aiming first at the goal $\forall_x[P(x) : \neg Q(x)]$ in line (n). The main symbol of this goal is ∀, hence it makes sense to try and reach this goal with ∀-intro. The new goal becomes ¬$Q(x)$, which is also ($\stackrel{val}{=\!=}$) $Q(x) \Rightarrow$ False, and hence requires ⇒-intro, etcetera.

In this manner, we have a strategy at our disposal to 'use' (or 'eliminate') a proposition of the form ∃$_x[P(x) : \neg Q(x)]$. This may help you further in developing a derivation.

Remark 15.2.1 *Also here we don't need to introduce a separate* ∃*-intro- or* ∃*-elim-rule: we can in both cases do the work with De Morgan.*

15.3 Alternatives for ∃

Dealing with ∃ in the system of natural deduction in the manner we have just explained in the previous section, is simple and sound. Still there are some disadvantages:
- it requires some 'technical' rewriting,
- it leads to long-winded derivations, and
- it is a bit far from intuition.

Especially this last disadvantage is a problem. The person giving a proof, wants to know precisely what he is doing, and the person reading a proof, must not be distracted by detours. In order to understand well what happens during such a proof, all the steps must be as self-evident as possible.

For this reason, we re-consider the ∃ in this section, but now from a practical point of view. It appears that there are alternative possibilities for both ∃-intro and ∃-elim, which are closer to intuition.

Our work in the previous section is not actually wasted: there are situations where the new rules that we will give in this section will not work (this holds in particular for the alternative ∃-*intro*), and hence we must return to the 'old' methods from Section 15.2.

(I) *An alternative* ∃-*intro*

Sometimes we can prove ∃$_x[P(x) : Q(x)]$ by providing a *witness*. This 'witness' is an element a which satisfies both P and Q, so for which both $P(a)$ and $Q(a)$ hold. This a 'proves' hence the existence of an x with $P(x)$ and $Q(x)$ (a itself is such an x).

Examples:

- If you want to prove that ∃$_x[x \in \mathbb{Z} : x^4 = 16]$, then you can use as witness the integer number 2 (also -2 is a good choice), because:

- 2 ∈ ℤ, and
- $2^4 = 16$.

Hence the number 2 satisfies both predicates, $x \in \mathbb{Z}$ and $x^4 = 16$.

- And if in the context

$$\underline{var}\ y;\ y \in \mathbb{R}$$

you want to prove $\exists_x [x \in \mathbb{R} : \ln(x) > y]$, then you can call every witness whose natural logarithm is greater than y, for example $e^y + 1$. In fact, $e^y + 1$ satisfies both predicates, $x \in \mathbb{R}$ and $\ln(x) > y$:
- $e^y + 1 \in \mathbb{R}$, and
- $\ln(e^y + 1) > y$, because $\ln(e^y + 1) > \ln(e^y)$ (as ln is a monotonic increasing function) and $\ln(e^y) = y$.

We make of the above a new ∃-introduction rule, which we call ∃*-*intro* :

∃*-introduction

$$\vdots$$

(k) $P(a)$

$$\vdots$$

(l) $Q(a)$

      { ∃*-intro on (k) and (l): }

(m) $\exists_x [P(x) : Q(x)]$

This ∃*-intro-rule works in practice very nicely, and requires much less work than the method from the previous section (the one where ∃ was replaced by ¬∀¬). Therefore we follow from now on the following standard strategy for an ∃-formula which, as a goal, occurs directly *under* the hole: we do *nothing* with it, leave it as it is and wait till a suitable 'witness' appears. We can try to find this witness with the help of our *knowledge* (which occurs *above* the hole). If this witness shows up, we are done. If it doesn't, we are still free to try the long-winded method '∃-intro via De Morgan' from Section 15.2.

We shall now show that the rule ∃*-intro is indeed correct. For this, we *assume* that $P(a)$ and $Q(a)$ both hold and then we show, *exclusively with* *the earlier given rules*, that then also $\exists_x[P(x) : Q(x)]$ holds. Because we fully trust these earlier rules, we conclude that the new rule is acceptable.

We start hence from the following situation:

{ Assume: }
(1) $\boxed{P(a)}$

       { Assume: }
(2) $\boxed{Q(a)}$

          $\vdots$

(n) $\exists_x[P(x) : Q(x)]$

and we try to give a derivation by closing the hole.

Because the ∃-formula appears *under* the hole, we apply what occurred in (**I**) in the previous section ('∃-intro via De Morgan'):

{ Assume: }
(1) $\boxed{P(a)}$

       { Assume: }
(2) $\boxed{Q(a)}$

          { Assume: }
(3) $\boxed{\forall_x[P(x) : \neg Q(x)]}$

             $\vdots$

(n − 2)   False
             { ⇒-intro on (3) and (n − 2), and Negation: }
(n − 1) $\neg\forall_x[P(x) : \neg Q(x)]$
             { De Morgan and Double Negation on (n − 1): }
(n) $\exists_x[P(x) : Q(x)]$

Now the ∀-formula $\forall_x[P(x) : \neg Q(x)]$ occurs above the hole. To which we can directly apply ∀-elim, because in line number (1) we have that a satisfies P. The result from this ∀-elimination is hence $\neg Q(a)$, which is also

$Q(a) \Rightarrow$ False. With this, together with $Q(a)$ from line number (2), we easily reach the goal: False. This gives:

{ Assume: }

(1) $\boxed{P(a)}$

      { Assume: }

(2) $\boxed{Q(a)}$

        { Assume: }

(3) $\boxed{\forall_x[P(x) : \neg Q(x)]}$

          { $\forall$-elim on (3) and (1): }

(4) $\neg Q(a)$

          { Contradiction on (2) and (4): }

(5)   False

       { $\Rightarrow$-intro on (3) and (5), and Negation: }

(6) $\neg\forall_x[P(x) : \neg Q(x)]$

       { De Morgan and Double Negation on (6): }

(7) $\exists_x[P(x) : Q(x)]$

We must make a marginal note for the $\exists$*-intro rule: it *does not always* work. You must have some luck in order to be able to find the 'witness' a which satisfies both P and Q. *It can even be that in some cases such a witness cannot be found at all*, no matter how hard you look and no matter how clever you are.

In that case we luckily still have at our disposal the method from the previous section ('$\exists$-intro via De Morgan', hence the replacement of '$\exists$' by '$\neg\forall\neg$'). *If* it is possible at all to derive $\exists_x[P(x) : Q(x)]$, then it will be possible with the (usual) method '$\exists$-intro via De Morgan'. Even though there may probably be a lot of work involved.

Said differently, sometimes there may well *exist* an x which satisfies P and Q, but without anyone being able to *give* such an x. In such a case we cannot do more than noting that the *non*-existence of such an x leads to a contradiction. Hence the assumption that $\neg\exists_x[P(x) : Q(x)]$ (which is by De Morgan $\forall_x[P(x) : \neg Q(x)]$) leads to False. This is precisely what the method of the previous section gives, as can easily be checked.

(II) *An alternative ∃-elim*

In order to show that, exactly as for ∃-intro, there is a 'natural' alternative for ∃-*elim*, we begin with an example.

Assume that we 'know':

$$\exists_x[x \in \mathbb{R} : \cos(x) = x].$$

We may for example have reached this conclusion by drawing the graphs of the functions $y = x$ and $y = \cos(x)$ in one figure and by noting that these graphs have a meeting point (as a matter of fact, they have a *unique* meeting point, but this does not matter here).

We want to use this knowledge in order to show that

$$\exists_u[u \in \mathbb{R} : \sin^2(u) + u = \tfrac{1}{2}].$$

The situation is hence as follows:

$$(1) \qquad \exists_x[x \in \mathbb{R} : \cos(x) = x]$$

$$\vdots$$

$$(n) \qquad \exists_u[u \in \mathbb{R} : \sin^2(u) + u = \tfrac{1}{2}]$$

In order to reach the goal in line number (n), it would be nice to find a 'witness' a with $a \in \mathbb{R}$ and $\sin^2(a) + a = \tfrac{1}{2}$. If we have such a witness, we can then apply ∃*-intro. We follow the standard strategy for this rule, which we have given earlier in this section: we do nothing with the ∃-formula in line number (n) and we wait for the witness a to come forward 'by itself'.

Let us hence start working with what we know. In this case, this is *only* what is written in line number (1). But what can we do with line number (1)? This line requires a kind of ∃-elim but we prefer not to use the '∃-elim via De Morgan' from Section 15.2, because it is long-winded and counter-intuitive. How can we use the fact that there *exists* a real x with $\cos(x) = x$ in an intuitive way? The simplest is to reason as follows: 'There *is* such an x, so now *pick one* and calculate with it further'. The x that we 'pick' satisfies hence $x \in \mathbb{R}$ and $\cos(x) = x$. Now we can go further. We use a known formula (the 'half-angle-formula'), which says that $\cos(\alpha) = 1 - 2\sin^2(\tfrac{1}{2}\alpha)$, in order to bring in the $\sin^2$-function occurring in the goal.

Now we can calculate as follows: For the x in question, it holds that:

$\cos(x) = x$,

hence $1 - 2\sin^2(\tfrac{1}{2}x) = x$,

hence $2\sin^2(\tfrac{1}{2}x) + x = 1$,

hence $\sin^2(\tfrac{1}{2}x) + \tfrac{1}{2}x = \tfrac{1}{2}$.

But now we also have a witness u for $\sin^2(u) + u = \frac{1}{2}$, simply take $\frac{1}{2}x$ for this u! (This $u = \frac{1}{2}x$ *also* satisfies $u \in \mathbb{R}$.)

Considering the reasoning in the above scheme we get:

(1) $\exists_x[x \in \mathbb{R} : \cos(x) = x]$

       $\{ \ \dots \ \}$

(2)   Pick an x with $x \in \mathbb{R}$ and $\cos(x) = x$

       $\{$ Mathematics: $\}$

(3)   Hence is $1 - 2\sin^2(\frac{1}{2}x) = x, \dots$

       $\{$ Mathematics: $\}$

(4)   hence $\sin^2(\frac{1}{2}x) + \frac{1}{2}x = \frac{1}{2}$.

       $\{$ Mathematics: $\}$

(5)   Moreover we have $\frac{1}{2}x \in \mathbb{R}$

       $\{$ $\exists^*$-intro on (5) and (4): $\}$

(6)   hence $\exists_u[u \in \mathbb{R} : \sin^2(u) + u = \frac{1}{2}]$

This leads us to incorporate the following alternative $\exists$-elimination rule in our system of natural deduction:

$\exists^*$-elimination

       $|||$

(k) $\exists_x[P(x) : Q(x)]$

       $|||$

       $\{$ $\exists^*$-elim on (k): $\}$

(l)   Pick an x with $P(x)$ and $Q(x)$.

It is *indeed* important here that the x that we 'pick' in line number (l) be 'new'. On grounds of (k), we have picked an arbitrary element which satisfies P and Q; we need to give this element a name which we did not already know.

And what about the x which already exists in line number (k)? Yes, but the x in line number (k) is a *bound* variable, which is hence only known within the $\exists$-formula in line number (k). Hence the x in line number (l) ('Pick an x') is definitely *new* with respect to the earlier x in line number (k).

Remark 15.3.1 *You can see now why such an extra rule 'Pick an x with $P(x)$ and $Q(x)$' is needed. As you know, the x which occurs after the $\exists$ in $\exists_x[P(x) : Q(x)]$ does not live any more outside this formula.*

If we want to work with such an x outside this formula, then we must introduce it from new again. This is exactly what we do in the sentence 'Pick an x with $P(x)$ and $Q(x)$'.

But of course we must not get in a mess with an x which occurs somewhere else in the derivation, for example a free x which occurs somewhere below line number (l). What will happen if x is *not* new at the moment where we want to write line number (l)? Then we simply take another letter, which is *definitely* new. And hence we write in line number (l), if y is such letter:

(k) Pick a y with $P(y)$ and $Q(y)$.

Why is the $\exists^*$-elim-rule a 'good' rule now? We have defended it *intuitively*, but this is different from having an absolute certainty of the correctness of the rule.

It suffices here to say that it can indeed be *proven exclusively with the earlier given rules*, that the method of the $\exists^*$-elim-rule is correct. This proof is quite involved and hence we leave it out.

Finally, we give an example in which both the $\exists^*$-elim and the $\exists^*$-intro appear.

We will now show that the following formula is derivable:

$$(*) \quad (\exists_x[P(x) : Q(x)] \wedge \forall_y[Q(y) : R(y)]) \;\Rightarrow\; \exists_z[P(z) : R(z)].$$

Remark 15.3.2 *In the formula $(*)$ there are three sub-formulas which begin with a quantifier. We have chosen the bound variables in such a way that they are different in each of these three sub-formulas: x is the bound variable in the first, y is the bound variable in the second and z is the bound variable in the third.*

In general this is a good habit, in order to avoid confusion. If you happen to come across quantified sub-formulas with the same bound variables, then first, make these variables different. This is always possible, due to the standard equivalence 'Bound Variable', see Section 9.2.

Example: you may change $\forall_x[P(x) : Q(x)] \Rightarrow \forall_x[P(x) : Q(x) \vee R(x)]$ into $\forall_x[P(x) : Q(x)] \Rightarrow \forall_y[P(y) : Q(y) \vee R(y)]$.

The above formula $(*)$ is an $\Rightarrow$-formula. And therefore it is quite reasonable to start the derivation as follows:

{ Assume: }

(1) $\boxed{\exists_x[P(x) : Q(x)] \wedge \forall_y[Q(y) : R(y)]}$

        $\vdots$

$(n-1)$ $\exists_z[P(z) : R(z)]$

       { $\Rightarrow$-intro on (1) and $(n-1)$: }

(n) $(\exists_x[P(x) : Q(x)] \wedge \forall_y[Q(y) : R(y)]) \Rightarrow \exists_z[P(z) : R(z)]$

The goal in line number $(n-1)$ is an $\exists$-formula, hence according to our new strategy, we don't do anything with it. We hope that soon, a certain a which satisfies $P(a)$ and $R(a)$ will offer itself.

Hence, we first work with what we 'know', which is for the moment *only* line (1). This is an $\wedge$-formula, which we divide with $\wedge$-elim in two parts:

{ Assume: }

(1) $\boxed{\exists_x[P(x) : Q(x)] \wedge \forall_y[Q(y) : R(y)]}$

      { $\wedge$-elim on (1): }

(2) $\exists_x[P(x) : Q(x)]$

      { $\wedge$-elim on (1): }

(3) $\forall_y[Q(y) : R(y)]$

        $\vdots$

$(n-1)$ $\exists_z[P(z) : R(z)]$

      { $\Rightarrow$-intro on (1) and $(n-1)$: }

(n) $(\exists_x[P(x) : Q(x)] \wedge \forall_y[Q(y) : R(y)]) \Rightarrow \exists_z[P(z) : R(z)]$

Now we can proceed further with the lines numbered (2) and (3). The latter is a $\forall$-formula, which is still not usable via $\forall$-elim, as long as we don't have a b such that $Q(b)$. But on line number (2), an $\exists$-formula *above* the hole, we can apply $\exists^*$-elim:

{ Assume: }

(1) $\boxed{\exists_x[P(x) : Q(x)] \wedge \forall_y[Q(y) : R(y)]}$

      { $\wedge$-elim on (1): }

(2) | $\exists_x[P(x) : Q(x)]$

{ $\wedge$-elim on (1): }

(3) | $\forall_y[Q(y) : R(y)]$

{ $\exists^*$-elim on (2): }

(4) | Pick an x with $P(x)$ and $Q(x)$.

       $\vdots$

$(n-1)$ | $\exists_z[P(z) : R(z)]$

{ $\Rightarrow$-intro on (1) and $(n-1)$: }

(n) | $(\exists_x[P(x) : Q(x)] \wedge \forall_y[Q(y) : R(y)]) \Rightarrow \exists_z[P(z) : R(z)]$

We have now 'picked' an x which amongst other things, satisfies $Q(x)$, and hence line (3) is now *indeed* applicable, by using $\forall$-elim:

{ Assume: }

(1) | $\boxed{\exists_x[P(x) : Q(x)] \wedge \forall_y[Q(y) : R(y)]}$

{ $\wedge$-elim on (1): }

(2) | $\exists_x[P(x) : Q(x)]$

{ $\wedge$-elim on (1): }

(3) | $\forall_y[Q(y) : R(y)]$

{ $\exists^*$-elim on (2): }

(4) | Pick an x with $P(x)$ and $Q(x)$.

{ $\forall$-elim on (3)and(4): }

(5) | $R(x)$

       $\vdots$

$(n-1)$ | $\exists_z[P(z) : R(z)]$

{ $\Rightarrow$-intro on (1) and $(n-1)$: }

(n) | $(\exists_x[P(x) : Q(x)] \wedge \forall_y[Q(y) : R(y)]) \Rightarrow \exists_z[P(z) : R(z)]$

But now we can 'close' the derivation: we were (see line number $(n-1)$) looking for an a with $P(a)$ and $R(a)$, which we have now found. To be precise, x 'does what is required': we know now, that both $P(x)$ (see line number (4)) and $R(x)$ (see line number (5)) hold. Hence the complete derivation becomes:

{ Assume: }

(1) $\quad \exists_x[P(x) : Q(x)] \wedge \forall_y[Q(y) : R(y)]$

$\quad$ { $\wedge$-elim on (1): }

(2) $\quad \exists_x[P(x) : Q(x)]$

$\quad$ { $\wedge$-elim on (1): }

(3) $\quad \forall_y[Q(y) : R(y)]$

$\quad$ { $\exists^*$-elim on (2): }

(4) $\quad$ Pick an x with $P(x)$ and $Q(x)$.

$\quad$ { $\forall$-elim on (3) and (4): }

(5) $\quad R(x)$

$\quad$ { $\exists^*$-intro on (4) and (5): }

(6) $\quad \exists_z[P(z) : R(z)]$

$\quad$ { $\Rightarrow$-intro on (1) and (6): }

(7) $\quad (\exists_x[P(x) : Q(x)] \wedge \forall_y[Q(y) : R(y)]) \;\Rightarrow\; \exists_z[P(z) : R(z)]$

15.4   Exercises

15.1 Prove the following. Always put the declaration of x and the corresponding hypothesis in a context flag.

(a) $\forall_x[x \in \mathbb{R} \wedge x < 0 : x^3 + x^2 - x - 1 \leq 0]$
(b) $\forall_x[x \in \mathbb{R} : \cosh^2(x) - \sinh^2(x) = 1]$

Note that $\sinh(x) = \frac{1}{2}(e^x - e^{-x})$ and $\cosh(x) = \frac{1}{2}(e^x + e^{-x})$.

15.2 You are given:

$$\forall_x[x \in \mathbb{R} : e^x - 1 \geq x].$$

Prove that:

$$\forall_y[y \in \mathbb{R} \wedge y > 0 : \ln(y) \leq y - 1].$$

Describe clearly where the $\forall$-elimination or the $\forall$-introduction are used.

Hint: Use the substitution: $[\ln(y) \text{ for } x]$.

15.3 Give derivations for the following tautologies using the methods given in Section 15.1:

(a) $\forall_x[P(x) \wedge Q(x)] \Rightarrow \forall_y[P(y)]$

(b) $\forall_x[P(x) \Rightarrow Q(x)] \Rightarrow (\forall_y[P(y)] \Rightarrow \forall_z[Q(z)])$

15.4 As Exercise 15.3 (**D** is a given set, a and b are given elements of **D**):

(a) $\forall_x[x \in \mathbf{D} : \forall_y[y \in \mathbf{D} : P(x,y)]] \Rightarrow \forall_z[z \in \mathbf{D} : P(z,z)]$

(b) $\forall_x[x \in \mathbf{D} : P(x,x) \Rightarrow \forall_y[y \in \mathbf{D} : P(x,y)]] \Rightarrow$
$(\neg P(a,a) \vee P(a,b))$

15.5 Give derivations of the following tautologies, where for $\exists$, you only use the methods of Section 15.2, *not* the alternative methods of Section 15.3.

Remark: It is advisable in this and in the following exercise, to rename some bound variables in order to make them all different.

(a) $\neg \exists_x \exists_y[P(x,y)] \Rightarrow \forall_x \forall_y[\neg P(x,y)]$

(b) $\forall_x[P(x) : Q(x)] \Rightarrow (\exists_x[P(x)] \Rightarrow \exists_x[Q(x)])$

15.6 Prove the following tautologies via logical derivations, using the methods given in Part II.

Remark: Also the alternative $\exists$-rules of Section 15.3 are allowed.

(a) $\exists_x[P(x) : Q(x)] \Rightarrow (\exists_x[P(x)] \wedge \exists_x[Q(x)])$

(b) $\exists_x[P(x) \vee Q(x)] \Rightarrow (\exists_x[P(x)] \vee \exists_x[Q(x)])$

15.7 As Exercise 15.6:

(a) $\exists_y \forall_x[P(x) \wedge Q(x,y)] \Rightarrow \forall_z[P(z)]$

(b) $\exists_x \forall_y[P(x) \Rightarrow Q(y)] \Rightarrow (\forall_u[P(u)] \Rightarrow \exists_v[Q(v)])$

15.8 As Exercise 15.6:

(a) $\exists_x \forall_y[P(x,y)] \Rightarrow \forall_v \exists_u[P(u,v)]$

(b) $\forall_y[Q(y) \Rightarrow (P(y) \Rightarrow \exists_x[P(x) \wedge Q(x)])]$

15.9 As Exercise 15.6:

$(\forall_x[x \in \mathbb{N} : P(x)] \Rightarrow \exists_y[y \in \mathbb{N} : Q(y)]) \Rightarrow \exists_z[z \in \mathbb{N} : P(z) \Rightarrow Q(z)]$

15.10 Prove again the truth of the proposition of Exercise 11.3 (c), but now using as much as possible the methods of Chapter 15.

Use here the following definitions:

$$x \text{ is a multiple of } 3 \;\overset{\text{def}}{=}\; \exists_u [u \in \mathbb{Z} : x = 3u],$$

$$x \text{ is a multiple of } 6 \;\overset{\text{def}}{=}\; \exists_v [v \in \mathbb{Z} : x = 6v].$$

Part III

Applications

Chapter 16

Sets

Put two and two together

16.1   Set construction

In this chapter and the next, we will *apply* logic. We will show how you can use a reasoning to *prove* that certain properties hold. In the chapters thereafter, we look at general mathematical structures which are also of great importance in computer science, in particular relations and mappings (or functions). In this chapter we concentrate on a fundamental concept in both mathematics and computer science: the concept of sets.

We have already seen sets in Section 10.2. In this chapter we look at certain issues which are standard in the theory of sets. We start by giving the important concepts both via formal definitions and via informal descriptions. Thereafter we show how the logic described in the previous chapters can be applied to give convincing arguments that certain conjectures about sets are or are not correct.

We use the mathematical notation for set construction,

$$\{x \in \mathbf{D} | P(x)\}$$

because, for the problems that will be considered in this chapter, it fits better than the computer science notation. This notation (see Section 10.2) describes the set of all x-s in the domain $\mathbf{D}$ for which the predicate P holds.

Below we show how you can use sets of the form $\{x \in \mathbf{D} | P(x)\}$ in a proof or in a reasoning. For this we give exactly as in chapters 12 and 15,

introduction and elimination rules, with which we can work in a similar way
to before.

(I) '∈-*intro*' via **Property of** ∈ :

How can we decide for an arbitrary object t whether it belongs to the set
$\{x \in \mathbf{D}|P(x)\}$? For this, it is obvious that t must first be an element of
$\mathbf{D}$. Moreover, the predicate P must hold for this t. We can state this as a
Property of ∈ :

Property of ∈ :

$t \in \{x \in \mathbf{D}|P(x)\} \overset{val}{=\!=\!=} t \in \mathbf{D} \wedge P(t)$

Remark 16.1.1 *Of course, the formula $t \in \mathbf{D} \wedge P(t)$ should be read as the*
conjunction $(t \in \mathbf{D}) \wedge P(t)$. In general, we give symbols connected with sets,
such as '∈', higher priority than logical symbols.

Hence, for the *introduction* of a statement of the form $t \in \{x \in \mathbf{D}|P(x)\}$,
we may proceed as follows:

$$\vdots$$
$$(l) \qquad t \in \mathbf{D}$$
$$\vdots$$
$$(m-1) \qquad P(t)$$
$$\{ \text{ Property of } \in \text{ on } (l) \text{ and } (m-1): \ \}$$
$$(m) \qquad t \in \{x \in \mathbf{D}|P(x)\}$$

It it wise to choose the bound variable in $\{x \in \mathbf{D}|P(x)\}$ such that it
does not occur free in t, otherwise we run the risk of confusion. If there
are problems with variable name x, we can rename it. For example, by
renaming it into y, we can use the equivalent formula $t \in \{y \in \mathbf{D}|P(y)\}$
instead of $t \in \{x \in \mathbf{D}|P(x)\}$.

(II) '∈-*elim*' via **Property of** ∈ :

On the other hand, if we *know* that $t \in \{x \in \mathbf{D}|P(x)\}$, then what can we
derive? We can derive two conclusions, namely that both $t \in \mathbf{D}$ and $P(t)$
hold. So we have the following two rules for the *elimination* of a statement
of the form $t \in \{x \in \mathbf{D}|P(x)\}$:

	$\|\|\|$		$\|\|\|$
(k)	$t \in \{x \in \mathbf{D}\|P(x)\}$	(k)	$t \in \{x \in \mathbf{D}\|P(x)\}$
	$\|\|\|$		$\|\|\|$
	{ Property of $\in$ on (k): }		{ Property of $\in$ on (k): }
(m)	$t \in \mathbf{D}$	(n)	$P(t)$

Remark 16.1.2 *We shall not use the names '$\in$-intro' and '$\in$-elim', instead we use the phrase 'Property of $\in$'.*

16.2   Universal set and subset

We shall often work with *abstract* sets of the form A, B or $\{x \in \mathbf{D} \mid P(x)\}$, not with *concrete* sets as for example $\{0, 1, 2\}$, $\mathbb{N}$ or $\{x \in \mathbb{R}|5 < x \le 20\}$. All properties that we shall prove for these abstract sets, are of course valid also for *concrete* sets, simply by filling the abstract with the concrete.

We assume that there is *an* 'abstract superset' $\mathbf{U}$, the *universal set*, of which all other abstract sets are a part. We can for example take $\mathbb{R}$ for $\mathbf{U}$, the set of real numbers, or, if this is not big enough, we take another suitable set.

All sets that we will consider are hence part of this universal set $\mathbf{U}$. It can of course be that one set A is a *subset* of another set B. This will be the case when all elements of A are also elements of B. This is written as: $A \subseteq B$. The definition of $\subseteq$ is hence:

$$A \subseteq B \stackrel{\text{def}}{=} \forall_x[x \in \mathbf{U} : x \in A \Rightarrow x \in B].$$

The symbol $\stackrel{\text{def}}{=}$ must be read here as: 'is defined by'. The proposition $A \subseteq B$ is pronounced as: 'A is included in B' or 'A is a subset of B', the sign $\subseteq$ is called the *inclusion sign*. The word 'inclusion' comes from Latin and literally means 'enclosure': A is *enclosed in* B.

The definition implies that every set is a subset *of itself*, because

$$A \subseteq A \stackrel{val}{=\!=} \forall_x[x \in \mathbf{U} : x \in A \Rightarrow x \in A] \stackrel{val}{=\!=} \forall_x[x \in \mathbf{U} : \text{True}] \stackrel{val}{=\!=}$$
True.

Hence it always holds that: $A \subseteq A$.

Consequently, the universal set $\mathbf{U}$ is itself also a subset of $\mathbf{U}$. The set $\mathbf{U}$ can also be written in the form $\{x \in \mathbf{U}|P(x)\}$: it is clear that, in this case, we can take `True` for $P(x)$:

$$\mathbf{U} = \{\, x \in \mathbf{U} \mid \text{True}\}.$$

Hence with the Property of $\in$ it follows that:

> **Property of U :**
> $t \in \mathbf{U} \overset{val}{=\!=\!=} \text{True}$

Because in what follows we implicitly look at sets whose elements come from the universal set $\mathbf{U}$ (hence for every x it holds that $x \in \mathbf{U}$), we can write our definition of $\subseteq$ in a compact way, by using $x \in \mathbf{U} \overset{val}{=\!=\!=} \text{True}$ and Domain Weakening:

$$A \subseteq B \overset{\text{def}}{=\!=} \forall_x[x \in A : x \in B].$$

In what follows we will use this latter version.

Remark 16.2.1 *If a proposition P is defined as Q, then P and Q are also equivalent. Hence:*

$$\text{If } P \overset{\text{def}}{=\!=} Q, \text{ then } P \overset{val}{=\!=\!=} Q .$$

This means for example, that on the basis of the above definition, we can replace $A \subseteq B$, either forwards or backwards by the equivalent proposition $\forall_x[x \in A : x \in B]$.

From the definition of $\subseteq$ it follows by $\forall$-elim that:

> **Property of $\subseteq$:**
> $A \subseteq B \wedge t \in A \overset{val}{\models\!=} t \in B$

The definition of $\subseteq$ can be applied in two ways:

(I) '$\subseteq$-intro' via Definition of $\subseteq$:

If $A \subseteq B$ is the *goal* of a reasoning-in-the-making, then, because of the definition of $\subseteq$, we may replace this 'backwards' by the equivalent proposition $\forall_x[x \in A : x \in B]$. Afterwards, we can try to prove the latter formula with $\forall$-*intro*.

In a scheme:

$$\{ \text{Assume: } \}$$

(1) $\boxed{\underline{\text{var } x};\ x \in A}$

       $\vdots$

$(m-2)$ $x \in B$

$$\{ \forall\text{-intro on } (1) \text{ and } (m-2)\text{: } \}$$

$(m-1)$ $\forall_x [x \in A : x \in B]$

$$\{ \text{Definition of } \subseteq \text{ on } (m-1)\text{: } \}$$

(m) $A \subseteq B$

(II) '$\subseteq$-elim' via Property of $\subseteq$:

If we 'know' on the other hand that $A \subseteq B$, then we can do something with it, as soon as we have an element t of A. Then the above mentioned Property of $\subseteq$ gives that $t \in B$. In a scheme:

       $\|\|\|$

(k) $A \subseteq B$

       $\|\|\|$

(l) $t \in A$

       $\|\|\|$

$$\{ \text{Property of } \subseteq \text{ on } (k) \text{ and } (l)\text{: } \}$$

(m) $t \in B$

Remark 16.2.2 *We shall not in what follows use the names '$\subseteq$-intro' and '$\subseteq$-elim', because –as we just saw above– they are not needed.*

16.3   Equality of sets

Two sets are *equal* if they contain exactly the same elements. So the set $\{n \in \mathbb{Z} | n > 0\}$ is equal to the set $\{n \in \mathbb{N} | n \neq 0\}$.

     Hence we have for two equal sets that: every element of one is contained in the other, and vice versa. This means that from $A = B$ it follows that both $A \subseteq B$, and $B \subseteq A$.

     We can also turn this round. Suppose that $A \subseteq B$ and $B \subseteq A$. Then every element of A is contained in B, and every element of B is contained in A. This means that A and B have *the same* elements, and are hence equal.

For this reason we can consider the equality of two sets as a double inclusion. This is given by the following *definition*:

$$A = B \overset{\text{def}}{=} A \subseteq B \ \wedge \ B \subseteq A.$$

Remark 16.3.1 *In the latter formula, again we used the convention that set symbols have higher priority than logical symbols: the formula on the right hand side must be read as* $(A \subseteq B) \wedge (B \subseteq A)$.

With the above definition, we are able now to *reason* with sets.

(I) '=-*intro*' via Definition of = :

If we must *prove* that a set A is equal to a set B, we can do this by proving that both $A \subseteq B$ holds and $B \subseteq A$ holds. In a scheme:

$$\vdots$$

$$(l) \quad A \subseteq B$$

$$\vdots$$

$$(m-2) \quad B \subseteq A$$

$$\{ \wedge\text{-intro on } (l) \text{ and } (m-2) \text{: } \}$$

$$(m-1) \quad A \subseteq B \wedge B \subseteq A$$

$$\{ \text{ Definition of } = \text{ on } (m-1) \text{: } \}$$

$$(m) \quad A = B$$

There are hence two new 'holes' with two new goals, which can both be rewritten backwards by means of the definition of $\subseteq$. If we for example work further with the first new goal, we get:

$$\{ \text{ Assume: } \}$$

$$(k) \quad \boxed{\text{var } x; \ x \in A}$$

$$\vdots$$

$$(l-2) \quad x \in B$$

$$\{ \forall\text{-intro on } (k) \text{ and } (l-2) \text{: } \}$$

$$(l-1) \quad \forall_x [x \in A : x \in B]$$

$$\{ \text{ Definition of } \subseteq \text{ on } (l-1): \}$$

(l) $A \subseteq B$

$$\vdots$$

$(m-2)$ $B \subseteq A$

$$\{ \wedge\text{-intro on } (l) \text{ and } (m-2): \}$$

$(m-1)$ $A \subseteq B \wedge B \subseteq A$

$$\{ \text{ Definition of } = \text{ on } (m-1): \}$$

(m) $A = B$

We see here that in order to show that $A = B$, it is enough to show that for an arbitrary x, we have both $x \in A \Rightarrow x \in B$, and $x \in B \Rightarrow x \in A$! We can also see this as follows, with a *calculation*:

(1) $A = B$

$\stackrel{val}{=\!=}$ $\{ \text{ Definition of } =: \}$

(2) $A \subseteq B \wedge B \subseteq A$

$\stackrel{val}{=\!=}$ $\{ \text{ Definition of } \subseteq, \text{ twice: } \}$

(3) $\forall_x [x \in A : x \in B] \wedge \forall_x [x \in B : x \in A]$

$\stackrel{val}{=\!=}$ $\{ \text{ Domain Weakening, twice: } \}$

(4) $\forall_x [x \in A \Rightarrow x \in B] \wedge \forall_x [x \in B \Rightarrow x \in A]$

$\stackrel{val}{=\!=}$ $\{ \text{ Lemma: } \}$

(5) $\forall_x [(x \in A \Rightarrow x \in B) \wedge (x \in B \Rightarrow x \in A)]$

$\stackrel{val}{=\!=}$ $\{ \text{ Bi-implication: } \}$

(6) $\forall_x [x \in A \Leftrightarrow x \in B]$

(A *lemma* is an auxiliary theorem, which we usually prefer to prove separately. The above step from line number (4) to line number (5) follows from the general truth of:

$$\forall_x [P(x)] \wedge \forall_x [Q(x)] \stackrel{val}{=\!=} \forall_x [P(x) \wedge Q(x)] \ .$$

Can you give a proof of this?)

From the above calculation, we can find a strategy for proving $A = B$ which is much simpler than a reasoning. It is namely enough to show (for example with a *calculation*) for an arbitrary x in the universal set that:

$$x \in A \stackrel{val}{=\!=} x \in B \ ,$$

which implies by Lemma 6.1.3 that $\forall_x[x \in A \Leftrightarrow x \in B]$ and hence (see above) that $A = B$!

We give this as a property of equality (of sets):

> **Property of $=$:**
>
> $A = B \overset{val}{=\!=} \forall_x[x \in A \Leftrightarrow x \in B]$

Remark 16.3.2 *It is not surprising that with equality of sets, calculating with formulas is easier than reasoning with the help of contexts. In fact, $=$ looks like $\Leftrightarrow$, and the method of calculating with formulas is especially suitable for bi-implications.*

(II) ' $=$-elim' via Definition of $=$:

On the other hand, if we *know* that $A = B$, then this implies that both $A \subseteq B$, and $B \subseteq A$ hold:

$$
\begin{array}{ll}
 & \|\|\| \\
(k) & A = B \\
 & \|\|\| \\
 & \{ \text{ Definition of } = \text{ on } (k)\text{: } \} \\
(m) & A \subseteq B \land B \subseteq A \\
 & \{ \land\text{-elim on } (m)\text{: } \} \\
(m+1) & A \subseteq B \\
 & \{ \land\text{-elim on } (m)\text{: } \} \\
(m+2) & B \subseteq A
\end{array}
$$

Both $A \subseteq B$ and $B \subseteq A$ can then be used in the standard way by applying the definition of $\subseteq$. (See the previous section for this definition.) This gives both $\forall_x[x \in A : x \in B]$ and $\forall_x[x \in B : x \in A]$. And hence: as soon as we have t in A, then we also have t in B because of $\forall$-elim, and vice versa.

We describe this in two properties of equality:

> **Properties of $=$:**
>
> $A = B \land t \in A \overset{val}{=\!=} t \in B$
>
> $A = B \land t \in B \overset{val}{=\!=} t \in A$

Remark 16.3.3 *A general version of the rule of Leibniz (see Section 6.2) holds for* equality: *if $u = v$, then we may replace u by v wherever u occurs in a formula (or v by u wherever v occurs), without changing the truth value of the formula.*

This is in particular the case for equality of sets. *In the text above we find two examples of this fact:*

– *The inclusion $A \subseteq A$ always holds (see Section 16.2). Now assume $A = B$. By the 'general rule of Leibniz', we may hence replace an A in $A \subseteq A$, for example the second one, by B. Thus we have shown directly that $A \subseteq B$ is a consequence of $A = B$.*

– *Assume $A = B$ and $t \in A$. By the general rule of Leibniz, it follows that $t \in B$. (This is a second manner to justify the Properties of $=$ given above.)*

Remark 16.3.4 *The names '$=$-intro' and '$=$-elim' will not be used anymore.*

16.4 Intersection and union

We can combine sets in different ways to obtain new sets. In this section we study the *intersection* and the *union* of two sets.

If A and B are sets, then the *intersection* of A and B is the set of all elements which are *both* in A *and* in B. This new set is written as $A \cap B$, and pronounced as 'A intersection B'.

The definition of $A \cap B$ is hence:

$$A \cap B \overset{\text{def}}{=} \{x \in \mathbf{U} | x \in A \wedge x \in B\}.$$

Note that this definition makes a connection between the *set* symbol $\cap$ and the *logical* symbol $\wedge$. These two symbols look alike!

Example 16.4.1

- $\{n \in \mathbb{N} | n > 5\} \cap \{n \in \mathbb{N} | n < 10\} = \{6, 7, 8, 9\}$,

- $\{n \in \mathbb{N} | n > 5\} \cap \{n \in \mathbb{N} | n > 10\} = \{n \in \mathbb{N} | n > 10\}$,

- $\{x \in \mathbb{Z} | x \geq 0\} \cap \{x \in \mathbb{Z} | x \leq 0\} = \{0\}$,

- $\mathbb{Z} \cap \mathbb{N} = \mathbb{N}$,

- $\{n \in \mathbb{Z} | n \text{ is even}\} \cap \{n \in \mathbb{Z} | n \text{ is odd}\} = \emptyset$.

(Here $\emptyset$ is the empty set, the set without elements. See also Section 16.7.)

Another combination of sets A and B can be done via the *union* of A and B. This set contains the elements which are either in A *or* in B (or in both!). Said differently: x is in the union of A and B if x is in *at least one of the two*. The union of A and B is written as $A \cup B$, and pronounced as 'A union B'.

As a definition:

$$A \cup B \stackrel{\text{def}}{=} \{x \in \mathbf{U} | x \in A \vee x \in B\}.$$

There is again a relation between $\cup$ and $\vee$. These symbols look alike, just like $\cap$ and $\wedge$.

Example 16.4.2

- $\{n \in \mathbb{N} | n > 5\} \cup \{n \in \mathbb{N} | n < 10\} = \mathbb{N}$,

- $\{n \in \mathbb{N} | n > 5\} \cup \{n \in \mathbb{N} | n > 10\} = \{n \in \mathbb{N} | n > 5\}$,

- $\{x \in \mathbb{Z} | x \geq 0\} \cup \{x \in \mathbb{Z} | x \leq 0\} = \mathbb{Z}$,

- $\mathbb{Z} \cup \mathbb{N} = \mathbb{Z}$,

- $\{n \in \mathbb{Z} | n \text{ is even }\} \cup \{n \in \mathbb{Z} | n \text{ is odd }\} = \mathbb{Z}$.

From the definitions of intersection and union, together with the Property of $\in$ (see Section 16.1), we get two useful *properties*:

Property of $\cap$:
$t \in A \cap B \stackrel{val}{=\!=} t \in A \wedge t \in B$

Property of $\cup$:
$t \in A \cup B \stackrel{val}{=\!=} t \in A \vee t \in B$

(We have left out the part '$t \in \mathbf{U}$', because this is equivalent to **True** – see Section 16.2. Use **True**-elimination.)

In what follows we shall use these properties a lot.

Both intersection and union are *commutative* and *associative*. This means that:

$$A \cap B = B \cap A, \quad A \cup B = B \cup A,$$

$$(A \cap B) \cap C = A \cap (B \cap C), \ (A \cup B) \cup C = A \cup (B \cup C) \ .$$

These equalities are not difficult to prove, for example with the 'properties' just listed above.

Note that the commutativity and the associativity of $\cap$ and $\cup$ meet those of the logical symbols $\wedge$ and $\vee$. This did not happen by chance. When delivering proofs, one can really see that for example the associativity of $\cap$ is a *consequence* of that of $\wedge$!

Because of the 'commutativity' and 'associativity' properties of $\cap$ and $\cup$, one can usually drop the parentheses for repeated intersection and repeated union. Hence, one writes for example $A \cap B \cap C$ for the intersection of the *triple* A, B and C. It does not actually matter how we combine these, as long as all the three sets are included in the combination. The result is always the same.

We get for example $A \cap B \cap C$ as follows:

- first combine A and C into $A \cap C$, and then intersect the result with B, or

- first combine C and B into $C \cap B$, and then intersect A with $C \cap B$.

(Side-remark: also for logical formulas, we drop the parentheses in case of associativity: $a \wedge b \wedge c$ was a shorthand for both $(a \wedge b) \wedge c$, and $a \wedge (b \wedge c)$. See Section 5.1.)

Remark 16.4.3 *In formulas like* $(A \cap B) \cup C$ *the parentheses* must *be kept, because it does* not *hold in general that:* $(A \cap B) \cup C = A \cap (B \cup C)$. *We can show this with a* concrete *counterexample: take* $A = \{1\}$, $B = \{2\}$ *and* $C = \{3\}$, *then* $(A \cap B) \cup C = \emptyset \cup \{3\} = \{3\}$, *but* $A \cap (B \cup C) = \{1\} \cap \{2, 3\} = \emptyset \neq \{3\}$.

16.5 Complement

As we said already in Section 16.2, we consider all sets as part of a *universal set* **U**. Take now such a set A which is part of **U**. Then the *complement* of A is the set of all elements of **U** which do *not* occur in A. The complement of A is written as A^c.

The definition of A^c is hence:

$$A^c \overset{\text{def}}{=} \{x \in \mathbf{U} \,|\, \neg(x \in A)\}$$

Examples, with $\mathbf{U} = \mathbb{Z}$:

- $\{x \in \mathbb{Z} \,|\, x \geq 0\}^c = \{x \in \mathbb{Z} \,|\, x < 0\}$,

- $\{-1, 0, 1\}^c = \{x \in \mathbb{Z} | x \leq -2\} \cup \{x \in \mathbb{Z} | x \geq 2\}$,
- $\{x \in \mathbb{Z} | x \text{ is even}\}^c = \{x \in \mathbb{Z} | x \text{ is odd}\}$,
- $\mathbb{Z}^c = \emptyset$,
- $\emptyset^c = \mathbb{Z}$.

Note that when taking the complement, it is important to know what the universal set is. For example:
– If **U** is equal to $\mathbb{N}$ then $\mathbb{N}^c = \emptyset$,
– but if **U** is equal to $\mathbb{Z}$, then $\mathbb{N}^c = \{x \in \mathbb{Z} | x < 0\}$.

As is the case for intersection and union, an important *property* of complement follows from the definition plus the Property of $\in$ (again with the implicit assumption that the term t belongs to **U**):

Property of ^{c}:

$t \in A^c \overset{val}{=\!=\!=} \neg(t \in A)$

If we combine *complement* with *union* and/or *intersection*, we get interesting lemmas. For example:

$$(A \cap B)^c = A^c \cup B^c, \ (A \cup B)^c = A^c \cap B^c \ .$$

If you think of 'complement' as a kind of 'negation of sets' (A^c is everything in **U** that is *not* in A), then these properties will look like De Morgan. They are indeed closely connected with De Morgan. This becomes clear if we for example, try to prove the first of these two. We do this by showing that for an arbitrary x:

$$x \in (A \cap B)^c \overset{val}{=\!=\!=} x \in A^c \cup B^c \ ,$$

which is sufficient (see Section 16.3).

    (1) $x \in (A \cap B)^c$
$\overset{val}{=\!=\!=}$ { Property of ^{c}: }
    (2) $\neg(x \in A \cap B)$
$\overset{val}{=\!=\!=}$ { Property of $\cap$: }
    (3) $\neg(x \in A \land x \in B)$
$\overset{val}{=\!=\!=}$ { De Morgan }
    (4) $\neg(x \in A) \lor \neg(x \in B)$
$\overset{val}{=\!=\!=}$ { Property of ^{c}, twice: }
    (5) $x \in A^c \lor x \in B^c$
$\overset{val}{=\!=\!=}$ { Property of $\cup$: }
    (6) $x \in A^c \cup B^c$

For the other proposition, $(A \cup B)^c = A^c \cap B^c$, a similar proof can be easily given, again using De Morgan.

16.6 Difference

We saw in Section 16.3 that the *intersection* of two sets consists of every-thing contained in *both*, and the *union* consists of everything which is *at least in one of the two*.

In this section we study the *difference* of two sets. The difference of A and B is everything contained in A , but *not* in B. The difference of A and B is denoted by $A \backslash B$. We pronounce this as 'A minus B'.

The definition of $A \backslash B$ is hence:

$$A \backslash B \stackrel{\text{def}}{=} \{x \in \mathbf{U} | x \in A \wedge \neg(x \in B)\} \ .$$

Remark 16.6.1 *The difference of A and B is also written as $A - B$.*

Example 16.6.2

- $\{n \in \mathbb{N} | n > 5\} \backslash \{n \in \mathbb{N} | n < 10\} = \{n \in \mathbb{N} | n \geq 10\}$,

- $\{n \in \mathbb{N} | n > 5\} \backslash \{n \in \mathbb{N} | n > 10\} = \{6, 7, 8, 9, 10\}$,

- $\{x \in \mathbb{Z} | x \geq 0\} \backslash \{x \in \mathbb{Z} | x \leq 0\} = \{x \in \mathbb{Z} | x > 0\}$,

- $\mathbb{Z} \backslash \mathbb{N} = \{x \in \mathbb{Z} | x < 0\}$,

- $\mathbb{N} \backslash \mathbb{Z} = \emptyset$.

From the definition of difference and the Property of $\in$, a useful property of the difference follows:

> **Property of $\backslash$:**
> $t \in A \backslash B \stackrel{val}{=\!=} t \in A \ \wedge \ \neg(t \in B)$

Note that 'difference' is not commutative: $A \backslash B$ is in general very differ-ent from $B \backslash A$. (See the last two examples above.) Also the difference is not associative: $(A \backslash B) \backslash C$ can be very different from $A \backslash (B \backslash C)$. Show this yourself by giving a (counter-)example.

There are many interesting relations between formulas containing the symbols $\cap$, $\cup$, ^{c} and $\backslash$. Below, we show with two examples how one can *prove* that such relations hold. Afterwards we show how a *counterexample* can be used to show that a property of sets does *not* in general hold.

First, we show that, for arbitrary sets A and B, the following relation holds:

$$A \backslash (A \cap B) = A \backslash B \ .$$

Because one is concerned here with the *equality* of two sets, a simple *calculation* lends itself:

$$(1) \quad x \in A \backslash (A \cap B)$$

$\overset{val}{=\!=} \quad \{ \text{ Property of } \backslash : \}$

$$(2) \quad x \in A \land \neg(x \in A \cap B)$$

$\overset{val}{=\!=} \quad \{ \text{ Property of } \cap : \}$

$$(3) \quad x \in A \land \neg(x \in A \land x \in B)$$

$\overset{val}{=\!=} \quad \{ \text{ De Morgan: } \}$

$$(4) \quad x \in A \land (\neg(x \in A) \lor \neg(x \in B))$$

$\overset{val}{=\!=} \quad \{ \text{ Distributivity: } \}$

$$(5) \quad (x \in A \land \neg(x \in A)) \lor (x \in A \land \neg(x \in B))$$

$\overset{val}{=\!=} \quad \{ \text{ Contradiction: } \}$

$$(6) \quad \mathtt{False} \lor (x \in A \land \neg(x \in B))$$

$\overset{val}{=\!=} \quad \{ \text{ True/False-elimination: } \}$

$$(7) \quad x \in A \land \neg(x \in B)$$

$\overset{val}{=\!=} \quad \{ \text{ Property of } \backslash : \}$

$$(8) \quad x \in A \backslash B$$

From this we immediately get the desired goal.

In the following example we show that

$$A \subseteq B^c \Rightarrow A \backslash B = A \ .$$

The beginning is simple:

$\{ \text{ Assume: } \}$

$$(1) \quad \boxed{A \subseteq B^c}$$

$$\qquad \vdots$$

$$(n-1) \quad A \backslash B = A$$

$\{ \Rightarrow\text{-intro on (1) and } (n-1): \}$

$$(n) \quad A \subseteq B^c \Rightarrow A \backslash B = A$$

At first sight, we may want to close the hole with a calculation. Note that the goal in line number $(n-1)$ is the *equality* of the sets $A \backslash B$ and A. Hence it is enough to give a calculation from which it follows that (for all $x \in \mathbf{U}$) the following holds:

$$x \in A \backslash B \overset{val}{=\!=} x \in A .$$

But this does not seem to work:

$$(2) \quad x \in A \backslash B$$
$$\stackrel{val}{=\!=\!=} \quad \{ \text{ Property of } \backslash : \}$$
$$(3) \quad x \in A \wedge \neg(x \in B)$$
$$\stackrel{val}{=\!=\!=} \quad \{ \text{ ??? } \}$$
$$(n\!-\!2) \quad x \in A$$

Of course we have $x \in A \wedge \neg(x \in B) \stackrel{val}{\models} x \in A$. But here we need the *equivalence* $x \in A \wedge \neg(x \in B) \stackrel{val}{=\!=\!=} x \in A$. In order to show that this holds *in this case*, we need the hypothesis that $A \subseteq B^c$ from line number (1)! However, in a calculation, we cannot in principle look further back than the *previous* line.

For this reason, we will proceed with a *reasoning*, instead of a calculation. This gives the desired result, although with a lot of work.

The overall frame of the derivation looks like this:

$$\{ \text{ Assume: } \}$$
$$(1) \quad \boxed{A \subseteq B^c}$$

$$\vdots$$

$$(m) \quad A \backslash B \subseteq A$$

$$\vdots$$

$$(n-3) \quad A \subseteq A \backslash B$$
$$\{ \wedge\text{-intro on } (m) \text{ and } (n-3): \}$$
$$(n-2) \quad A \backslash B \subseteq A \ \wedge \ A \subseteq A \backslash B$$
$$\{ \text{ Definition of } = \text{ on } (n-2): \}$$
$$(n-1) \quad A \backslash B = A$$
$$\{ \Rightarrow\text{-intro on } (1) \text{ and } (n-1): \}$$
$$(n) \quad A \subseteq B^c \Rightarrow A \backslash B = A$$

The full derivation can be found below:

$$\{ \text{ Assume: } \}$$
$$(1) \quad \boxed{A \subseteq B^c}$$
$$\{ \text{ Assume: } \}$$

(2)   ⎢ $\boxed{\underline{\text{var }} x;\ x \in A\backslash B}$

          ⎢   { Property of \ on (2): }
(3)   ⎢ $x \in A \land \neg(x \in B)$

          ⎢   { $\land$-elim on (3): }
(4)   ⎢ $x \in A$

          ⎢ { $\forall$-intro on (2) and (4): }
(5)   ⎢ $\forall_x[x \in A\backslash B : x \in A]$

          ⎢ { Definition of $\subseteq$ on (5): }
(6)   ⎢ $A\backslash B \subseteq A$

          ⎢ { Assume: }
(7)   ⎢ $\boxed{\underline{\text{var }} x;\ x \in A}$

          ⎢   { Definition of $\subseteq$ on (1): }
(8)   ⎢ $\forall_y[y \in A : y \in B^C]$

          ⎢   { $\forall$-elim on (8) and (7): }
(9)   ⎢ $x \in B^C$

          ⎢   { Property of ^{C} on (9): }
(10)   ⎢ $\neg(x \in B)$

          ⎢   { $\land$-intro on (7) and (10): }
(11)   ⎢ $x \in A \land \neg(x \in B)$

          ⎢   { Property of \ on (11): }
(12)   ⎢ $x \in A\backslash B$

          ⎢ { $\forall$-intro on (7) and (12): }
(13)   ⎢ $\forall_x[x \in A : x \in A\backslash B]$

          ⎢ { Definition of $\subseteq$ on (13): }
(14)   ⎢ $A \subseteq A\backslash B$

          ⎢ { $\land$-intro on (6) and (14): }
(15)   ⎢ $A\backslash B \subseteq A \ \land\ A \subseteq A\backslash B$

          ⎢ { Definition of $=$ on (15): }
(16)   ⎢ $A\backslash B = A$

          { $\Rightarrow$-intro on (1) and (16): }
(17) $A \subseteq B^C \Rightarrow A\backslash B = A$

(Note that in line number (8) we used as a name for the bound variable the letter y and not the letter x. We do this in order to avoid ambiguity; the name x is actually already 'in use', see line number (7).)

In what follows, we shall often write reasonings like the one given above, in *shorter form* and without arguments. The same reasoning then looks as follows:

(1)	$A \subseteq B^c$
(2)	$\boxed{\text{var } x; \ x \in A \backslash B}$
(3)	$x \in A \wedge \neg(x \in B)$
(4)	$x \in A$
(5)	$\forall_x [x \in A \backslash B : x \in A]$
(6)	$A \backslash B \subseteq A$
(7)	$\boxed{\text{var } x; \ x \in A}$
(8)	$\forall_y [y \in A : y \in B^c]$
(9)	$x \in B^c$
(10)	$\neg(x \in B)$
(11)	$x \in A \wedge \neg(x \in B)$
(12)	$x \in A \backslash B$
(13)	$\forall_x [x \in A : x \in A \backslash B]$
(14)	$A \subseteq A \backslash B$
(15)	$A \backslash B \subseteq A \ \wedge \ A \subseteq A \backslash B$
(16)	$A \backslash B = A$
(17)	$A \subseteq B^c \Rightarrow A \backslash B = A$

If we change the last result of the above reasoning a little bit, by replacing the final A by B, it will *not* always be valid:

It does not hold in general that: $A \subseteq B^c \Rightarrow A \backslash B = B$.

We show this with a counterexample. Such a counterexample can be found by *trying* things out:

- Take $\mathbf{U} = \mathbb{Z}$, $A = \mathbb{N}$ and $B = \emptyset$, then $A \subseteq B^c$. But $A \backslash B \neq B$, because the left hand side is $A \backslash B = \mathbb{N} \backslash \emptyset = \mathbb{N}$, whereas the right hand side $B = \emptyset$.

- Or: take $\mathbf{U} = \{0, 1, 2\}$, $A = \{0\}$ and $B = \{2\}$, then $B^c = \{0, 1\}$ hence $A \subseteq B^c$, but $A \backslash B = \{0\} \neq B$.

Obviously, *one* counterexample is enough. Make it however *as concrete as possible*. When looking for a counterexample it does help to draw a picture (a so-called '*Venn diagram*') on which you choose a number in every 'picture part'. This is in fact what we have done in the second counterexample above: see Figure 16.1.

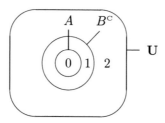

Figure 16.1: A Venn diagram of sets A and B where $A \subseteq B^c$.

16.7   The empty set

The *complement* of the universal set is the *empty set*. We have already seen this set which we denote by $\emptyset$.

In the same manner as *every* element belongs to the universal set, *no* element belongs to the empty set. Hence $\emptyset$ is the set *without elements*. (There is precisely *one* such set.)

The set $\emptyset$ can also be written as $\{x \in \mathbf{U} | P(x)\}$, when we take `False` as the predicate $P(x)$.

Hence we have:

$$\emptyset = \{\, x \in \mathbf{U} \mid \texttt{False}\,\}\,.$$

Again with the Property of $\in$ it follows that:

Property of $\emptyset$:

$t \in \emptyset \overset{val}{=\!=\!=} \texttt{False}$

Now it is easy to show that $\emptyset \subseteq A$, for every A:

(1) $\emptyset \subseteq A$
$\overset{val}{=\!=\!=}$ { Definition of $\subseteq$: }
(2) $\forall_x[x \in \emptyset : x \in A]$
$\overset{val}{=\!=\!=}$ { Property of $\emptyset$: }
(3) $\forall_x[\mathtt{False} : x \in A]$
$\overset{val}{=\!=\!=}$ { Empty Domain: }
(4) $\mathtt{True}$

(Of course it also holds that $A \subseteq \mathbf{U}$, for every A.)

We will now look at how one can use $\emptyset$ in reasonings. We separate between $A = \emptyset$ as a *goal*, see (**I**) below, and $A = \emptyset$ as a proposition that we *'know'*, see (**II**).

(I) '$\emptyset$-intro' via Property of $\emptyset$:

If we must show that a certain A is *equal* to $\emptyset$, it is enough to show that $A \subseteq \emptyset$, because $\emptyset \subseteq A$ is always true (see above). And in order to prove $A \subseteq \emptyset$, it is sufficient to have a proof of $\forall_x[x \in A : x \in \emptyset]$, that is, a proof of $\forall_x[x \in A : \mathtt{False}]$. We summarize this in the following property:

Property of $\emptyset$:
$A = \emptyset \quad \overset{val}{=\!=\!=} \quad \forall_x[x \in A : \mathtt{False}]$

A *calculation* which makes the above reasoning precise, is the following:

(1) $A = \emptyset$
$\overset{val}{=\!=\!=}$ { Definition of $=$: }
(2) $A \subseteq \emptyset \ \wedge \ \emptyset \subseteq A$
$\overset{val}{=\!=\!=}$ { $\emptyset \subseteq A \overset{val}{=\!=\!=} \mathtt{True}$; True/False-elimination: }
(3) $A \subseteq \emptyset$
$\overset{val}{=\!=\!=}$ { Definition of $\subseteq$: }
(4) $\forall_x[x \in A : x \in \emptyset]$
$\overset{val}{=\!=\!=}$ { Property of $\emptyset$ (the one given earlier in this section): }
(5) $\forall_x[x \in A : \mathtt{False}]$

Remark 16.7.1 *Check that we can also rewrite* $\forall_x[x \in A : \mathtt{False}]$ *to* $\forall_x[\neg(x \in A)]$ *or to* $\neg\exists_x[x \in A]$.

(The complementary Property for $\mathbf{U}$ is:

$A = \mathbf{U} \quad \overset{val}{=\!=\!=} \quad \forall_x[x \in A : \texttt{True}]$.

But in practice, we shall rarely need this property.)

Proving $A = \emptyset$ can hence simply be done by starting from $x \in A$ and showing $\texttt{False}$. This latter can be done with a derivation, but under some circumstances, it can simply be done with a calculation.

We give an example where it must be proven that a certain set is empty. We will show that:

$$A \subseteq B \Rightarrow A \backslash B = \emptyset \ .$$

Because in the proof of $A \backslash B = \emptyset$ we need the context $A \subseteq B$, a *calculation* in the standard sense is not directly possible. Therefore, we give first a *reasoning*. Thereafter, we shall show that also a calculation can offer a solution, although we must stretch a bit the rules for calculations.

$\{$ Assume: $\}$

(1) $\boxed{A \subseteq B}$

$\quad\quad$ $\{$ Assume: $\}$

(2) $\quad$ $\boxed{\underline{\text{var } x};\ x \in A \backslash B}$

$\quad\quad\quad$ $\{$ Property of $\backslash$ on (2): $\}$

(3) $\quad\quad$ $x \in A \wedge \neg(x \in B)$

$\quad\quad\quad$ $\{$ $\wedge$-elim on (3): $\}$

(4) $\quad\quad$ $x \in A$

$\quad\quad\quad$ $\{$ Property of $\subseteq$ on (1) and (4): $\}$

(5) $\quad\quad$ $x \in B$

$\quad\quad\quad$ $\{$ $\wedge$-elim on (3): $\}$

(6) $\quad\quad$ $\neg(x \in B)$

$\quad\quad\quad$ $\{$ Contradiction on (5) and (6): $\}$

(7) $\quad\quad$ $\texttt{False}$

$\quad\quad$ $\{$ $\forall$-intro on (2) and (7): $\}$

(8) $\quad$ $\forall_x[x \in A \backslash B : \texttt{False}]$

$\quad\quad$ $\{$ Property of $\emptyset$ on (8): $\}$

(9) $\quad$ $A \backslash B = \emptyset$

$\quad$ $\{$ $\Rightarrow$-intro on (1) and (9): $\}$

(10) $A \subseteq B \Rightarrow A \backslash B = \emptyset$

We can replace a part of the reasoning, namely the part appearing in the inside flag, by a *calculation*. We can replace line numbers (3) to (7), by the following:

$$(3') \quad x \in A \land \neg(x \in B)$$
$$\overset{val}{\models} \quad \{ \text{ Monotonicity on } (3'), \text{ use } (1): \}$$
$$(4') \quad x \in B \land \neg(x \in B)$$
$$\overset{val}{=\!=} \quad \{ \text{ Contradiction on } (4'): \}$$
$$(7') \quad \texttt{False}$$

This leads to benefits. Note that when giving reasons for line number $(4')$ we have gone outside the scheme of a calculation, because there we have called line number (1)! (From (1) it actually follows that $x \in A \overset{val}{\models} x \in B$.)

Hence we have here the possibility to make better use of calculations, because when moving from line number (m) to line number $(m+1)$ we can also call anything which we *earlier* already 'knew' (provided that it is still valid).

This expanded form of 'calculating with formulas' shall play a useful role especially in the derivation of correct programs. In this book we only touch the possibility, we shall not use it further.

Finally we give a version of this proof as it would appear in a mathematics book. Check that all important elements of the above reasoning(s) can be found in it!

Lemma 16.7.2

$$A \subseteq B \Rightarrow A \backslash B = \emptyset .$$

Proof: Assume $A \subseteq B$. If $x \in A \backslash B$, then $x \in A$ and $x \notin B$. From $A \subseteq B$ and $x \in A$ it follows that $x \in B$. Contradiction. Hence $A \backslash B$ must be empty.

(II) '$\emptyset$-elim' via Property of $\emptyset$:

If we *know* that $A = \emptyset$, then we apply this by using the second Property of $\emptyset$. This Property tells us that we also 'know' $\forall_x [x \in A : \texttt{False}]$. Hence as soon as we have an element t in A, we get **False**.

As a scheme this looks as follows:

$$\|\|\|$$

(k) $A = \emptyset$

$$\|\|\|$$

(m) $t \in A$

{ Property of $\emptyset$ on (k): }

$(m+1)$ $\forall_x[x \in A : \texttt{False}]$

{ $\forall$-elim on $(m+1)$ and (m): }

$(m+2)$ $\texttt{False}$

Remark 16.7.3 *We shall not use the names '$\emptyset$-intro' and '$\emptyset$-elim' any further.*

16.8   Powerset

Every set has subsets. Even the empty set has a subset: itself! For a given set A you can form the *set of all its subsets*, the so-called *powerset* of A. Notation: $\mathcal{P}(A)$.

Be careful: an *element* of $\mathcal{P}(A)$ is itself a *set*, namely a subset of A.

Example 16.8.1

- *Take $A = \{5, 8\}$. The elements of $\mathcal{P}(A)$ are the subsets of A, hence the sets: $\emptyset$, $\{5\}$, $\{8\}$ and $\{5, 8\}$.*

- *Take $A = \{1, 2, 3\}$. Then:*

$$\mathcal{P}(A) = \{ \ \emptyset, \{1\}, \{2\}, \{3\}, \{1, 2\}, \{1, 3\}, \{2, 3\}, \{1, 2, 3\} \ \} \ .$$

  Hence for example $\{1, 3\} \in \mathcal{P}(A)$, $\emptyset \in \mathcal{P}(A)$, $\{2\} \in \mathcal{P}(A)$, but not *$2 \in \mathcal{P}(A)$, because 2 is not a subset of $\{1, 2, 3\}$, but an element of it.*

- *Take $A = \emptyset$. Then $\mathcal{P}(A)$ is the* one-element set *(!) $\{\emptyset\}$.*

- *Take $A = \mathbb{N}$. Then the following sets are for example elements of $\mathcal{P}(\mathbb{N})$:*

$$\emptyset, \{37\}, \{5, 8, 23\}, \{n \in \mathbb{N} | n \text{ is odd }\}, \mathbb{N} \backslash \{0\}, \mathbb{N} \ .$$

Let A be a *finite* set with n elements. Then the number of elements of $\mathcal{P}(A)$ is equal to 2^n. This is simple to check. See also the first three of the above listed examples:

- $\{5, 8\}$ has 2 elements and its powerset has 2^2.

- $\{1, 2, 3\}$ has 3 elements and the powerset of $\{1, 2, 3\}$ has $2^3 = 8$.

- $\emptyset$ has 0 elements and the powerset of $\emptyset$ has $2^0 = 1$.

Remark 16.8.2 *For finite sets A, the number of elements of $\mathcal{P}(A)$ is two to the* power *of the number of elements of A. This is hence the origin of the* name power*set. The symbol $\mathcal{P}$ comes from 'power'. The powerset $\mathcal{P}(A)$ is therefore also denoted by 2^A. For finite A it also holds that: $\#(2^A) = 2^{\#(A)}$, which says: the number of elements of the powerset of A is two to the power of the number of elements of A ...*

Hence, from the definition of 'powerset' it follows that:

Property of $\mathcal{P}$:

$C \in \mathcal{P}(A) \overset{val}{=\!=\!=} C \subseteq A$

When reasoning about powersets, it is important to separate *elements* and *sets*. A can be both a set and at the same time an *element* of another set, for example a powerset! So you must keep track of the circumstances under which you are studying this A.

We give an example to show how powerset can be used in proofs. We show that:

$A \subseteq B \Rightarrow \mathcal{P}(A) \subseteq \mathcal{P}(B)$.

The start is simple (we combine two steps on the way from line number $(n-2)$ to line number $(n-1)$):

$\{$ Assume: $\}$

(1) $\boxed{A \subseteq B}$

      $\{$ Assume: $\}$

(2) $\boxed{\underline{\text{var }} X;\ X \in \mathcal{P}(A)}$

      $\vdots$

$(n-2)$ $X \in \mathcal{P}(B)$

          $\{$ $\forall$-intro on (2) and $(n-2)$, definition of $\subseteq$: $\}$

$(n-1)$ $\mathcal{P}(A) \subseteq \mathcal{P}(B)$

          $\{$ $\Rightarrow$-intro on (1) and $(n-1)$: $\}$

(n) $A \subseteq B \Rightarrow \mathcal{P}(A) \subseteq \mathcal{P}(B)$

On the basis of the above Property of $\mathcal{P}$, we rewrite the propositions in which $\mathcal{P}$ appears in the above proof. This concerns the lines numbered (2) and $(n-2)$. We rewrite the first one forward and the other (the goal) backwards:

$$\{ \text{Assume: } \}$$

(1) $\boxed{A \subseteq B}$

$\qquad \{ \text{Assume: } \}$

(2) $\qquad \boxed{\underline{\text{var }} X;\ X \in \mathcal{P}(A)}$

$\qquad\qquad \{ \text{Property of } \mathcal{P} \text{ on (2): } \}$

(3) $\qquad\qquad X \subseteq A$

$\qquad\qquad \vdots$

$(n-3)$ $\qquad\qquad X \subseteq B$

$\qquad\qquad \{ \text{Property of } \mathcal{P} \text{ on } (n-3) \text{: } \}$

$(n-2)$ $\qquad\qquad X \in \mathcal{P}(B)$

$\qquad \{ \forall\text{-intro on (2) and } (n-2), \text{ definition of } \subseteq \text{: } \}$

$(n-1)$ $\qquad \mathcal{P}(A) \subseteq \mathcal{P}(B)$

$\quad \{ \Rightarrow\text{-intro on (1) and } (n-1) \text{: } \}$

(n) $\quad A \subseteq B \Rightarrow \mathcal{P}(A) \subseteq \mathcal{P}(B)$

Note that we have moved here from the *element*-level, for example (see line (2)) $X \in \mathcal{P}(A)$, to the (sub)*set*-level, for example (see line (3)) $X \subseteq A$.

Now we can easily complete the proof, because it is intuitively clear that the propositions $X \subseteq A$ in line number (3) and $A \subseteq B$ in line number (1) together have as conclusion that $X \subseteq B$. This latter can be shown as follows:

$$\{ \text{Assume: } \}$$

(1) $\boxed{A \subseteq B}$

$\qquad \{ \text{Assume: } \}$

(2) $\qquad \boxed{\underline{\text{var }} X;\ X \in \mathcal{P}(A)}$

$\qquad\qquad \{ \text{Property of } \mathcal{P} \text{ on (2): } \}$

(3) $\quad X \subseteq A$

$\quad$ { Assume: }

(4) $\quad$ $\boxed{\text{var } x;\ x \in X}$

$\quad\quad$ { Property of $\subseteq$ on (3) and (4): }

(5) $\quad\quad x \in A$

$\quad\quad$ { Property of $\subseteq$ on (1) and (5): }

(6) $\quad\quad x \in B$

$\quad$ { $\forall$-intro on (4) and (6), definition of $\subseteq$: }

(7) $\quad X \subseteq B$

$\quad$ { Property of $\mathcal{P}$ on (7): }

(8) $\quad X \in \mathcal{P}(B)$

$\quad$ { $\forall$-intro on (2) and (8), definition of $\subseteq$: }

(9) $\quad \mathcal{P}(A) \subseteq \mathcal{P}(B)$

$\quad$ { $\Rightarrow$-intro on (1) and (9): }

(10) $\quad A \subseteq B \Rightarrow \mathcal{P}(A) \subseteq \mathcal{P}(B)$

16.9   Cartesian product

We have already (Section 4.1) dealt with the *Cartesian product*:

$$A \times B \ := \ \{\,(a,b) \in \mathbf{U} \mid a \in A \wedge b \in B\,\}\,.$$

So, if A and B are sets, then the Cartesian product $A \times B$ consists of all *pairs* (a,b) where $a \in A$ and $b \in B$. From this it follows directly that:

Property of $\times$:

$(a,b) \in A \times B \quad \overset{val}{=\!=} \quad a \in A \ \wedge \ b \in B$

Similarly, the Cartesian product $A \times B \times C$ consists of all '*triples*' (a,b,c) where $a \in A$, $b \in B$ and $c \in C$. We can go on on like that forming Cartesian products of more than three sets. The Cartesian product $A_1 \times \ldots \times A_n$ contains all *n-tuples* $(a_1, \ldots, a_n)$ where $a_i \in A_i$.

The *order* is important for these pairs, triples, ..., n-tuples. For example, the pair $(3, 5)$ is different from the pair $(5, 3)$. It is also important that the ith element of the n-tuple $(a_1, \ldots, a_n)$, that is a_i, comes from the ith set, hence from A_i.

Example 16.9.1

- $\mathbb{N} \times \mathbb{Z}$ *is the Cartesian product of* $\mathbb{N}$ *and* $\mathbb{Z}$, *that is, the set of all pairs* (n, x) *where* $n \in \mathbb{N}$ *and* $x \in \mathbb{Z}$. *Hence, elements of* $\mathbb{N} \times \mathbb{Z}$ *are for example* $(2, 8)$, $(2, 2)$, $(2, 0)$ *and* $(2, -2)$, *but* not $(2, \pi)$, $(\pi, -2)$ *or* $(-2, 2)$.

- *The Cartesian product* $\mathbb{R} \times \mathbb{R} \times \mathbb{R}$ *contains all triples* (x, y, z) *where* x, y *and* $z \in \mathbb{R}$. *Hence* $(\pi, -3, \sqrt{2})$ *and* $(0, 0, 0) \in \mathbb{R} \times \mathbb{R} \times \mathbb{R}$, *but not the pair* $(2, \pi)$ *or the triple* $(\sqrt{-1}, 2, -5)$.

- *The Cartesian product* $(A \times B) \times C$ *consists of the* pairs (x, c) *where* x *is itself a pair in* $A \times B$, *whereas* c *is an element of* C.

A Cartesian product of a set with itself is denoted as a *power*: $\mathbb{N}^2 = \mathbb{N} \times \mathbb{N}$ and $\mathbb{R}^3 = \mathbb{R} \times \mathbb{R} \times \mathbb{R}$.

In order to show how one can do reasonings with Cartesian products, we give the following simple example:

$$A \subseteq B \Rightarrow A^2 \subseteq B^2 \ .$$

The beginning is straightforward:

$$\{ \text{Assume: } \}$$

(1) $\boxed{A \subseteq B}$

$\qquad \vdots$

$(n-1)$ $A^2 \subseteq B^2$

$\qquad \{ \Rightarrow\text{-intro on (1) and } (n-1)\text{: } \}$

(n) $A \subseteq B \Rightarrow A^2 \subseteq B^2$

In order to reach the goal $A^2 \subseteq B^2$, we replace it by a $\forall$-formula, by the use of the definition of $\subseteq$:

$$A^2 \subseteq B^2 \stackrel{val}{=\!=\!=} \forall_{(x,y)}[(x, y) \in A^2 : (x, y) \in B^2] \ .$$

Be careful: we are considering all the *elements* of A^2, which are here *pairs* of elements from A. Such pairs must be taken as 'arbitrary' elements, hence (x, y) is a good choice.

(Note: We cannot take (x, x) because this is not general enough! Take as example $\mathbb{N}^2$, the (x, y) can be any pair of natural numbers, but (x, x) can only be one of the pairs $(0,0)$, $(1,1)$, $(2,2)$, ...)

This gives:

$$\{ \text{ Assume: } \}$$

(1) $\boxed{A \subseteq B}$

$$\vdots$$

$(n-2)$ $\quad \forall_{(x,y)}[(x, y) \in A^2 : (x, y) \in B^2]$

$\quad \{ \text{ Definition of } \subseteq \text{ on } (n-2): \}$

$(n-1)$ $\quad A^2 \subseteq B^2$

$\quad \{ \Rightarrow\text{-intro on (1) and } (n-1): \}$

(n) $\quad A \subseteq B \Rightarrow A^2 \subseteq B^2$

The rest of the proof is not difficult anymore:

$$\{ \text{ Assume: } \}$$

(1) $\boxed{A \subseteq B}$

$$\{ \text{ Assume: } \}$$

(2) $\boxed{\underline{\text{var }} (x, y); \; (x, y) \in A^2}$

$\quad \{ \text{ Property of } \times \text{ on (2): } \}$

(3) $\quad x \in A \wedge y \in A$

$\quad \{ \wedge\text{-elim on (3): } \}$

(4) $\quad x \in A$

$\quad \{ \text{ Property of } \subseteq \text{ on (1) and (4): } \}$

(5) $\quad x \in B$

$\quad \{ \wedge\text{-elim on (3): } \}$

(6) $\quad y \in A$

$\quad \{ \text{ Property of } \subseteq \text{ on (1) and (6): } \}$

(7) $\quad \Big\Vert \quad y \in B$

$\quad\quad\quad \Big\Vert \quad \{ \ \wedge\text{-intro on (5) and (7): } \}$

(8) $\quad \Big\Vert \quad x \in B \wedge y \in B$

$\quad\quad\quad \Big\Vert \quad \{ \ \text{Property of } \times \text{ on (8): } \}$

(9) $\quad \Big\Vert \quad (x, y) \in B^2$

$\quad\quad \Big\Vert \quad \{ \ \forall\text{-intro on (2) and (9): } \}$

(10) $\quad \Big\Vert \quad \forall_{(x,y)}[(x, y) \in A^2 : (x, y) \in B^2]$

$\quad\quad \Big\Vert \quad \{ \ \text{Definition of } \subseteq \text{ on (10): } \}$

(11) $\quad \Big\Vert \quad A^2 \subseteq B^2$

$\quad\quad \{ \ \Rightarrow\text{-intro on (1) and (11): } \}$

(12) $\quad A \subseteq B \Rightarrow A^2 \subseteq B^2$

Finally, it is good to know when two pairs are *equal* – and when they are not. The pair (a, b) is equal to (a', b') if, and only if, both $a = a'$ and $b = b'$.

So in $\mathbb{N} \times \mathbb{Z}$, the pair $(2, -2)$ is only equal to itself, and to no other pair like $(2, 2)$ or $(0, -2)$. Moreover, if $(x, y) = (2, -2)$, then $x = 2$ and $y = -2$; and also the other way round. Of course, we may allow some mathematical calculations, such as $(2 + 3, -2 + 1) = (5, -1)$, because $2 + 3 = 5$, etc.

We state this 'equality for pairs' as another Property of $\times$:

> **Property of $\times$:**
>
> $(a, b) = (a', b') \ \stackrel{val}{=\!=\!=} \ a = a' \ \wedge \ b = b'$

Of course, equality of pairs can be easily extended to equality of triples or to n-tuples in general, for example:

$$(a_1, \ldots, a_n) = (a'_1, \ldots, a'_n) \ \stackrel{val}{=\!=\!=} \ \forall_k[k \in \{1, \ldots, n\} : a_k = a'_k] \ .$$

16.10   Exercises

16.1 Check whether the following propositions always hold. If so, give a proof; if not, give a counterexample.

(a) $(A \subseteq B \wedge \neg(A = B)) \Rightarrow \neg(B \subseteq A)$

(b) $\neg(A \subseteq B) \wedge \neg(A = B) \Rightarrow B \subseteq A$

16.2 As Exercise 16.1:

(a) $(A \subseteq B \wedge \neg(B \subseteq C)) \Rightarrow \neg(A \subseteq C)$

(b) $(A \subseteq B \wedge B \subseteq C) \Rightarrow A \subseteq C$

16.3 As Exercise 16.1:

(a) $(A \cup B) \cap C = A \cup (B \cap C)$

(b) $(A \cup B) \cap (A \cup C) = A \cup (B \cap C)$

16.4 Prove (you may leave out the justifications, i.e., the arguments between the braces):

(a) $((A \cap B) = A) \Rightarrow A \subseteq B$

(b) $((A \cup B) = B) \Rightarrow A \subseteq B$

(c) $(A \cup B = A \cap B) \Rightarrow A = B$

(d) $(A \subseteq B \wedge B \subseteq C) \Rightarrow (A \cup B) \subseteq C$

16.5 Prove:

(a) $(A^c)^c = A$

(b) $A \backslash B = A \cap B^c$

16.6 Check whether the following propositions always hold. If so, give a proof; if not, give a counterexample.

(a) $(A \subseteq B) \Rightarrow (A^c \subseteq B^c)$

(b) $(A \subseteq B) \Rightarrow (B^c \subseteq A^c)$

16.7 As Exercise 16.6:

(a) $(A \backslash B) \backslash C = A \backslash (B \backslash C)$

(b) $A \backslash (B \cap C) = (A \backslash B) \cup (A \backslash C)$

(c) $A \backslash C \subseteq ((A \backslash B) \cup (B \backslash C))$

(d) $A \backslash (B \backslash A) = A$

16.8 Prove (you may leave out the justifications):

(a) $A \cup B = \emptyset \Rightarrow A \cap B = \emptyset$

(b) $A \backslash B = \emptyset \Rightarrow A \subseteq B$

16.9 Check whether the following propositions always hold. If so, give a proof; if not, give a counterexample.

(a) $A \cup B = B \cap C \Rightarrow A\backslash B = \emptyset$

(b) $A\backslash B = \emptyset \Rightarrow A \cup B = B \cap C$

16.10 As Exercise 16.9:

(a) $\mathcal{P}(A) \cap \mathcal{P}(B) = \mathcal{P}(A \cap B)$

(b) $\mathcal{P}(A) \cup \mathcal{P}(B) = \mathcal{P}(A \cup B)$

16.11 Take $A = \{1, 2, 3, 4\}$, $B = \{1, 4\}$ and $C = \{1\}$.

(a) Give $B \times A$, $B \times B$ and $B \times C$.

(b) What is $B \times \emptyset$?

(c) How many elements does $A \times B \times C$ have?

16.12 Prove or give a counterexample:

(a) $A \times B = B \times A$

(b) $A \subseteq B \Rightarrow A \times C \subseteq B \times C$

(c) $A \times A \subseteq B \times C \Rightarrow A \subseteq B \cap C$

(d) $A \times B = C \times D \Rightarrow A = C$

Chapter 17

Relations

Having good connections

17.1 Relations between sets

A *(binary) relation* is in principle nothing more than a *two-place predicate*. (See Chapter 8.) Look for example at the two-place predicate P from Section 8.2, which is defined on $\mathbb{R} \times \mathbb{N}$ by $3m + n > 3$. It is simple to check that $P(1, 2)$ holds but $P(-1, 2)$ does not. (See also Figure 8.1.) We say that P *relates* $1 \in \mathbb{R}$ and $2 \in \mathbb{N}$, but not -1 and 2.

Hence, a two-place predicate (or relation) *relates* elements of two sets (such as $\mathbb{R}$ and $\mathbb{N}$ in the example above). Let A and B be such sets. A *relation between A and B* states which $a \in A$ is related to which $b \in B$. (One also says: a relation *from A to B* or a relation *on $A \times B$*.)

Example 17.1.1

- *The relation 'is-a-child-of'. This relates children and parents, as in the sentence: 'Prince Charles is-a-child-of Prince Philip'.*

- *The relation 'is-greater-than' (or simply: '>'). This is usually a relation between pairs of numbers. For example, the proposition '5 is-greater-than 3' holds, but not '3 is-greater-than 5'.*

- *The relation 'is-equivalent-to' (or: $\overset{val}{=\!=\!=}$) between abstract propositions. For example: $a \Rightarrow b \overset{val}{=\!=\!=} \neg a \vee b$, but not: $a \Rightarrow b \overset{val}{=\!=\!=} b \Rightarrow a$. Another standard relation between abstract propositions is the relation 'is-stronger-than' (or: $\overset{val}{\models\!=}$).*

231

- *In computer science, relations are also used to give structure to a set of data. One can introduce order in an unstructured data base by defining relations between the data.*

  For example, if W is the set of employees of a company, then the relation 'is-the-boss-of' is used to give some structure to the set of employees. This relation can be built by making a list of all the pairs (w_1, w_2) of employees for which it holds that 'w_1 is-the-boss-of w_2'. We can also define the relation 'has-salary' from W to $\mathbb{N}$, where 'w has-salary n' means that employee w earns salary n (for example in euros per year).

  If V is the set of all airports, then the relation 'has-direct-connection-with' expresses whether one airport has a connection via a direct flight (without changing flights) with another airport. Also here, the relation can be written as a list of all pairs of airports (v_1, v_2) which are directly connected. Another relation can be 'flies-to', which relates airline companies to airports which are used by these companies: 'The airline company KLM flies-to Kennedy Airport'.

- *In object-oriented programming languages, many relations can exist between the objects in a program, like the relation 'inherits-from': If it holds that 'Object B inherits-from Object A', then all the data and methods of Object A are also valid ('usable') for Object B.*

For relations, the letter R (of relation) is more used than the letter P (of predicate). That R is a relation between A and B, is usually written as: $R : A \rightarrow B$ or as $R \subseteq A \times B$.

We give now a more abstract example of a relation between A and B.

Let $A = \{0, 1, 2\}$ and $B = \{0, 1, 2, 3\}$. The relation R between A and B is defined by the following connections:
- between the element 1 of A and the element 0 of B,
- between the element 2 of A and the element 2 of B, and
- between the element 2 of A and the element 3 of B.

There are two notations in use to express this in a compact manner. We can describe the relation R of this example by:
(1) $(1, 0) \in R$, $(2, 2) \in R$ and $(2, 3) \in R$, or by:
(2) $1R0$, $2R2$ and $2R3$.
We will look in more details at these two descriptions:

(1) In the first case, R is identified with a *set*, namely with

$$R = \{(1, 0), (2, 2), (2, 3)\} \ .$$

This set is a subset of the Cartesian product $A \times B$. The so-called *Cartesian graph*, of this relation can be found in Figure 17.1. The relation is the collection of the pairs of co-ordinates of the points in the circles (there are three such pairs).

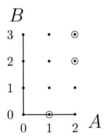

Figure 17.1: The Cartesian graph of the relation $R = \{(1,0), (2,2), (2,3)\}$.

Not only $R = \{(1,0), (2,2), (2,3)\}$, but *every* subset of $A \times B$ determines a relation between A and B. As we see in our example $\#(A) = 3$ and $\#(B) = 4$, hence $\#(A \times B) = 3 \times 4 = 12$. A set with 12 elements has 2^{12} subsets, hence between these A and B there are $2^{12} = 4096$ different relations possible. The R above is only one of these!

Two extreme cases are the *empty relation*, $R^{\perp} = \emptyset$, and the *full relation*, $R^{\top} = A \times B$. The empty relation holds if there is *no* connection at all between any element of A and any element of B (no elements are related), the full relation holds if *every* element of A is related to *every* element of B. (What do the Cartesian graphs of $R^{\perp}$ and $R^{\top}$ look like?)

(2) In the second case, the connections are directly described by putting the letter R between the relevant elements of A and B: 2R3 says that $2 \in A$ is related to $3 \in B$. (Hence we don't write $R(x, y)$ as is standard for predicates, but we use the *infix-notation*: xRy, with the symbol R *between* the elements.) Instead of this letter R, we can also use an arrow, for example: $2 \to 3$. A diagram which expresses this is the *arrow graph*, where arrows are drawn between the points which are related. In our example, this is given in Figure 17.2.

The arrows always *begin* in A and *end* in B. Moreover, there are no restrictions, except that there may, between a given $a \in A$ and a given $b \in B$, never be *more than one* arrow . Hence 0, 1, ..., up to at most $\#(B)$ arrows can depart from a point in A, and 0, 1, ..., up to at most $\#(A)$ arrows can arrive to a point in B.

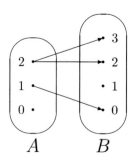

Figure 17.2: The arrow graph of the relation R with $1R0$, $2R2$ and $2R3$.

Remark 17.1.2 *Diagrams (or graphs) of relations between A and B are especially useful if A and B are* finite *sets which are not too large. If the sets are* infinite, *then the diagrams can only give a sketch of the whole situation.*

17.2   Relations on a set

Often in mathematics and computer science, one comes across relations between A and B where A and B are *the same* set. Then, we are dealing with a relation R between A and A. Such an R is usually called a *relation on A*.

From the examples at the beginning of the previous section these are:
– The relation 'is-a-child-of' on M, the set of all persons.
– The relation '$>$' on $\mathbb{R}$.
– The relations '$\overset{val}{=\!=\!=}$', '$\overset{val}{\models}$' and '$\overset{val}{=\!=\!\dashv}$' on the set of all abstract propositions.
– The relation 'is-the-boss-of' on W, the set of all employees of a company.
– The relation 'has-direct-connection-with' on V, the set of all airports.
– The relation 'inherits-from' on the set of all objects of a certain program.

Also for a relation on A there are two ways to describe R:
(1) as a subset of the Cartesian product $A \times A$, or
(2) as a set of connections xRy (or $x \to y$).

As before, one can draw a *diagram* of such a relation R on A by either drawing a Cartesian graph or an arrow graph, but there is also a third way: the so-called *directed graph*. This graph looks like an arrow graph, but then in one set A. The points of this graph represent the elements of A, the arrows say which points $x \in A$ are related to which points $y \in A$.

Example: Let R be the relation on $\mathbb{N}$ given by:

$$x\,R\,y \text{ if } x = 2y .$$

A (small) part of the corresponding directed graph is given in Figure 17.3.

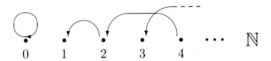

$$0 \quad 1 \quad 2 \quad 3 \quad 4$$

Figure 17.3: The directed graph of the relation $R = \{(x,y) \in \mathbb{N} \times \mathbb{N} \,|\, x = 2y\}$.

Remark 17.2.1 *A graph* consists of a set of nodes ('points') and a set of *connections between these nodes ('lines'). For a* directed *graph, every line has a direction, and therefore, such a line is often drawn as an* arrow.
    The graph given in Figure 17.3 has $\mathbb{N}$ as the set of points. Its lines (in this case arrows) correspond to the subset of $\mathbb{N} \times \mathbb{N}$ which is written as $\{(0,0), (2,1), (4,2), (6,3), \ldots\}$.
    Note that a tree, as was introduced in Section 2.4, is a special kind of graph.

17.3   Special relations on a set

Relations can have special properties which make them sometimes simpler and more pleasant to use. We mention three such possible properties: reflexivity, symmetry and transitivity. We shall discuss these properties here, one by one.

(1) *Reflexivity*

A relation R on A is said to be *reflexive* if:

$$\forall_x [x \in A : x R x] .$$

Hence in a reflexive relation, every element of A is related to itself.

    In a directed graph, we recognize a reflexive relation because every point is connected to itself via an arrow; see Figure 17.4.

$$x$$

Figure 17.4: For a *reflexive* relation on A, *every* point x is related to itself.

Examples of reflexive relations include:

- ' $\stackrel{val}{=\!=\!=}$ ' on the set of all abstract propositions; this is reflexive because it is always the case that $P \stackrel{val}{=\!=\!=} P$ (see Lemma 6.1.1 (1)).

- ' $\stackrel{val}{=\!\!\mid}$ ' and ' $\stackrel{val}{=\!\!\mid}$ ' on the set of all abstract propositions.

- '=', '$\geq$' and '$\leq$' on $\mathbb{R}$. For all $x \in \mathbb{R}$ it holds for example that $x \leq x$.

Examples of *non*-reflexive relations are:

- 'is-a-child-of' on the set M of all people. (*Not everybody* is a child of him/herself; even much more than that: *nobody* is.)

- 'has-a-direct-connection-with' on the set V of all airports (unless *every* airport offers round-flights).

- '>' and '<' on $\mathbb{R}$.

- 'is-the-boss-of' on W, the employees.

- The relation R on $\mathbb{N}$ where xRy is defined by $x = 2y$ (see Section 17.2). (Because not *for all* $x \in \mathbb{N}$ it holds that xRx. Be careful: it *does* hold that $0R0$, but this is not enough for reflexivity. Indeed: $1R1$ does *not* hold. This is a *counterexample*.)

(2) *Symmetry.*

A relation R on A is called *symmetric* if:

$$\forall_{x,y}[x, y \in A : xRy \Rightarrow yRx] \ .$$

Hence symmetry means that: as soon as x is related to y, then y must also be related to x. Be careful however, the *condition* before the implication arrow needs not hold: an x does not *have* to be related at all to y, but *if it is*, then the other direction must hold as well.

Figure 17.5: For a *symmetric* relation on A it holds that: if x is related to y, then also y is related to x.

Hence in a directed graph we have the situation as depicted in Figure 17.5.

Examples of symmetric relations are:

- '$\stackrel{val}{=\!=\!=}$' on the set of all abstract propositions, because if $P \stackrel{val}{=\!=\!=} Q$, then also $Q \stackrel{val}{=\!=\!=} P$ (see Lemma 6.1.1 (2)).

- '=' on $\mathbb{R}$.

- 'has-direct-connections-with' on the set V of all airports (assuming that every flight has also a return flight).

Non-symmetric relations are:

- '$\stackrel{val}{=\!\models}$', '$\stackrel{val}{=\!\models}$', since for example it holds that False $\stackrel{val}{=\!\models}$ True, but not True $\stackrel{val}{=\!\models}$ False.

- '>', '<', '$\geq$', '$\leq$' on $\mathbb{R}$. *Counterexample* for the last relation: $5 \leq 7$, but not: $7 \leq 5$.

- The earlier described relation 'is-a-child-of'.

- Similarly for: 'is-the-boss-of' (unless no-one is the boss in the company!).

(3) *Transitivity.*

A relation R on A is called *transitive* if:

$$\forall_{x,y,z}[x, y, z \in A : (xRy \wedge yRz) \Rightarrow xRz] \ .$$

This property says that: if x is related to y and this y in turn is related to z, then the initial x is also related to z. Here we have again a condition, even a double one: x need not be related to y, and y need not be related to z. But *if both relations hold*, then x must be related to z, as well.

In a directed graph, things look as shown in Figure 17.6.

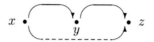

Figure 17.6: For a *transitive* relation on A it holds that: if x is related to y and this y is related to z, then also x is related to z.

Examples of transitive relations are:

- '$\overset{val}{=\!=\!=}$' on the set of abstract propositions, because if $P \overset{val}{=\!=\!=} Q$ and $Q \overset{val}{=\!=\!=} R$, then also $P \overset{val}{=\!=\!=} R$ (see Lemma 6.1.1 (3)).

- '$\overset{val}{\models}$' and '$\overset{val}{=\!=\!\dashv}$' on the same set.

- '$=$', '$>$', '$<$', '$\geq$' and '$\leq$' on $\mathbb{R}$. For all x, y and $z \in \mathbb{R}$ it holds for example that: if $x \leq y$ and $y \leq z$, then $x \leq z$.

The following are examples of *non*-transitive relations:

- 'is-a-child-of'.

- 'is-the-boss-of'.

- 'has-direct-connection-with'.

17.4   Equivalence relations

In the previous section we saw that some relations can be reflexive and/or symmetric and/or transitive. If a relation R on A has *all these three* properties, then we call it an *equivalence relation*.

Example 17.4.1

- '$\overset{val}{=\!=\!=}$' *on the set of all abstract propositions is an equivalence relation. In Chapter 4 we saw that the collection of all abstract propositions can be divided into* classes *of equivalent propositions. See the picture at the end of that chapter.*

- '$=$' *on (for example)* $\mathbb{R}$ *is an equivalence relation.*

An important equivalence relation is the relation 'modulo n' on $\mathbb{Z}$, with n a fixed natural number ≥ 2. This relation is defined as follows:

Let $n \in \mathbb{N}$ and $n \geq 2$. We say for $k, l \in \mathbb{Z}$ that $k = l$ *modulo* n, if $k - l$ is a multiple of n.

(A *multiple of* n is as the name describes, a number which is the product of an integer and n, hence for example $3.n$ or $-5.n$, but also n itself (because $n = 1.n$) and 0 (because $0 = 0.n$).)

Example 17.4.2

- $27 = 7$ *modulo* 5, *because the difference* $27 - 7$ *is a multiple of 5.*

- $3 = 102$ *modulo* 11, *because* $3 - 102 = -99$ *and* -99 *is a multiple of 11.*

- $15 = 15$ *modulo* 23, *because* $15 - 15$ *is a multiple of 23 (indeed,* $15 - 15 = 0 \times 23$).

We will use in this book a special notation for the relation 'is-equal-to-modulo-n', namely $\equiv_n$. Hence our examples above are written as: $27 \equiv_5 7$, $3 \equiv_{11} 102$ and $15 \equiv_{23} 15$ respectively.

The definition of the relation $\equiv_n$ on $\mathbb{Z}$ is hence:

$$x \equiv_n y \text{ if } x - y \text{ is a multiple of } n \ .$$

We will *prove* now that $\equiv_n$ is indeed an equivalence relation on $\mathbb{Z}$. For this we need to show:

(1) $\equiv_n$ is reflexive: $\forall_x [x \in \mathbb{Z} : x \equiv_n x]$.
(2) $\equiv_n$ is symmetric: $\forall_{x,y} [x, y \in \mathbb{Z} : x \equiv_n y \Rightarrow y \equiv_n x]$.
(3) $\equiv_n$ is transitive: $\forall_{x,y,z} [x, y, z \in \mathbb{Z} : (x \equiv_n y \wedge y \equiv_n z) \Rightarrow x \equiv_n z]$.

(1) A proof of the *reflexivity of* $\equiv_n$ begins as follows:

$\quad\quad$ { Assume: }

(1) $\quad$ | var x; $x \in \mathbb{Z}$ |

$\quad\quad\quad$ | $\vdots$

$(l-1)$ $\quad$ | $x \equiv_n x$

$\quad\quad\quad$ { $\forall$-intro on (1) and $(l-1)$: }

(l) $\quad$ $\forall_x [x \in \mathbb{Z} : x \equiv_n x]$

The goal is to prove now that $x \equiv_n x$. According to the definition of $\equiv_n$ this means: $x - x$ is a multiple of n. But $x - x = 0$ and 0 is indeed a multiple of n.

Hence, the full proof is as follows:

{ Assume: }

(1) | var x; $x \in \mathbb{Z}$ |

        { Mathematics: }
(2) | 0 is a multiple of n

        { Mathematics: $x - x = 0$: }
(3) | $x - x$ is a multiple of n

        { Definition of $\equiv_n$ on (3): }
(4) | $x \equiv_n x$

      { $\forall$-intro on (1) and (4): }
(5) $\forall_x[x \in \mathbb{Z} : x \equiv_n x]$

Remark 17.4.3 *Actually, there is in the proposition 'a is a multiple of n' a hidden existential quantifier, because this means: $\exists_k[k \in \mathbb{Z} : a = k \cdot n]$. Therefore, if we really want to do the above proof very precisely, then we need to apply an introduction rule for $\exists$. In this case, the core of the proof will for example look as follows:*

        { Mathematics: }
(2a) $x - x = 0 \cdot n$

        { Mathematics: }
(2b) $0 \in \mathbb{Z}$

        { $\exists^*$-intro on (2a) and (2b): }
(2c) $\exists_k[k \in \mathbb{Z} : x - x = k \cdot n]$

        { Definition of 'multiple of n' on (2c): }
(3) $x - x$ is a multiple of n

        { Definition of $\equiv_n$ on (3): }
(4) $x \equiv_n x$

Like this, we make the proof much more difficult than is needed. The first given reasoning is convincing enough. For this reason, in this kind of *proofs we shall not bring to light the 'hidden' $\exists$-quantifier in propositions of the form 'a is a multiple of n'. See also the following two proofs.*

(2) We give now a proof of the *symmetry of* $\equiv_n$.

In the core of such a proof, we must show that $x \equiv_n y \Rightarrow y \equiv_n x$, hence: 'If $x - y$ is a multiple of n, then $y - x$ is also a multiple of n'. This is not difficult to see, because $y - x$ is the *inverse* of $x - y$, hence if $x - y = k \cdot n$ for a certain $k \in \mathbb{Z}$, then $y - x = (-k) \cdot n$, and hence $y - x$ is also a multiple of n. (Note that $-k$ is also an element of $\mathbb{Z}$).

Hence, the proof becomes:

{ Assume: }

(1)   var x, y; $x, y \in \mathbb{Z}$

     { Assume: }

(2) $x \equiv_n y$

       { Definition of $\equiv_n$ on (2): }

(3) $x - y$ is a multiple of n, say $x - y = k \cdot n$

       { Mathematics on (3): }

(4) $y - x = (-k).n$, hence $y - x$ is a multiple of n

       { Definition of $\equiv_n$ on (4): }

(5) $y \equiv_n x$

     { $\Rightarrow$-intro on (2) and (5): }

(6) $x \equiv_n y \Rightarrow y \equiv_n x$

   { $\forall$-intro (twice) on (1) and (6): }

(7) $\forall_{x,y}[x, y \in \mathbb{Z} : x \equiv_n y \Rightarrow y \equiv_n x]$

Note that for convenience, we have combined *two* flags in line number (1): the flag for x and the flag for y. This is possible here, because we strike these flags out (retract them) *together* after line number (6).

(3) Finally, we prove the *transitivity of* $\equiv_n$.

The core of the proof here is: if we know that $x \equiv_n y$ and $y \equiv_n z$, then why is $x \equiv_n z$? This is not difficult: from $x \equiv_n y$ it follows that $x - y = k.n$ for some $k \in \mathbb{Z}$, and likewise, it follows from $y \equiv_n z$ that $y - z = l.n$ for some $l \in \mathbb{Z}$ (this l can obviously be very different from this k!). What about $x - z$ now? Is this also a multiple of n? Yes, this follows because $x - z$ is equal to $(x - y) + (y - z)$, and hence to $k.n + l.n$, and hence to $(k + l).n$, and this latter is a multiple of n because $k + l$ is again an integer number.

Hence, the proof looks as follows (in line number (1), we even combine *three* flags!):

{ Assume: }

(1) $\boxed{\underline{\text{var }} x, y, z;\ x, y, z \in \mathbb{Z}}$

      { Assume: }

(2) $\boxed{x \equiv_n y \wedge y \equiv_n z}$

        { $\wedge$-elim on (2), and definition of $\equiv_n$ (twice): }

(3) $x - y$ is a multiple of n, and $y - z$ is a multiple of n

        { Mathematics on (3): }

(4) $x - y = k.n$ and $y - z = l.n$ for certain k and $l \in \mathbb{Z}$

        { Mathematics on (4): }

(5) $x - z = (x - y) + (y - z) = k.n + l.n = (k + l).n$

        { Definition of $\equiv_n$ on (5); note that $k + l \in \mathbb{Z}$: }

(6) $x \equiv_n z$

      { $\Rightarrow$-intro on (2) and (6): }

(7) $(x \equiv_n y \wedge y \equiv_n z) \Rightarrow x \equiv_n z$

      { $\forall$-intro (three times) on (1) and (7): }

(8) $\forall_{x,y,z}[x, y, z \in \mathbb{Z} : (x \equiv_n y \wedge y \equiv_n z) \Rightarrow x \equiv_n z]$

17.5   Equivalence classes

An equivalence relation R on a set A ensures that the elements of A are related *group-wise*. If for example a is related to b and also a is related to c, then there is a relation between *every* pair of the three elements a, b and c. We show this here:

(1) aRb (*assumption*).
(2) aRc (*assumption*).
(3) aRa (by the reflexivity of R).

(4) bRa (follows from (1), by the symmetry of R).
(5) bRb (by the reflexivity of R).
(6) bRc (follows from (4) and (2), by the transitivity of R).
(7) cRa (follows from (2), by the symmetry of R).
(8) cRb (follows from (6), by the symmetry of R).
(9) cRc (by the reflexivity of R).

If we begin with a certain $a \in A$ and search for all the elements to which a is related, then we get a subset $K(a) \subseteq A$. We can define $K(a)$ as follows:

$$K(a) = \{b \in A | aRb\} \ .$$

Such a subset $K(a)$ is called the *equivalence class* of a (with respect to R). Similarly to what we explained above in the case that aRb and aRc, we can conclude that within such an equivalence class, *every* element is related to *every* (other) element. Within such a class, there is hence a kind of a *maximal relation*: an arrow runs 'round' from *every* point to itself, and moreover, an arrow runs between *every* pair of different points within this class (and hence for every pair of points there are arrows in both directions). The relation R is hence the *full* relation on such a class.

From the definition of $K(a)$ it follows that: if a is related to a', then a' is in the equivalence class of a. But if a is *not* related to a', then a' is *outside* $K(a)$ and we can then look for the equivalence class of a', or $K(a')$. Now it is simple to prove that in such a case, also the whole class $K(a')$ is *outside* the class $K(a)$, that hence $K(a) \cap K(a')$ is empty. Because, from assuming that $x \in K(a) \cap K(a')$, a contradiction follows. We show this in a similar way to what we did in Chapter 16 (see in particular Section 16.7):

{ Assume: }

(1) $\neg(aRa')$

    { Assume: }

(2) $\underline{\text{var } x};\ x \in K(a) \cap K(a')$

       { Property of $\cap$ on (2): }

(3) $x \in K(a) \land x \in K(a')$

       { Definition of $K(a)$ resp. $K(a')$ on (3): }

(4) $aRx \land a'Rx$

       { Symmetry of R on (4): }

(5) $aRx \land xRa'$

$$
\begin{array}{ll}
& \quad \{ \text{ Transitivity of } R \text{ on (5): } \} \\
(6) & \quad aRa' \\
& \quad \{ \text{ Contradiction on (6) and (1): } \} \\
(7) & \quad \texttt{False} \\
& \quad \{ \ \forall\text{-intro on (2) and (7): } \} \\
(8) & \quad \forall_x [x \in K(a) \cap K(a') : \texttt{False}] \\
& \quad \{ \text{ Property of } \emptyset \text{ on (8): } \} \\
(9) & \quad K(a) \cap K(a') = \emptyset \\
& \quad \{ \ \Rightarrow\text{-intro on (1) and (9): } \} \\
(10) & \quad \neg(aRa') \Rightarrow (K(a) \cap K(a') = \emptyset)
\end{array}
$$

Hence, for any two equivalence classes – say the classes of a and a' – corresponding to a given relation R, there are only two possibilities:

- the equivalence classes of a and a' *coincide*, i.e. $K(a) = K(a')$; this is the case if aRa',

- the equivalence classes of a and a' *have no overlap*, i.e. $K(a) \cap K(a') = \emptyset$; this is the case if $\neg(aRa')$.

It is hence not possible that for an equivalence relation, two equivalence classes overlap *partly* (some of their elements are common and some are not).

We return now to the equivalence relation $\equiv_n$ on $\mathbb{Z}$ (see Section 17.4). How do the equivalence classes look like for $\equiv_n$? In order to focus our attention, we take $n = 5$ and we study $\equiv_5$. What is now for example $K(4)$? This consists of all integer numbers x with $4 \equiv_5 x$, hence with: '$4 - x$ is a multiple of 5'. So:
$$K(4) = \{ \ldots, -16, -11, -6, -1, 4, 9, 14, 19, 24, \ldots \}.$$
The directed graph which corresponds to this class is pictured in Figure 17.7.

Apart from $K(4)$, there are four more equivalence classes for $\equiv_5$:
$$
\begin{aligned}
K(0) &= \{ \ldots, -20, -15, -10, -5, 0, 5, 10, 15, 20, \ldots \}, \\
K(1) &= \{ \ldots, -19, -14, -9, -4, 1, 6, 11, 16, 21, \ldots \}, \\
K(2) &= \{ \ldots, -18, -13, -8, -3, 2, 7, 12, 17, 22, \ldots \}, \\
K(3) &= \{ \ldots, -17, -12, -7, -2, 3, 8, 13, 18, 23, \ldots \}.
\end{aligned}
$$

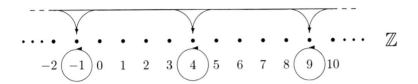

Figure 17.7: The directed graph for the equivalence class $K(4)$ of $\equiv_5$.

The *names* that we choose here for the five equivalence classes ($K(0)$ to $K(4)$) are clear, but in principle rather arbitrary. No-one forbids us for example from calling $K(3)$ henceforth $K(228)$, because this is the same subset of $\mathbb{Z}$ (in fact: $3 \equiv_5 228$, hence 3 and 228 are in the same class).

Note that the five equivalence classes $K(0)$ to $K(4)$ are *mutually disjoint* (they always have an empty intersection) and that the *union* of these five classes gives the whole $\mathbb{Z}$.

We let go now of the choice $n = 5$ and we return to the general $n \in \mathbb{N}$ with $n \geq 2$. It will be clear that for the equivalence relation $\equiv_n$ on $\mathbb{Z}$ there are precisely n different equivalence classes. We can give these classes the names $K(0)$ to $K(n-1)$. They are characterized as follows:

$K(0) =$ the set of the multiples of n,
$K(1) =$ the set of the multiples of n, with 1 added to each of them,
$K(2) =$ the set of the multiples of n, with 2 added to each, ...,
$K(n-1) =$ the set of the multiples of n, with $(n-1)$ added to each.

The *set of the equivalence classes* is in this case

$$\{K(0), K(1), K(2), \ldots, K(n-1)\} \, .$$

This set has n elements (each of these elements is itself a set!).

It is possible to consider each of these n classes as independent *objects*, a kind of super-numbers, with which you can calculate: you can define for these objects (=classes) an *addition* and a *multiplication* . These addition and multiplication of classes have themselves nice properties and 'lift' the arithmetic to a higher level of abstraction. Examples for $n = 5$:

– addition: $K(4) + K(2) = K(6) = K(1)$,
– multiplication: $K(4) \times K(2) = K(8) = K(3)$.

This falls under (higher) algebra. We will not go further into these matters.

The set of the equivalence classes for an equivalence relation R is called the *class-division* or the *partition* for this R. Hence in the above case it holds that:

$\{K(0), K(1), K(2), \ldots, K(n-1)\}$ is the partition of $\mathbb{Z}$ which corresponds to $\equiv_n$.

Remark 17.5.1 *Another example of an equivalence relation, which we have already come across, is the relation $\stackrel{val}{=\!=}$ on abstract propositions. Check that also in this case we are dealing with equivalence classes, of which there are now not n, but infinitely many. They have again characteristic properties, such as:*

- *a class is never empty; moreover, in every class, every proposition is related by the $\stackrel{val}{=\!=}$-relation to itself and to every other proposition from this class,*

- *two different classes are always disjoint; a proposition in a class is never in relation with a proposition in another class.*

- *all elements of all classes form together precisely the collection of all abstract propositions (the union of the classes gives the whole collection, hence: every proposition occurs in – precisely – one class).*

The figure at the end of Chapter 4 gives a clear idea of the class-division (the partition) that we obtain there.

17.6   Composing relations

In Sections 17.1 and Section 17.2, we studied respectively the notions of a relation *between* two sets and a relation *on* a set.

In Sections 17.3, 17.4 and 17.5, we looked at relations with special properties including the so-called equivalence relations.

In the present section we look at the *composition* of relations. This can be briefly summarized by saying that we 'glue' the two relations 'together' by first applying one, and then applying the other. Take for example the two relations 'is-a-child-of' and 'is-a-sister-of'. If we have that both 'Xerxes is-a-child-of Yvonne' and 'Yvonne is-a-sister-of Zelda' then we can conclude that also Xerxes and Zelda are related by some relation, namely: 'Xerxes is-a-child-of-a-sister-of Zelda'. We can take 'is-a-child-of-a-sister-of' as the composition of 'is-a-child-of' and 'is-a-sister-of'.

In general, from the relation R between A and B and the relation S between B and C, we can build a new relation $R;S$ between A and C, which can be defined as follows:
for $x \in A$ and $z \in C$ we have $x\,R;S\,z$ if $\exists_y[y \in B : xRy \wedge ySz]$.

The relation $R;S$ is called the *composition* of R and S.

Hence, the x in A and the z in C must be related to each other via *some* (at least one) y in B, in the sense that xRy and ySz. See the example below, where 'Xerxes is-a-child-of-a-sister-of Zelda' follows from the fact that there is a person Y (namely Yvonne) for whom the following hold:

(1) 'Xerxes is-a-child-of Y' and

(2) 'Y is-a-sister-of Zelda'.

In order to be able to compose R and S into $R;S$, the domains must be compatible. By this we mean that: If a relation R holds between some A and some B, then S must be a relation between *the same* B and some C.

Remark 17.6.1 *We can pronounce $R;S$ as 'R followed by S'. One can also say 'R before S', or 'S after R'.*

Often, the symbol '$\circ$' is used instead of the semi-colon, where $R \circ S$ is written for the composition of R and S. Moreover, it is quite common to exchange R and S in this case, hence writing $S \circ R$ (in reversed order!) for $R;S$. The reason for this is that, when composing functions, the 'reversed' order is the one that is mostly used. For further details, see Section 18.6.

If both relations R and S are between A and *the same* A, in other words both are relations *on* A, then R and S can be connected either way and hence both $R;S$ and $S;R$ are well-defined. (In the above example, these are respectively 'is-a-child-of-a-sister-of' and 'is-a-sister-of-a-child-of' – which obviously are different relations.)

We can also compose a relation R on A *with itself*, and then we get $R;R$, also denoted by R^2. So for example, 'is-a-child-of' composed with 'is-a-child-of' is the same as 'is-a-child-of-a-child-of' (hence a grandchild). Note that for the composed relation R^2, we have as before that xR^2z holds if there *is* a (at least one) y such that xRy and yRz. For example, 'Anna is-a-child-of-a-child-of Charles' if there is a person 'B' where 'Anna is-a-child-of B' and 'B is-a-child-of Charles'. Hence, *one* of the parents of Anna (Bernard? Berta?) must be a child of Charles.

We can repeat the above process, to obtain $R;R;R$ (or R^3), etc. For t and $w \in A$ it holds then that tR^3w if there are u and $v \in A$ such that tRu, uRv and vRw. We can continue this process: $R^4, R^5, \ldots$.

The *transitive closure* of R, denoted by R^+, is the relation where

xR^+y if $\exists_n[n \in \mathbb{N}\backslash\{0\} : xR^ny]$.

In other words: xR^+y holds for x and $y \in A$ if there are zero or more elements: $u_1, u_2, \ldots, u_{n-1}$, all in A, which are 'between' x and y, meaning that xRu_1, u_1Ru_2, $\ldots$, $u_{n-2}Ru_{n-1}$ and $u_{n-1}Ry$. Hence xR^+y means that we can go from x to y via *one* R-step, or via two R-steps, or via three R-steps, or ... .

In the above example, the relation 'is-a-child-of' has as transitive closure 'is-a-child-of-a-child-of-a-child-of-...', in other words: 'is-a-descendant-of'.

Remark 17.6.2 *Sometimes, one speaks of the* reflexive-transitive *closure of R, denoted by R^*, which is an extension of the transitive closure R^+ by making it also reflexive, so that we always have, in particular, that xR^*x. This means that it is also allowed that we do* zero *steps.*

17.7   Equality of relations

Finally, we look at the question: when are two relations *equal*? First of all, the *domains* must be the same, hence if R is a relation between A and B, then S must also be a relation between (these same) A and B. But this is not enough, we must also have:

$\forall_{a,b}[a \in A, b \in B : aRb \Leftrightarrow aSb]$.

Hence the relations R and S, both between A and B, are *equal* if each pair which is in the R-relation is also in the S-relation, and vice versa.

For example: Take the relations R and S on $\mathbb{Z}$ where:

xRy if $x + y$ is even,

xSy if $x - y$ is even.

Now, for all whole numbers x and y we have that $xRy \Leftrightarrow xSy$, because $x + y$ is even if and only if x and y are either both even, or both odd; and the same holds for $x - y$.

Another proof is:

$$x + y \text{ is even}$$
$$\overset{val}{=\!=} \quad \{ -2y \text{ is also even: } \}$$
$$x + y - 2y \text{ is even}$$
$$\overset{val}{=\!=} \quad \{ \text{ Mathematics: } \}$$
$$x - y \text{ is even}$$

Hence R and S are equal on $\mathbb{Z}$.

Note that these R and S are *not* equal on $\mathbb{R}$. Counterexample: $\frac{3}{2} + \frac{1}{2}$ is even, but $\frac{3}{2} - \frac{1}{2}$ is not.

17.8 Exercises

17.1 The relation R on $\{1, 2, 3, 4, 5\}$ is given by the following table:

	1	2	3	4	5
1	1	0	0	1	0
2	0	1	1	0	0
3	0	1	1	0	0
4	1	0	0	1	0
5	0	0	0	0	1

(A symbol 1 in line k and column l means that the number before line k is related to the number above column l, a 0 means: these numbers are *not* related.)

(a) Give an arrow graph of R.

(b) Give the directed graph which corresponds to R.

(c) What is so special with this R?

17.2 The relation R on $\{0, 1, 2, 3, 4\}$ is given by:

$x R y$ if $(x = y) \vee (2x = y)$.

(a) Give the Cartesian graph of R.

(b) Give the arrow graph of R.

(c) Give the directed graph of R.

17.3 Check whether each of the following relations is reflexive, symmetric and/or transitive:

(a) R on $\mathbb{Z}$ with $x R y$ if $x + y$ is even.

(b) R on $\mathbb{Z}$ with $x R y$ if $x + y$ is a multiple of three.

(c) R on $\mathbb{N}^+$ with $k R l$ if l is a divisor of k.
   (For a definition of 'divisor', see Section 20.2.)

(d) R on $\mathcal{P}(\mathbf{U})$ with $A R B$ if $A \subseteq B$.

17.4 Let V be a set and R a relation on V which is symmetric and transitive. Prove:

$\forall_x [x \in V : \exists_y [y \in V : x R y]] \Rightarrow (R$ is an equivalence relation$)$.

17.5 The relation R on $\mathbb{R}$ is given by

$x R y$ if $(xy > 0) \vee (x = y = 0)$.

(a) Show that R is an equivalence relation.

(b) What are the classes for R?

17.6 Let n be a natural number greater than 1.

(a) Prove that: $\forall_{x,y}[x, y \in \mathbb{Z} : x \equiv_n y \Rightarrow x^3 \equiv_n y^3]$.

(b) Check whether the following holds or not:
$\forall_{x,y}[x, y \in \mathbb{Z} : x^3 \equiv_4 y^3 \Rightarrow x \equiv_4 y]$.

(c) Check whether the following holds or not:
$\forall_{x,y}[x, y \in \mathbb{Z} : x^3 \equiv_5 y^3 \Rightarrow x \equiv_5 y]$.

17.7 The relation R on $\mathbb{Z}$ is given by:

$x R y$ if $x^2 - y^2$ is a multiple of five.

(a) Prove that R is an equivalence relation.

(b) Prove that: $\forall_{x,y}[x, y \in \mathbb{Z} : x \equiv_5 y \Rightarrow x R y]$.

(c) How many equivalence classes are there for R?

17.8 Let $a, a', b, b' \in \mathbb{Z}$ and assume that $a \equiv_n a'$ and $b \equiv_n b'$. Prove that:

(a) $a + b \equiv_n a' + b'$.

(b) $ab \equiv_n a'b'$.

17.9 Let R be an equivalence relation on V. Let $K(x)$ denote, for each $x \in V$, the class of x with respect to R. Let $a, a', a'', b \in V$. Prove that:

(a) $a \in K(a)$.

(b) $(a' \in K(a) \wedge a'' \in K(a)) \Rightarrow a' R a''$.

(c) $a R b \Leftrightarrow K(a) = K(b)$.

17.10 Consider the equivalence relation $\equiv_n$ on $\mathbb{Z}$. Let $a, b \in \mathbb{Z}$.

(a) Prove the following: If n is a prime number, then we have:
$(K(ab) = K(0)) \Rightarrow (K(a) = K(0) \vee K(b) = K(0))$.
Hint: Use the fact: if p is prime and $p \,|\, ab$, then $p \,|\, a$ or $p \,|\, b$.
(Here $x \,|\, y$ means: x divides (= is a divisor of) y.)

(b) Does the last implication also hold if n was not a prime number?

17.11 The relations R and S, both on $\mathbb{N} \backslash \{0\}$, are given by:

$x R y$ if x is a *proper* divisor of y (this means that x is a divisor of y – for a formal definition, see Section 20.2 – but also that x is *not equal* to y),

$x S y$ if $x + 1 = y$.

(a) Describe in words the relations $R;S$ and $S;R$.

(b) Is it the case that $R;S = S;R$?

(c) Describe in words the relations R^2 and S^2.

(d) Prove that: $R^+ = R$ and $S^+ = <$.

(e) What are R^* and S^*?

Chapter 18

Mappings

From reliable sources

18.1   Mappings from one set to another

Mappings play an essential role both in mathematics and in computer science. (Mappings which are described by some formula are mostly called *functions*.) We give the following examples of mappings (functions):

- the *polynomial functions*, for example $y = x^2$ or $y = 5x^3 - 3x^2 + 2x - 1$,
- the *rational functions*, for example $y = \frac{x^3+1}{x-1}$,
- the *trigonometric functions*, like the sine, the cosine and the tangent,
- the *exponential function* $y = e^x$ and the *natural logarithm* $y = \ln(x)$.

These functions take real numbers as 'input' and deliver real numbers as 'output'. But there are also mappings which work with natural or integer numbers, like for example l.c.m. (the least common multiple) or g.c.d. (the greatest common divisor). Further examples include the *truth-functions* of Section 4.1 which are mappings from Boolean values (0 or 1) to Boolean values; more precisely: from $\{0,1\}^n$ to $\{0,1\}$. In 'higher' mathematics and in computer science, many kinds of mappings are important. These mappings are often based on sets that may be very different from sets of 'numbers'.

What is a mapping now in more general terms? A mapping can be seen as a special kind of relation between two sets, say A and B: every element of A gets *mapped* to an element of B. This means, in our terminology (see Section 17.1, part (2)) that: from every element of A there is an arrow to an element of B. Note that A and B may be different sets.

Look for example at the mapping (or function) from $\mathbb{N}$ to $\mathbb{Z}$ which corresponds to the formula: $y = -x^2 + 4x - 2$. Here, it holds indeed that every element of $\mathbb{N}$ is related to an element of $\mathbb{Z}$. For example: $x = 0 \in \mathbb{N}$ is related to $y = -2 \in \mathbb{Z}$, $x = 1$ is related to $y = 1$, 2 is related to 2, 3 is related to 1, and so on.

Mappings from A to B are hence a special kind of relations. For this reason we can in general make for mappings the same kind of 'graphs' or 'diagrams' or 'maps' as we made for relations (see Section 17.1). For the mapping $y = -x^2 + 4x - 2$ from $\mathbb{N}$ to $\mathbb{Z}$, for example, we can give a *Cartesian graph* (see Figure 18.1), and also an *arrow graph* (see Figure 18.2).

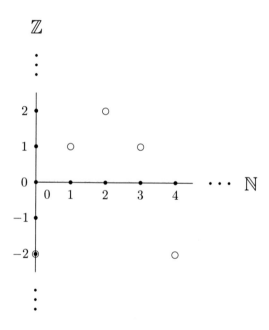

Figure 18.1: The Cartesian graph of the function $y = -x^2 + 4x - 2$.

Let R be a relation from A to B. When is R a *mapping*? Basically this holds when we have what we suggested above: *each a of A is related to exactly one b in B.* (A certain 'input' gives *one* 'output', no less and no more.) Hence, if we take a certain a, then:

 – there is a certain $b \in B$ such that aRb,

 – but this b is also unique: there cannot be a c, different from b, such that aRc.

In the above given example, it is simple to check that this property holds (see in particular Figure 18.2). Hence it holds that: $0R$–2, but not $0Ry$ for any other $y \in \mathbb{Z}$.

What is *not* allowed for a mapping is drawn schematically on the left halves of Figures 18.3 and 18.4:

- There cannot be a point in A that is *not* related to any point in B, and:

- There cannot be a point in A that is related to *two or more* points in B.

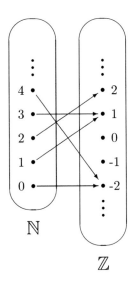

Figure 18.2: The arrow graph of the function $y = -x^2 + 4x - 2$.

But be careful: A mapping can very well fit the situation drawn on the right half of Figure 18.3: there may be points b in B to which no point a in A is related. See the example of Figure 18.2, where $-1 \in \mathbb{Z}$ is such a point. Also, the situation drawn on the right half of Figure 18.4 can very well happen, namely that *two* (or more) different elements of A are related to one and the same element of B. See again the example in Figure 18.2, where for $-2 \in \mathbb{Z}$ both $0R$–2 and $4R$–2 hold.

Remark 18.1.1 *The strict condition that for every $a \in A$ there must be precisely one $b \in B$ with aRb, is sometimes weakened in practice: it is*

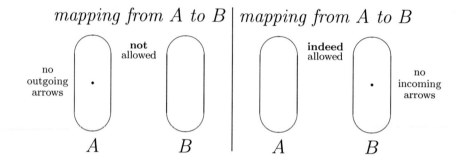

Figure 18.3: In a mapping, it is not allowed to have no outgoing arrows but it is indeed allowed to have zero incoming arrows.

enough that for $a \in A$ at most *one* such $b \in B$ exists (hence the non-existence of such b is also acceptable). In the latter case (when there are a's in A that are not related to any b's in B), one speaks also of a partial function. This means for example that the function $y = \frac{x^3+1}{x-1}$ is in this view a 'good' mapping from $\mathbb{R}$ to $\mathbb{R}$, despite the fact that for $x = 1$ there is no corresponding value y. The same holds for the function described by $y = \tan(x)$, which is often called a mapping from $\mathbb{R}$ to $\mathbb{R}$, although no y-value is given to $x = \frac{\pi}{2} + k\pi$.

In this book we keep to the strict condition that a relation from A to B can only be a mapping (or a function) if for *every* $a \in A$ there is *precisely one* $b \in B$ such that aRb.

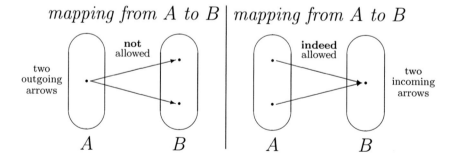

Figure 18.4: In a mapping, two outgoing arrows are not allowed, whereas two incoming arrows are indeed allowed.

18.2 The characteristics of a mapping

In the previous section we described when a relation R between A and B can be called a mapping. This description can be written in the form of a formula as follows:
$$\forall_x [x \in A : \exists^1_y [y \in B : xRy]] \ .$$

We use here the *new quantifier* $\exists^1$ for the so-called *unique existence*: *there is precisely one* .... How can we *prove* now for a given $x \in A$ that $\exists^1_y [y \in B : xRy]$?

For this, we look first at the general case of a unique existence, hence at a formula of the form $\exists^1_y [y \in B : P(y)]$, for some predicate P. This formula says:

There is *precisely one* $y \in B$ with the property $P(y)$.

We divide this in two parts:

(1) there is *at least one* $y \in B$ with $P(y)$, *and*

(2) there is *at most one* $y \in B$ with $P(y)$.

For (1) we immediately get a formula:
$$\exists_y [y \in B : P(y)] \ .$$

For (2) we must think a bit. The simplest is to express 'at most one' as 'not: two or more'. And this latter can be formulated as:
$$\forall_{y_1, y_2} [y_1, y_2 \in B : (P(y_1) \wedge P(y_2)) \Rightarrow (y_1 = y_2)] \ .$$

This says that: if P holds for both y_1 and y_2 in B, then these y_1 and y_2 cannot be different (because otherwise P will hold for two elements of B). And if P cannot hold for two elements of B, then it cannot hold either for more than two.

We now return to our case $\exists^1_y [y \in B : xRy]$. From the above we have:

$$\exists^1_y [y \in B : xRy] \overset{val}{=\!=\!=} $$
$$\exists_y [y \in B : xRy] \ \wedge $$
$$\forall_{y_1, y_2} [y_1, y_2 \in B : (xRy_1 \wedge xRy_2) \Rightarrow (y_1 = y_2)]$$

The last equivalence can be applied in proofs where unique existence plays a role.

A mapping from A to B is usually denoted not by the letter R of 'relation', but for example by the letter F of 'function', or by lower-case letters: f, g.

If F is a mapping from A to B, we write: $F : A \to B$. Also, it is normal practice for a mapping, to write the relation between $a \in A$ and $b \in B$ differently: if a is related to b, we don't write aFb, but instead we write $F(a) = b$. This latter notation is familiar: one writes $\cos(2\pi) = 1$ and not: $2\pi \cos 1$.

In this notation we can write the earlier described characteristic property of a mapping as follows:

Property of 'mapping' $F : A \to B$ **:**
$\forall_x [x \in A : \exists^1_y [y \in B : F(x) = y]]$

The set A is called the *domain* of F, the set B the *range* of F.

Remark 18.2.1 *How does the above fit for functions of more than one variable? For example: $z = \sin(x + y)$, or $f(x, y, z) = x^2 + y^2 + z^2$. These can still be seen as mappings from A to B, but then with a Cartesian product for A: the first example can be a function from $\mathbb{R} \times \mathbb{R}$ to $\mathbb{R}$, the second from $\mathbb{R}^3$ to $\mathbb{R}$. Hence, also functions of more than one variable fall under our abstract concept of mappings.*

18.3   Image and source

In the previous sections we saw that for every mapping F from A to B, there is a kind of 'asymmetry' between the domain A and the range B (see also Figures 18.3 and 18.4):

- All elements from A are included in the mapping, and in addition, *precisely* one arrow departs from every such $a \in A$. (See the above given Property of 'mapping'.)

  (You can for instance see A and B as two clubs, one of letter writers (A) and the other of letter receivers (B). The agreement is that every member of A writes *one* letter to a member of B. The function F specifies for every member a of A the member b in B to whom he/she should write this letter.)

- But how things are in B can vary quite a lot: there can be b's in B which receive no incoming arrows at all and there can be some which receive one incoming arrow, or two, or more, and even infinitely many.

  (It depends on F how many letters a certain b in B will receive.)

We now explain two different concepts that are important for a given mapping $F : A \to B$: the *image* of a subset of the domain A, and the *source* of a subset of the range B.

(1) Image

Assume first that A' is a subset of the domain A. Sometimes it is interesting to know *where* precisely all the arrows that begin in A' will end (these are precisely the b's in B that receive a letter from an a' in the subclub A'). This subcollection of B is called the *image* of A' under F. Notation: $F(A')$. Hence:

$$F(A') = \{b \in B | \exists_x [x \in A' : F(x) = b]\}.$$

Remark 18.3.1 *In computer science notation, this can be written more elegantly as follows:*
$$F(A') = (\text{Set } x : x \in A' : F(x)).$$

We give a number of examples in which we describe images of subsets, relative to domains of well-known functions.

Example 18.3.2

- *Look at the function* $\sin : \mathbb{R} \to \mathbb{R}$. *For the subset* $I = \langle 0, \pi \rangle$ *of the domain* $\mathbb{R}$ *(I is the interval of the numbers between 0 and π), we have: the image of I under* $\sin$ *(denoted by* $\sin(I)$*) is* $\langle 0, 1]$ *(that is: the interval of the numbers between 0 and 1, including 1 itself). (Note that in mathematics books,* $\langle 0, \pi \rangle$ *is often written as* $(0, \pi)$*.)*

- *Look at the function* $F : \mathbb{Z} \to \mathbb{N}$ *with formula* $F(x) = x^2 + 5$. *Then it holds that: the image of* $\{-2, -1, 0, 1, 2\} \subseteq \mathbb{Z}$ *under F is* $\{5, 6, 9\} \subseteq \mathbb{N}$ *and the image of* $\mathbb{Z}$ *(in its entirety) under F (hence* $F(\mathbb{Z})$*) is the set* $\{5, 6, 9, 14, 21, 30, \ldots\}$. *The latter set may also be written, more clearly, as:* $\{0 + 5, 1 + 5, 4 + 5, 9 + 5, 16 + 5, 25 + 5, \ldots\}$. *In computer science notation:* $F(\mathbb{Z}) = (\text{Set } x : x \in \mathbb{Z} : x^2 + 5)$.

- *Note that for a mapping* $F : A \to B$ *it holds in general that the image of the whole A under F is always a subset of B:* $F(A) \subseteq B$. *This image $F(A)$ can be the whole B (see Section 18.4, 'surjection'), but it can also be a strict subset of B. For the function* $\sin : \mathbb{R} \to \mathbb{R}$, *for example, this image* $\sin(\mathbb{R})$ *is equal to* $[-1, 1]$, *a 'proper' (or strict) subset of the range* $\mathbb{R}$.

Note that the notation $F(A')$ for *the image of A' under the mapping F*, is 'abuse' of notation: we pretend here that F acts on a *set*, while actually, F acts on *elements* of a set.

Remark 18.3.3 *So we assign a double role to each function-symbol F: in the first place, such an F acts on arbitrary elements x of the domain A; and only secondarily, we allow F to act on subsets A' of A, as well. There is, however, a relation between these two roles of F: we may consider $F(A')$ (hence with F in the second role) as being a shorthand for* the set of all $F(a')$ *(with F in the first role), where a' ranges over all elements of A'.*

(2) Source

Consider now a subset B' of the range B. It can be useful to know where the arrows arriving in B have come from (which letter writers from A have sent a letter to someone in the subclub B'). This is called the *source* of B' under F. Notation: $F^-(B')$. Hence:

$$F^-(B') = \{a \in A | F(a) \in B'\}.$$

Example 18.3.4

- *Look again at the function* $\sin : \mathbb{R} \to \mathbb{R}$. *Take the subset* $\mathbb{Z}$ *in the range* $\mathbb{R}$. *What is the source under* $\sin$? *This is the set of all the x's in $\mathbb{R}$ for which* $\sin(x) \in \mathbb{Z}$. *This latter can only hold if* $\sin(x) \in \{-1, 0, 1\}$, *because* $|\sin(x)| \leq 1$. *The answer is hence: the set of all the x's such that x is an integer multiple of $\frac{\pi}{2}$.*

  In summary: $\sin^-(\mathbb{Z}) = \{x \in \mathbb{R} | x$ is a multiple of $\frac{\pi}{2}\}$.

  (In computer science notation this can be written more nicely in the following form: $\sin^-(\mathbb{Z}) = (\text{Set } u : u \in \mathbb{Z} : u \times \frac{\pi}{2})$.*)*

- *Take again the function* $F : \mathbb{Z} \to \mathbb{N}$ *with* $F(x) = x^2 + 5$. *Then the source of* $B' = \{0, 1, 2, \ldots, 10\}$ *under F is the set of the x's in $\mathbb{Z}$ for which* $x^2 + 5 \in B'$. *It will be clear that this set consists of* $\{-2, -1, 0, 1, 2\}$ *because, for precisely these integer numbers it holds that* $x^2 + 5 \in \{0, 1, 2, \ldots, 10\}$.

  The source of $\mathbb{N}$ *in its entirety (hence:* $F^-(\mathbb{N})$) *is* $\mathbb{Z}$.

- *The latter also holds in general: if* $F : A \to B$ *is a mapping, then the source of the whole B under F is always equal to the whole A, hence* $F^-(B) = A$.

Remark 18.3.5 *Take again the mapping* $F : A \to B$ *and let* $B' \subseteq B$. *The symbol* F^- *in* $F^-(B')$ *operates on the subset B', not on its elements! The result* $F^-(B')$ *is also called* complete source *instead of (simply) source. The term 'inverse image' is also used.*

We summarize our knowledge about image and source once again, both in words and in a picture:

Let $F : A \to B$ be a mapping and assume that $A' \subseteq A$ respectively $B' \subseteq B$. Then:

– the image $F(A')$ consists of all the *end* points of the arrows which *begin* in A'.

– The source $F^-(B')$ consists of all the *begin* points of the arrows which *end* in B'.

We show this in Figure 18.5.

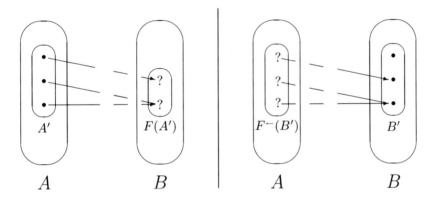

Figure 18.5: Image and source in a picture.

We establish a couple of important properties of image and source. Let F again be a mapping from A to B.

(1) We begin with the image $F(A')$ of a subset A' of A. The following holds:

Properties of 'image':

$x \in A' \overset{val}{\models} F(x) \in F(A')$

$y \in F(A') \overset{val}{=\!=\!=} \exists_x [x \in A' : F(x) = y]$

The first property is a sort of monotonicity-property: if x is in A', then $F(x)$ is in the image of A'. This follows from the definition of $F(A')$ and from the Property of $\in$ that we formulated in Section 16.1. Also the second Property of 'image' follows from the definition of $F(A')$ and this Property of $\in$, combined with the fact that $F(A') \subseteq B$ (cf. Example 18.3.2).

It is worth noting that the first Property of 'image' does not hold in general for the other direction! The reason for this is that there may be points x *outside* A' with $F(x) \in F(A')$. For such an x it holds that $F(x) \in F(A')$, but *not* that $x \in A'$.

This situation is illustrated in Figure 18.6.

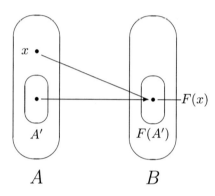

Figure 18.6: If $F(x) \in F(A')$, then it does not need to hold that $x \in A'$.

A concrete example is the following. Take $F : \mathbb{Z} \to \mathbb{N}$ with $F(x) = x^2$. Consider the two-element subset $\{0, 2\}$ of $\mathbb{Z}$. Then: $F(\{0, 2\}) = \{0, 4\}$. For the number -2 it also holds that $F(-2) \in F(\{0, 2\})$, whereas it does *not* hold that: $-2 \in \{0, 2\}$. Hence, the number -2 is a point *outside* $\{0, 2\}$ which after application of F still falls in $F(\{0, 2\})$.

(2) Next we give a standard property for the source of a subset B' of B:

Property of 'source':

$x \in F^-(B') \quad \overset{val}{=\!=\!=} \quad F(x) \in B'$

Also this property follows directly from the definition of F^- and from the Property of $\in$ given in Section 16.1.

We close this section with an example of a lemma about image and source. The lemma states:

Lemma 18.3.6 *Let $F : A \to B$ be a mapping and $A' \subseteq A$. Then it holds that:*
$$F^-(F(A')) \supseteq A'.$$

First we give a proof for this proposition as an informal reasoning. We will again consider the club A (with subclub A') of letter writers and the club B of letter receivers. Call $F(A')$ simply B'. What is the subclub B'? This is the club of all receivers of letters written by members of A'. We must know something about $F^-(F(A'))$, which is $F^-(B')$. Which elements are in it? These are *all* the writers in A which have written to members of B'. Definitely all the members of the subclub A' will appear there (see above), and maybe more. Hence it holds that: $A' \subseteq F^-(B')$. And that is what the lemma states.

In a formal proof, we cannot of course talk about letter writers and letter receivers. Instead, we must use the techniques given in Chapter 16 ('Sets'). The proof is deceptively simple. The reader is advised to check what happens exactly, and that this fits with the informal reasoning given above.

{ Assume: }

(1) | var x; $x \in A'$ |

    { First property of 'image' on (1): }

(2) | $F(x) \in F(A')$

    { Property of 'source' on (2): }

(3) | $x \in F^-(F(A'))$

  { $\forall$-intro on (1) and (3): }

(4) $\forall_x[x \in A' : x \in F^-(F(A'))]$

  { Definition of $\subseteq$ on (4): }

(5) $A' \subseteq F^-(F(A'))$

Try to give an example where $F^-(F(A'))$ is really *bigger* than A'.

The mirror image of the above proven Lemma 18.3.6 is:

Lemma 18.3.7 *Let $F : A \to B$ be a mapping and $B' \subseteq B$. Then we have:*
$F(F^-(B')) \subseteq B'$.

Prove this lemma on your own, first informally and thereafter with a formal reasoning. Give also an example where it appears that $F(F^-(B'))$ is really *smaller* than B'.

18.4   Special mappings

We have already seen that for a mapping $F : A \to B$, the number of incoming arrows to a certain b in B can vary. For some b there can be zero such arrows, for others there can be one, or two, or more, up to an infinite number.

We will in this section look at special classes of mappings where the number of incoming arrows to a certain b in B is restricted:

(1) There are mappings where each b in B has *at least one* incoming arrow. Such a mapping is called a *surjection*. Hence, for a surjection, the right half of Figure 18.3 changes: 'indeed allowed' is changed into 'not allowed'. See Figure 18.7.

(2) There are mappings where each b in B has *at most one* incoming arrow. Such a mapping is called an *injection*. Hence, for an injection the right half of Figure 18.4 changes. See Figure 18.8.

(3) There are also mappings where each b in B has *precisely one* incoming arrow. Such a mapping is both surjective and injective. Such a mapping is called a *bijection*.

We will go deeper into each of these kinds of mappings.

(1) *Surjection.*

The characteristic property of a surjection is:

Property of 'surjection' $F : A \to B$:
$\forall_y [y \in B : \exists_x [x \in A : F(x) = y]]$

Hence, for a surjection it does not only hold that $F(A) \subseteq B$, we even have $F(A) = B$: every b in B is the image of at least one a in A.

Example 18.4.1

- *The function* sin $: \mathbb{R} \to \mathbb{R}$ *is not a surjection, because there does not exist for every* $y \in \mathbb{R}$ *an* x *such that* $\sin(x) = y$. *Take for example* $y = 2$ *(this is a* counterexample*). Note that being surjective or not, depends on the given range. If we take* sin *as a function from* $\mathbb{R}$ *to* $[-1, 1]$, *then it becomes indeed a surjective function (in fact,* $\sin(\mathbb{R}) = [-1, 1]$*).*

- Also the function $F : \mathbb{Z} \to \mathbb{N}$ with formula $F(x) = x^2 + 5$ is not surjective. If we had instead considered the function with formula $F(x) = |x|$, then it would indeed have been a surjection.

- The function $f : \mathbb{R} \to \mathbb{R}$ with $f(x) = x^n$ is surjective for every odd $n \in \mathbb{N}$ and not surjective for every even $n \in \mathbb{N}$.

- The exponential function with formula $y = e^x$ is not surjective if the mapping is from $\mathbb{R}$ to $\mathbb{R}$, because e^x is always positive.

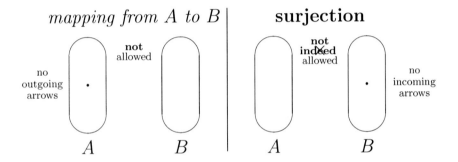

Figure 18.7: For a *surjection* there is for each b in B *at least one* incoming arrow.

In a Cartesian graph of a function from A to B, we have: the function is surjective if and only if every horizontal line drawn from a point of B has at least one intersection point with the graph. Check yourself that this is indeed the case for the above given examples.

Remark 18.4.2 *The word 'surjection' is French/Latin and means 'a throw-upon'. A surjective mapping 'throws' the domain A 'upon' the range B, the whole range becomes hence covered.*

A surjection is also called 'a mapping-onto': saying that 'f is a mapping from A onto B' means that $f : A \to B$ is a surjection.

(2) Injection.

For an injection $F : A \to B$, the characteristic property is that for every element $b \in B$ there is at most one $a \in A$ with $F(a) = b$. Hence, there can never be two *different* a's in A which have the same image b in B (see also Figure 18.8). Because of this last observation we can write the

characteristic property of injection in the form of a formula, just as we did
at the beginning of Section 18.2 for the expression 'at most one':

Property of 'injection' $F : A \to B$:
$\forall_{x_1, x_2}[x_1, x_2 \in A : (F(x_1) = F(x_2)) \Rightarrow (x_1 = x_2)]$

For an injection $F : A \to B$, not every b in B needs to be an end point
of an arrow, but *if* an arrow ends in b, then there is *only one* such arrow.
In the latter case, there is clearly a unique $a \in A$ where this arrow begins
(hence with $F(a) = b$).

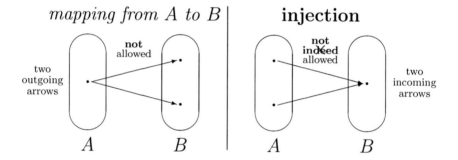

Figure 18.8: For an *injection* there is for each b in B *at most one* incoming
arrow.

Example 18.4.3

- *The function* $\sin : \mathbb{R} \to \mathbb{R}$ *is not an injection. We can show this with
  a counterexample:* $\sin(\frac{\pi}{4}) = \sin(\frac{3\pi}{4}) = \frac{1}{2}\sqrt{2}$.

- *The function* $F : \mathbb{Z} \to \mathbb{N}$ *with formula* $F(x) = x^2 + 5$ *is not injective,
  because for example* $F(-1) = F(1)$. *The function from* $\mathbb{Z}$ *to* $\mathbb{N}$ *with
  formula* $F(x) = |x|$, *is not injective, either.*

- *The function* $f : \mathbb{R} \to \mathbb{R}$ *with* $f(x) = x^n$ *is injective for odd* $n \in \mathbb{N}$ *but
  not injective for even* $n \in \mathbb{N}$.

- *The exponential function with formula* $y = e^x$, *given as a mapping
  from* $\mathbb{R}$ *to* $\mathbb{R}$, *is indeed injective, because for a given* y, *if* $y \le 0$ *then
  there is no* x *with* $y = e^x$, *and if* y *is positive then there is precisely
  one* x *with* $y = e^x$ *(namely* $x = \ln(y)$*).*

Remark 18.4.4 *The word 'injection' means something like 'a throw-in'. This does not say much. An injection is also called a 'one-to-one-mapping'. This term is a bit out of date.*

For a Cartesian graph of a function we have that: the function is injective if and only if every horizontal line drawn from a point in B has at most one intersection point with the graph. Check that this is indeed the case for the examples given above.

(3) *Bijection.*

A bijection is at the same time a surjection and an injection. This means that for every $b \in B$ there is *precisely one* $a \in A$ with $F(a) = b$:

Property of 'bijection' $F : A \rightarrow B$:
$\forall_y[y \in B : \exists^1_x[x \in A : F(x) = y]]$

The only difference with the Property of 'surjection' is that there is a number 'one' next to the symbol '$\exists$' (meaning: the existence not of 'at least one', but of 'precisely one' element with a certain property).

In proofs, instead of the last mentioned formula, usually the conjunction of 'surjective' and 'injective' is used: F is bijective if

$$\forall_y[y \in B : \exists_x[x \in A : F(x) = y]] \wedge$$
$$\forall_{x_1, x_2}[x_1, x_2 \in A : (F(x_1) = F(x_2)) \Rightarrow (x_1 = x_2)]$$

Remark 18.4.5 *The word 'bijection' contains the Greek prefix 'bi', which means 'double'. This expresses the fact that a bijection is both a surjection and an injection.*

Example 18.4.6

- *The function $f : \mathbb{R} \rightarrow \mathbb{R}$ with $f(x) = x^n$ is bijective for every odd $n \in \mathbb{N}$ (we already saw above that it is surjective and injective).*

- *The function sin is not bijective as a function from $\mathbb{R}$ to $\mathbb{R}$, but it is as a function from $[0, \frac{\pi}{2}]$ to $[0, 1]$. The same holds for cos. The function tan is bijective as a function from $\langle -\frac{\pi}{2}, \frac{\pi}{2} \rangle$ to $\mathbb{R}$.*

- *The exponential function $y = e^x$ from $\mathbb{R}$ to $\mathbb{R}$ is not bijective, but it is as a mapping from $\mathbb{R}$ to $\mathbb{R}^+$, the positive real numbers.*

- *Also the logarithmic function $y = \ln(x)$ is bijective as a mapping from $\mathbb{R}^+$ to $\mathbb{R}$.*

In a Cartesian graph we have: a function is bijective if and only if every horizontal line drawn through a point in B has precisely one intersection point with the graph. Check this yourself.

We close this section with two examples of lemmas where the concept 'injection' plays a role, and a theorem about surjection.

The first noticeable thing is that for an *injection*, the first Property of 'image' does *indeed* have two sides, hence for x in A not only the following holds

$$x \in A' \overset{val}{\models} F(x) \in F(A') \ ,$$

but also

$$x \in A' \overset{val}{\Longrightarrow} F(x) \in F(A') \ .$$

(See Section 18.3 for a counterexample showing that the latter does not need to hold if F was not an injection.)

We formulate this as a lemma:

Lemma 18.4.7 *Let $F : A \to B$ be an* injection *and take $A' \subseteq A$. Then for every $x \in A$ we have:*
$(F(x) \in F(A')) \Rightarrow (x \in A')$.

Proof. Assume that $F : A \to B$ is a mapping and that $A' \subseteq A$. Then we must fill the hole in the following reasoning:

$\qquad$ { Assume: }

(1) $\quad$ | F is an injection |

$\qquad\qquad$ { Assume: }

(2) $\qquad$ | var x; $x \in A$ |

$\qquad\qquad\qquad$ { Assume: }

(3) $\qquad\qquad$ | $F(x) \in F(A')$ |

$\qquad\qquad\qquad\qquad \vdots$

(n) $\qquad\qquad$ $x \in A'$

(At the end one should actually add a couple of lines expressing how one gets via $\Rightarrow$-intro and $\forall$-intro to $\forall_x[x \in A : (F(x) \in F(A')) \Rightarrow (x \in A')]$. For convenience, we leave these steps out.)

For clarity, we will abbreviate $F(x)$ with the letter y:

{ Assume: }

(1) $\boxed{F \text{ is an injection}}$

     { Assume: }

(2) $\boxed{\underline{\text{var}} \ x; \ x \in A}$

        { Assume: }

(3) $\boxed{F(x) \in F(A')}$

          { Define: }

(4) $y := F(x)$

          { then (3) becomes: }

(5) $y \in F(A')$

          $\vdots$

(n) $x \in A'$

Now we use the second Property of 'image' and $\exists^*$-elim:

{ Assume: }

(1) $\boxed{F \text{ is an injection}}$

     { Assume: }

(2) $\boxed{\underline{\text{var}} \ x; \ x \in A}$

        { Assume: }

(3) $\boxed{F(x) \in F(A')}$

          { Define: }

(4) $y := F(x)$

          { then (3) becomes: }

(5) $y \in F(A')$

          { Property of 'image' on (5): }

(6) $\exists_{x'}[x' \in A' : F(x') = y]$

          { $\exists^*$-elim on (6): }

(7)   Pick an x' with $x' \in A'$ and $F(x') = y$

$$(n) \quad \left|\;\right|\;\right|\quad \vdots \\ \qquad\qquad\; x \in A'$$

Note here that we have picked an x' in A' and not an x, because we already had an x, namely the $x \in A$ from line number (2).

Now we have both that $F(x) = y$ (a consequence of line number (4), the definition of y) and $F(x') = y$. Hence $F(x) = F(x')$. From the fact that F is an injection, it follows that $x = x'$. Hence, because $x' \in A'$, then $x \in A'$. And this was the goal!

So the full reasoning becomes:

$\{$ Assume: $\}$

(1) $\boxed{F \text{ is an injection}}$

        $\{$ Assume: $\}$

(2) $\boxed{\underline{\text{var}}\ x;\ x \in A}$

          $\{$ Assume: $\}$

(3) $\boxed{F(x) \in F(A')}$

            $\{$ Define: $\}$

(4) $y := F(x)$

            $\{$ then (3) becomes: $\}$

(5) $y \in F(A')$

            $\{$ Property of 'image' on (5): $\}$

(6) $\exists_{x'}[x' \in A' : F(x') = y]$

            $\{$ $\exists^*$-elim on (6): $\}$

(7)   Pick an x' with $x' \in A'$ and $F(x') = y$

            $\{$ Mathematics on (4) and (7): $\}$

(8) $F(x) = F(x')$

            $\{$ Property of 'injection' on (1): $\}$

(9) $\forall_{u_1, u_2}[u_1, u_2 \in A : (F(u_1) = F(u_2)) \Rightarrow (u_1 = u_2)]$

            $\{$ $\forall$-elim (twice) and $\Rightarrow$-elim on (9), (2), (7) and (8): $\}$

(10) $x = x'$

            $\{$ Mathematics on (7) and (10): $\}$

(11) $\big|\ \big|\ \big|\ \ x \in A'$

$\{\ \Rightarrow$-intro on (3) and (11): $\}$

(12) $\big|\ \big|\ \ (F(x) \in F(A')) \Rightarrow (x \in A')$

Hence, we are ready: this is a derivation that contains the complete proof of Lemma 18.4.7.

In what follows we show that Lemma 18.3.6 of Section 18.3 can be refined in the case where F is an injection:

Lemma 18.4.8 *Let* $F : A \rightarrow B$ *be an* injection *and* $A' \subseteq A$. *Then we have:*
$F^-(F(A')) = A'$.

From Lemma 18.3.6 we know already that $F^-(F(A')) \supseteq A'$, hence the only thing that we still need to show is:

$$F^-(F(A')) \subseteq A' \ .$$

This is very simple with the help of the above proven Lemma 18.4.7:

$\{\ $Assume: $\}$

(1) $\boxed{\text{var } x;\ x \in F^-(F(A'))}$

$\{\ $Property of 'source' on (1): $\}$

(2) $\big|\ \ F(x) \in F(A')$

$\{\ \forall$-elim and $\Rightarrow$-elim on Lemma 18.4.7 (F is an injection!): $\}$

(3) $\big|\ \ x \in A'$

$\{\ \forall$-intro on (1) and (3): $\}$

(4) $\forall_x [x \in F^-(F(A')) : x \in A']$

$\{\ $Property of $\subseteq$ on (4): $\}$

(5) $F^-(F(A')) \subseteq A'$

Now, show yourself the following refinement of Lemma 18.3.7 of Section 18.3 which holds if F is a *surjection*:

Lemma 18.4.9 *Let* $F : A \rightarrow B$ *be a* surjection *and take* $B' \subseteq B$. *Then we have:*
$F(F^-(B')) = B'$.

18.5   The inverse function

If $F : A \to B$ is a *bijection*, then we have something rather nice:

- By the fact that F is a *mapping*, from every point in A there is precisely one outgoing arrow, and

- because F is moreover a *bijection*, to every point in B there is precisely one incoming arrow.

This means that the points in A and B are paired to each other via F. In Figure 18.9, an example is given of such a pairing.

Hence, in the case of a bijection F from A to B, to each a in A there corresponds precisely one b in B, but we can just as well say that to each b in B there corresponds precisely one a in A.

This means that we can turn all the arrows round *and we get again a mapping*, this time from B to A. This mapping, which gives the same relation as F but in the other direction, is called the *inverse* of F and is denoted by F^{-1}. Note that, the inverse of F exists *only* if F is a bijection!

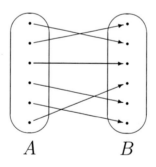

$$A \qquad\qquad B$$

Figure 18.9: Example how a *bijection* from A to B pairs the elements together.

For the inverse function, the following property holds:

Property of 'inverse function' $F^{-1} : B \to A$ for *bijective* $F : A \to B$:
$F(x) = y \overset{val}{=\!=\!=} F^{-1}(y) = x$

Remark 18.5.1 *If we apply this property to the Property of 'bijection' of Section 18.4, namely:*

$\forall_y [y \in B : \exists_x^1 [x \in A : F(x) = y]],$

we get:

$\forall_y [y \in B : \exists_x^1 [x \in A : F^{-1}(y) = x]].$

But this corresponds precisely to the characteristic Property of a 'mapping' of Section 18.2, if we fill there $F^{-1} : B \to A$ instead of $F : A \to B$! This implies once again, that $F^{-1} : B \to A$ is indeed a mapping.

For each bijection $F : A \to B$ there is hence a unique inverse function $F^{-1} : B \to A$. Because such an inverse function does precisely the opposite of what the function itself does, the following follows easily:

$\forall_x [x \in A : F^{-1}(F(x)) = x].$

In fact, if $F(a) = b$, then F^{-1} returns point b back to point a, hence $F^{-1}(F(a)) = F^{-1}(b) = a$.

In the same way it follows that

$\forall_y [y \in B : F(F^{-1}(y)) = y].$

We give a couple of examples of bijective functions and their inverses:

Example 18.5.2

- *The square function $f : \mathbb{R}^+ \to \mathbb{R}^+$ with $f(x) = x^2$ is a bijection. (Remark: If we took $\mathbb{R}$ (all real numbers) as domain instead of $\mathbb{R}^+$ (the positive real numbers), it would not have been a bijection.) The inverse function $f^{-1} : \mathbb{R}^+ \to \mathbb{R}^+$ is the root function: $f^{-1}(x) = \sqrt{x}$. Check yourself that $f^{-1}(f(x)) = x$ and that $f(f^{-1}(y)) = y$.*

- *The exponential function $y = e^x$ (domain: $\mathbb{R}$, range: $\mathbb{R}^+$) has as inverse the natural logarithm $y = \ln(x)$ (domain: $\mathbb{R}^+$, range: $\mathbb{R}$).*

- *If we restrict the domain of the sine function to $[-\frac{\pi}{2}, \frac{\pi}{2}]$ and the range to $[-1, 1]$, then it becomes a bijection, with as inverse the arcsin function. The cosine function with domain $[0, \pi]$ and range $[-1, 1]$ has as inverse the arccos function.*

- *Restrict the tangent function to the domain $\langle -\frac{\pi}{2}, \frac{\pi}{2} \rangle$. The range is the whole $\mathbb{R}$. We then have one continuous 'swing' of the graph of the tangent, which corresponds to a bijection. The inverse is the arctan function.*

Finally we point out that, for an arbitrary mapping $F : A \to B$, the source $F^{\leftarrow}$ is very different from the inverse function F^{-1}:

- $F^{\leftarrow}$ works on *subsets* from B and is always defined, this means: for every $B' \subseteq B$, $F^{\leftarrow}(B')$ is a well-defined subset of A.

- But F^{-1}, which is an 'ordinary' mapping and works on *elements* of B, is only defined if F is also a *bijection*.

There is only one case for which $F^{\leftarrow}$ and F^{-1} coincide. Namely, if F is a bijection, then it holds for every subset $B' \subseteq B$ that the *source* $F^{\leftarrow}(B')$ is equal to the *image* (!!) $F^{-1}(B')$. Check this.

18.6   Composite mappings

As we have already seen at the start of this chapter, mappings are special relations (see Sections 18.1 and 18.2). We have also seen that we can combine (or *compose*) two relations, see Section 17.6. But we can only do this if these relations fit each other: that is, if R is a relation between A and B, and S is a relation between *(the same!)* B, and C, then in this case $R;S$ is a relation between A and C, and it is called the *composition* of R and S.

Similarly, we can also compose mappings, under the same conditions: if F is a mapping from A to B and G is a mapping from (the same) B to C, then we can make a composite mapping from A to C. Note the condition that the *range* of the first mapping F, must be the same as the *domain* of the second mapping G. This *composite mapping* is denoted as $G{\circ}F$ (hence in the reversed order).

When does it now hold, for $x \in A$ and $z \in C$, that x $G{\circ}F$ z? Or, in mappings' notation, that $G{\circ}F(x) = z$? Again, as in Section 17.6, we need a $y \in B$ such that xFy and yGz. In mappings' notation: *such that* $F(x) = y$ and $G(y) = z$. It is obvious that we do not have *any choice* for this y: there is exactly *one* y such that $F(x) = y$, because F is a mapping, and if we apply the G on *this* y, we obtain z. In summary:

Property of 'composite mapping' $G{\circ}F : A \to C$
for $F : A \to B$ **and** $G : B \to C$ **:**
$G{\circ}F(x) = z \overset{val}{=\!=} G(F(x)) = z$

Hence in order to apply the composite mapping, we must first apply F on x obtaining the result $F(x)$, and then thereafter, we must apply G on this $F(x)$, obtaining the result $G(F(x))$. (It should now be obvious why $G{\circ}F$ is pronounced as G *after* F.)

In this way, the following takes place in the corresponding arrow graph: in order to calculate $G \circ F(x)$, you first follow the arrow from x to $F(x)$

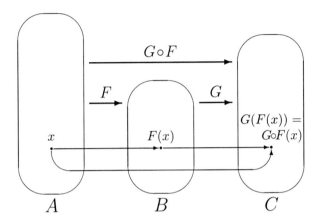

Figure 18.10: The arrow graph of the composite mapping $G{\circ}F$.

(there is exactly *one*), and then you follow the arrow from $F(x)$ to $G(F(x))$ (again here there is exactly *one*). See Figure 18.10.

When proving properties of composition functions, we will usually again 'decompose' $G{\circ}F$ in the composed functions F and G. See the following example, in the form of a lemma.

Lemma 18.6.1 *Assume that $F : A \to B$ and $G : B \to C$ are mappings and that they are both surjections. Then the composite mapping $G{\circ}F : A \to C$ is also a surjection.*

The proof of this statement is straightforward. It is so simple that we can even easily express it in words, namely as follows:

1. In order that $G{\circ}F : A \to C$ be surjective, every $z \in C$ must be an endpoint of a $G{\circ}F$–arrow, hence we have to show that there is an $x \in A$ such that $G{\circ}F(x) = z$.

2. But a z in C must surely be an endpoint of a G–arrow, because G from B to C is surjective. Hence there is a $y \in B$ (at least *one*) where $G(y) = z$.

3. Pick such a y in B, then this must be itself an endpoint of an F–arrow, because F from A to B is also surjective. Hence there is an $x \in A$ (again: at least *one*) where $F(x) = y$.

4. This is such an x that we have been looking for, because it satisfies $G \circ F(x) = G(F(x)) = G(y) = z$.

In a formal natural deduction proof, things are as follows:

{ Assume: }

(1) | var z; $z \in C$ |

{ G is a surjection, hence: }

(2) $\exists_y[y \in B : G(y) = z]$

{ $\exists^*$-elim on (2): }

(3)   Pick a y with $y \in B$ and $G(y) = z$

{ Also F is a surjection, hence: }

(4) $\exists_x[x \in A : F(x) = y]$

{ $\exists^*$-elim on (4): }

(5)   Pick an x with $x \in A$ and $F(x) = y$

{ From (5) and (3) we obtain: }

(6) $G(F(x)) = G(y) = z$

{ Property of 'composite mapping' on (6): }

(7) $G \circ F(x) = z$

{ $\exists^*$-intro on (5) and (7): }

(8) $\exists_x[x \in A : G \circ F(x) = z]$

{ $\forall$-intro on (1) and (8): }

(9) $\forall_z[z \in C : \exists_x[x \in A : G \circ F(x) = z]]$

{ Definition of surjection on (9): }

(10) $G \circ F$ is a surjection

So in this derivation we find the complete proof of Lemma 18.6.1.

Now prove yourself the corresponding lemma for *injections*:

Lemma 18.6.2 *Assume that $F : A \to B$ and $G : B \to C$ are mappings which are both injections. Then the composite mapping $G \circ F : A \to C$ is also an injection.*

If F is a mapping from A to *this same A*, i.e. $F : A \rightarrow A$, then we can also compose F *with itself*: we get $F \circ F(x)$ by first evaluating $F(x)$ and then again applying F to this $F(x)$ (because $F \circ F(x) = F(F(x))$).

If F is, for example, the function from $\mathbb{R}$ to $\mathbb{R}$ where $F(x) = x^2 + 1$, then we have:
$$F \circ F(x) = F(F(x)) = F(x^2 + 1) = (x^2 + 1)^2 + 1 = x^4 + 2x^2 + 2.$$

Repeated applications of the same function are called *iterations*. One calls $F \circ F$ the *second iteration* of F. This is also denoted by $F^{(2)}$. In the same way, one can build higher iterations, such as $F^{(3)}$, $F^{(4)}$; formally:
$$F^{(n+1)} := F \circ F^{(n)}, \text{ for } n \in \mathbb{N}, n \geq 2.$$
So for example: $F^{(3)} = F \circ F^{(2)} = F \circ (F \circ F)$. It follows from this that: $F^{(3)}(x) = F(F(F(x)))$, for every x in the domain of F.

Usually one also extends this definition to $n = 1$ and $n = 0$ by declaring that:
$$F^{(1)} := F, \text{ and}$$
$F^{(0)} :=$ the identity function (the *identity function* is the function which 'keeps every point in its place', hence $F^{(0)}(x)$ is always the same as x itself).

Now show that the equality $F^{(n+1)} = F \circ F^{(n)}$ also holds for $n = 1$ and $n = 0$.

18.7 Equality of mappings

Just as in Section 17.7 we spoke of equality of *relations*, we can also speak of *equality of mappings*. For this we have similar conditions.

First of all we only speak of the equality of the mappings F and G if both mappings have the same domain, *and* both have the same range. Hence if F is a mapping from domain A to range B then – to begin with – G can *only* be equal to F, if G is also a mapping from domain A to range B.

(Sometimes one deviates from this and allows that only the *domains* be equal, and so the function G can be a function with a different range B'; we do not allow this.) Moreover, in order to be equal, F and G must *do* the same thing with the elements of the domain, hence:
$$\forall_x [x \in A : F(x) = G(x)].$$
To summarize, if F and G are equal mappings, then they are indistinguishable as far as *behaviour* is concerned. Take for example the mappings F and G, both from $\{-1, 0, 1\}$ to $\mathbb{N}$, where:
$$F(x) = x^2,$$
$$G(x) = |x|.$$

Then these mappings are *equal*, because on their common domain, the set $\{-1, 0, 1\}$, we have that: $F(-1) = G(-1) = 1$, $F(0) = G(0) = 0$ and $F(1) = G(1) = 1$. Hence they are indistinguishable in their *behaviour*.

On the other hand if we take F and G both on a larger domain such as $\{-2, -1, 0, 1, 2\}$, or $\mathbb{N}$, then they are no longer equal.

18.8   Exercises

18.1 The relation R on $\mathbb{N}\backslash\{0\}$ is given by xRy if $y = $ l.c.m.$(8, x)$.

(The abbreviation l.c.m.(m, n) means: the least common multiple of m and n.)

(a) Check whether R is a mapping.

(b) Write the function values for $x = 1, 2, \ldots, 12$.

(c) Give $R(\{2, 4, 6, 8\})$ and $R(\{1, 2, \ldots, 12\}$.

(d) Give $R^{-}(\{8, 24\})$ and $R^{-}(\{1, 2, \ldots, 12\})$.

18.2 The mapping $f : \mathbb{R} \to \mathbb{R}$ is defined by $f(x) = x^2$.

(a) Show that there are $S, T \subseteq \mathbb{R}$ such that $f(S \cap T) \neq f(S) \cap f(T)$.

(b) Show that there is an $S \subseteq \mathbb{R}$ such that $f^{-}(f(S)) \neq S$.

(c) Show that there is a $U \subseteq \mathbb{R}$ such that $f(f^{-}(U)) \neq U$.

18.3 Let $f : A \to B$ be a mapping and $S, T \subseteq A$. Prove that:

(a) $S \subseteq T \Rightarrow f(S) \subseteq f(T)$.

(b) $f(S \cap T) \subseteq f(S) \cap f(T)$.

(c) $f(S\backslash T) \supseteq f(S)\backslash f(T)$.

18.4 Let $f : A \to B$ be a mapping and $U, V \subseteq B$. Prove that:

(a) $U \subseteq V \Rightarrow f^{-}(U) \subseteq f^{-}(V)$.

(b) $f^{-}(U \cap V) = f^{-}(U) \cap f^{-}(V)$.

(c) $f^{-}(U\backslash V) = f^{-}(U)\backslash f^{-}(V)$.

18.5 Give examples of mappings $f : \mathbb{N} \to \mathbb{N}$ such that

(a) f is a bijection.

(b) f is an injection, but not a surjection.

(c) f is a surjection, but not an injection.

(d) f is neither a surjection nor an injection.

18.6 The mapping f has as domain $\mathbb{R}$ and as range a certain (open or closed) interval Y. The mapping g has as domain a certain (open or closed) interval X and as range $\mathbb{R}$.

(a) What can you say about Y if f is a surjection, and
$f(x) = \sin(x)$, $f(x) = \tan(x)$ respectively $f(x) = e^x$?

(b) What can you say about X if g is an injection and
$g(x) = \sin(x)$, $g(x) = \tan(x)$ respectively $g(x) = e^x$?

18.7 Let F be a mapping from A to B and take $B' \subseteq B$. Prove that:

(a) $F(F^{\leftarrow}(B')) \subseteq B'$.

(b) If F is a surjection, then $F(F^{\leftarrow}(B')) = B'$.

18.8 (See also exercise 18.3 (b) and (c).)

Let $f : A \to B$ be an injection and $S, T \subseteq A$. Prove that:

(a) $f(S \cap T) = f(S) \cap f(T)$.

(b) $f(S \backslash T) = f(S) \backslash f(T)$.

18.9 (a) Give a bijection from $\mathbb{N}$ to the set Ω of the odd natural numbers.

(b) Give a bijection from $\mathbb{N}$ to $\mathbb{Z}$.

(c) Give a bijection from $\mathbb{N}$ to $\mathbb{N} \times \mathbb{N}$. (You don't need to give any formula, only a description of the mapping.)

18.10 If V is a *finite* set, one calls a bijective mapping from V to V a *permutation of V*.

(a) Give all permutations of $\{1, 2, 3\}$.

(b) Say which permutations of part (a) are inverses of each other.

(c) How many mappings are there from $\{1, 2, \ldots, n\}$ to $\{1, 2, \ldots, n\}$? How many of these are permutations?

18.11 (a) Show that the composition of mappings is *associative*, which means:

for every three mappings $F : A \to B$, $G : B \to C$ and $H : C \to D$ we have that $(F \circ G) \circ H = F \circ (G \circ H)$.

(b) Let $F : A \to A$ and $G : A \to A$ be two mappings.
Does it always hold that $F \circ G = G \circ F$? If so, give a proof; if not, give a counterexample.

18.12   (a) The function $f : \mathbb{R} \to \mathbb{R}$ is given by
$$f(x) = 2x - 1.$$
Give formulas for $f^{(0)}(x)$, $f^{(2)}(x)$ and $f^{(n)}(x)$.

(b) Find a function $g : \mathbb{R} \to \mathbb{R}$ with the properties:
$\forall_n [n \in \mathbb{N} : g^{(n)} \neq g^{(n+1)}]$, and
$\forall_n [n \in \mathbb{N} : g^{(n)} = g^{(n+2)}]$.

Chapter 19

Numbers and structures

19.1   Sorts of numbers

Numbers were originally only meant for *counting*: 'one', 'two', 'three', 'four'
.... These numbers are called *natural numbers*. The set of these is denoted
by $\mathbb{N}$. The number *zero* was added later to this set. It is important to note
that in somewhat older books of mathematics – say from *before* 1960 – the
symbol $\mathbb{N}$ represented the set $\{1, 2, 3, \ldots\}$, but that nowadays it almost always represents $\{0, 1, 2, 3, \ldots\}$, hence including 0. The elements of $\mathbb{N}$ *except*
0 are called the *positive* natural numbers (notation: $\mathbb{N}^{+}$).

By writing a minus sign before the natural numbers, 'minus *one*', 'minus
two', and so on, we can count 'the other way round': that is, we do not count
what we have, but what we are short of. We call a positive natural number
preceded by a minus sign, *negative*. The positive and negative numbers
together, also with 0 included, are called *whole numbers* (or *integers*). The
standard symbol for the set of all integers is $\mathbb{Z}$, with the Z for 'Zahlen'
(German for 'numbers'). Of course it holds that $\mathbb{N} \subseteq \mathbb{Z}$. If we want to do
more than the counting of 'entities', we can break these entities into pieces,
for example in *three* parts. And then we can count again, with these smaller
entities: one-third, two-thirds, three-thirds, four-thirds, ..., or minus-seven-
thirds, and so on. In this way we reach the *fractional numbers* or *fractions*.
A fraction can always be written as a whole number divided by another
whole number, with the condition that this *latter* number must not be zero
(dividing by 0 is undefined).

We use the symbol $\mathbb{Q}$ for the set of fractions, with the Q of Quotient.

One also counts whole numbers as fractions, hence $\mathbb{Z} \subseteq \mathbb{Q}$. In fact, every whole number can also be written as a fraction: $5 = 5/1 = 20/4$. Elements of $\mathbb{Q}$ are also called *rational numbers* (from the Latin word *ratio*, which originally only meant 'calculation', but later came to also mean 'ratio' or 'fraction').

But, not all possible number values are in $\mathbb{Q}$. For example $\sqrt{2}$, the square root of 2, is not a rational number. Other examples of non-rational (or *irrational*) numbers include π (the proportion between the circumference and the diameter of a circle) and e (the base of the natural logarithm). Rational and irrational numbers together form the *real numbers*, whose set is denoted by $\mathbb{R}$. And so it holds that $\mathbb{Q} \subseteq \mathbb{R}$. The set of the irrational numbers is $\mathbb{R} \backslash \mathbb{Q}$.

We can also represent the real numbers as points on the *number line*: an imaginary straight line which is infinite on both sides and where the whole numbers are used as a scale.

Furthermore, at a higher level, we find the *complex numbers* – 'complex' here means: 'composed' – denoted by $\mathbb{C}$. These are numbers $a + bi$ where a and $b \in \mathbb{R}$ and i is the so-called *imaginary entity*. Hence, $a + bi$ is *composed* from a *real part* a and an *imaginary part* bi. The symbol i is also described as the square root of -1, since *by axiom* it holds that $i^2 = -1$. This number $\sqrt{-1}$ does not 'exist' in the real world, and for this reason i is called 'imaginary'. Nonetheless, complex numbers are very useful, for example to calculate with equations. We refer to the mathematical literature for further details.

Note that we have: $\mathbb{R} \subseteq \mathbb{C}$ (indeed, if the b in $a + bi$ is equal to 0, then we get the real number a).

In the rest of this chapter we concentrate first on the natural and whole numbers. We will study their structure (Section 19.2) and the proof and construction methods which are based on the natural and whole numbers (Sections 19.3, 19.4, 19.5 and 19.6). Only towards the end will the big number systems appear in the picture: $\mathbb{Q}$ and $\mathbb{R}$ (Sections 19.9 and 19.10), and then with an eye to the question: *How* 'big' are they actually. We will not be concerned with $\mathbb{C}$ any more.

19.2   The structure of the natural numbers

In this section we look at the fundamental properties of natural numbers and at how these can be formally written. As we have already seen, 'counting' is the basis of the natural numbers.

What can we say about this counting? *Intuitively* speaking, counting is a *process* which gets started at a certain moment in time and which gets carried out step by step.

To be more precise:

(1) Counting must *start* somewhere: there is a *start-number*.

(2) Once started, the counting continues *stepwise*: it continues to deliver *new numbers*.

(3) It is not known in advance when counting will *finish*: there is *no fixed end-number*. Even stronger, we can continue to count until the end of our days; in principle, the counting goes on forever!

We can formalize all this as follows.

- As a set of all the 'counting numbers' we take $\mathbb{N}$ (hence including 0).

- As a start-number we take $0 \in \mathbb{N}$.

- The other numbers in $\mathbb{N}$ can then be obtained by continually appointing a *successor*. In order to be able to find such a successor, we use the so-called *successor function* s. Hence, $s(x)$ is the successor of x. This s must naturally be a function from $\mathbb{N}$ to $\mathbb{N}$.

So, first we have 0, then the successor of 0, then the successor of the successor of 0, and so on. In other words: we get a sequence 0, $s(0)$, $s(s(0))$, etc. Hence, $s(0)$ is the element of $\mathbb{N}$ that we normally take to be 1, $s(s(0))$ is 2, and so on. Note that in this way, we only 'really' need two symbols: 0 and s. By adding some parentheses around, we can describe with these two symbols, every natural number. The number 8 for example is in this notation $s(s(s(s(s(s(s(s(0))))))))$. Probably it is not very convenient to describe it this way, but it is consistent.

Note that the function s is *iterated* (see Section 18.6) in order to generate all the different counting numbers one after one. Another way of writing the number $s(s(s(s(s(s(s(s(0))))))))$ is $s^{(8)}(0)$. In general, it is the case that the number n can be 'constructed via the successor function by using $s^{(n)}(0)$.

However, we are still not there. Because no one can so far guarantee us that we continuously obtain *new* numbers, which is actually an important condition (see (2) above). In fact, in our abstract setting, it can well be for example that $s(s(s(s(0)))) = 0$ or that $s(s(s(s(s(0))))) = s(s(0))$.

In the first case we are 'back to the beginning' after four counting steps, in the second case we make a back jump after five steps (and again every three following steps ...). If we use the 'usual' numbers, then we count in the first case as follows: $0, 1, 2, 3, 0, 1, 2, 3, 0, 1, 2, 3, ...$ and in the second case our counting goes $0, 1, 2, 3, 4, 2, 3, 4, 2, 3, 4, ...$ This is not what we expect from counting.

In order to overcome such things, we require the following two things for the successor function:

1. There is no counting number with successor 0. (This will block the first case above, where $s(3) = 0$.)

2. The successors of two different numbers can never be equal. (With this, the second case $s(4) = s(1)$, becomes impossible.)

Putting everything together, we are now in a position to describe formally what the nature of the natural numbers is. We may describe it as a so-called *mathematical structure* $\langle \mathbb{N}, 0, s \rangle$ (see also Remark 19.2.1 below), where:

– $\mathbb{N}$ is a set,

– 0 is a fixed element of $\mathbb{N}$,

– and s is a mapping from $\mathbb{N}$ to itself.

Moreover, we have for this structure $\langle \mathbb{N}, 0, s \rangle$ the following two basic properties (so-called *axioms*):

1. $\forall_n [n \in \mathbb{N} : s(n) \neq 0]$, and

2. s is an injection.

(Verify that the injectivity of s covers precisely what we have just assumed, namely that the successors of two different numbers are never equal!)

The formal description of the mathematical structure $\langle \mathbb{N}, 0, s \rangle$ was given for the first time by the Italian Giuseppe Peano.[1] He added to the two axioms 1 and 2 above, four (two times two) more axioms in order to formalize addition and multiplication (see also Exercise 19.12) and a further axiom on the proof principle called *induction*. (This induction principle will be described in the following section). With this, Peano succeeded to pin down the nature of the natural numbers – on purely formal grounds! This is quite an achievement.

In order to facilitate things for us, we can now *define* $1 := s(0)$, $2 := s(1)$, and so on. It can be shown that the 'normal' manner in which we calculate with the natural numbers $0, 1, 2, \ldots$, corresponds to the calculations on the basis of $0, s(0), s(s(0)), \ldots$, in $\langle \mathbb{N}, 0, s \rangle$. Hence, we can use these 'newly defined' numbers $0, 1, 2, \ldots$, as we are accustomed to.

Remark 19.2.1 *The concept of 'mathematical structure' that we use above for $\langle \mathbb{N}, 0, s \rangle$, appears often in the literature. It is a bit different from an n-tuple (see Section 16.9). In order to see this, we look in more details at the mathematical structure $\langle \mathbb{N}, 0, s \rangle$, which looks like a triple (or a three-tuple) but which is not. This is the case because in a given triple like $(\pi, -3, \sqrt{2})$ the three elements are* independent. *However, for the structure $\langle \mathbb{N}, 0, s \rangle$, the second element, 0, depends on the first because 0 must be in $\mathbb{N}$. And also*

---

[1] Giuseppe Peano: *Formulaire de Mathématique*, Bocca, Turin, 1894–1908.

the third element, s, depends on the first; in fact, the assumption is that
$s : \mathbb{N} \rightarrow \mathbb{N}$. *In other words, in a mathematical structure, you can only give*
the k-th element (k > 1) if its preceding elements have already been given.

19.3 Inductive proofs

In the previous section we formally analyzed $\mathbb{N}$, the basis of all sets of
numbers. It appears that $\mathbb{N}$ is not *just* a set, but one *with a structure*.
The important factor in its structure is that the elements of $\mathbb{N}$ will appear
one by *one* if we start with 0 and then continuously repeat the successor
function. The elements of $\mathbb{N}$ can be so constructed step by step, just as
if we are climbing an infinite ladder with steps 0, $s(0)$, $s(s(0))$, and so on.
(As we have seen, this is related to 'counting', where the natural numbers
appear one after one.)

For this reason it is not surprising that for this $\mathbb{N}$ we have a special *proof*
principle, that fits well with this stepwise building process. This principle
is called *induction*. We first describe this proof principle in words, and then
later on, we present it formally.

We start with the situation that $A(n)$ is a one-place predicate over the
domain $\mathbb{N}$ of natural numbers. We assume also that for this predicate, the
following two properties hold:

(1) The predicate holds for 0.

(2) *If* the predicate holds for some arbitrary i in $\mathbb{N}$, then it also holds for
the successor of i.

We can say this in another way:

(1) The proposition $A(0)$ is true.

(2) The proposition $A(i) \Rightarrow A(s(i))$ is true for every $i \in \mathbb{N}$.

The second property can also be described as follows, by successively
filling 0, $s(0)$, $s(s(0))$ ... for i (hence by applying repeated $\forall$-elim):

(2′) $A(0) \Rightarrow A(s(0))$ is true,

(2″) $A(s(0)) \Rightarrow A(s(s(0)))$ is true,

(2‴) $A(s(s(0))) \Rightarrow A(s(s(s(0))))$ is true...

From this we can conclude that:

– $A(0)$ is true (this appears in (1)),

– $A(s(0))$ is true (from the previous line and (2′), by $\Rightarrow$-elim).

– $A(s(s(0)))$ is true (from the previous line and (2″), by $\Rightarrow$-elim).

– $A(s(s(s(0))))$ is true (from the previous line and (2‴), by $\Rightarrow$-elim).

And so on!

It is hence intuitively obvious, that $A(n)$ must be true for *every* $n \in \mathbb{N}$. Also $A(s(s(...(s(0))...)))$, where after the letter A a hundred – or several millions! – s's appear, must be true. In fact, we can repeat the above process until we reach the line where A is followed by these hundred – or these millions of - s's, it just takes some time before we are that far...

However, the problem is that we can only show that $A(n)$ indeed holds for *every* $n \in \mathbb{N}$, if we carry the above process *infinitely* forward. As a matter of fact, the whole $\mathbb{N}$ is infinitely big. It is really beyond a proof system like the one we developed in Part II to do *infinitely many* steps. For this, we must be able to do an infinitely long reasoning, but this is impossible.

Still, we would like in the above case, to be able to directly conclude that $A(n)$ is true for every $n \in \mathbb{N}$, because it is so 'obvious'. To achieve this, there is one formal thing we can do, and that is to *extend* our proof system with a new proof rule which can be especially applied to this case. Because the above described way of concluding is called *induction*, the corresponding proof rule is called the *proof rule for induction*.

We can write the proof rule for induction formally as follows (this induction rule is also one of the *axioms of Peano*):

induction:

$$\vdots$$

$(k) \qquad A(0)$

$$\vdots$$

$(l) \qquad \forall_i[i \in \mathbb{N} : A(i) \Rightarrow A(i+1)]$

$\qquad\qquad \{ \text{ Induction on } (k) \text{ and } (l): \ \}$

$(m) \qquad \forall_n[n \in \mathbb{N} : A(n)]$

Hence, a proof by induction amounts to the filling of the two dotted parts: (i) a proof of the *basis* $A(0)$, and (ii) a proof of the *step* $\forall_i[i \in \mathbb{N} : A(i) \Rightarrow A(i+1)]$.

These proofs are in principle independent, and so the line numbers (k) and (l) in the above schema can be interchanged.

Remark 19.3.1 *Note that we take the bound variables in the lines numbered (l) and (m) to be different: i resp. n. This is in order to avoid confusion. Note also that, as usual, we wrote $i + 1$ instead of $s(i)$; we shall do the same in what follows.*

The second part of the proof leads to the 'step-formula', which has the form $\forall i[i \in \mathbb{N} : A(i) \Rightarrow A(i+1)]$. This is a $\forall$-formula, with an internal $\Rightarrow$-formula. A standard proof of induction shall hence have the following form:

$$\vdots$$

(k) $A(0)$
     { Assume: }

$(k+1)$ $\boxed{\text{var } i; \ i \in \mathbb{N}}$
       { Assume: }

$(k+2)$ $\boxed{A(i)}$

           $\vdots$

$(l-2)$ $A(i+1)$
         { $\Rightarrow$-intro on $(k+2)$ and $(l-2)$: }

$(l-1)$ $A(i) \Rightarrow A(i+1)$
       { $\forall$-intro on $(k+1)$ and $(l-1)$: }

(l) $\forall_i[i \in \mathbb{N} : A(i) \Rightarrow A(i+1)]$
     { Induction on (k) and (l): }

(m) $\forall_n[n \in \mathbb{N} : A(n)]$

In the part of the proof which must be filled in the second sequence of dots, between line number $(k+2)$ and line number $(l-2)$, we can *use* that $A(i)$ holds, for the i which is introduced in line number $(k+1)$. This $A(i)$ is called the *induction hypothesis* or the *induction assumption*. The purpose of this second part of the proof is to *prove* that $A(i+1)$ holds if we 'know' that the induction hypothesis $A(i)$ holds.

Note the big difference between the status of $A(i)$ in this proof skeleton ($A(i)$ is an assumption that we may <u>use</u> between lines $(k+2)$ and $(l-2)$), and that of $A(i+1)$ (which we may <u>not use</u> in these lines, because we still have to show it). Those who don't distinguish these two points, will get greatly confused and will probably get lost.

Remark 19.3.2 *The concept of 'induction' comes from the natural sciences: if we observe in an experiment that a certain phenomenon covers a big number of cases, then it is reasonable to conjecture (and this is 'induction') that a pattern is in place. For example, if, for a large number of times, we pick up a stone and then open our hand, and in each case the stone falls* *down and never up; then the conclusion that this stone will* always *fall down is justified ('induction').*

The word *'induction' comes from Latin. 'To induce' means 'to lead to'. And indeed, the observed fact that the stone falls every time when you let it go, leads to the conclusion that the stone shall always fall. Similarly, the truth of the two propositions $A(0)$ and $A(i) \Rightarrow A(i+1)$ (for every i), leads to the conclusion that $A(n)$ must be true for every $n \in \mathbb{N}$.*

As an example, we give an inductive proof of a well known mathematical formula, the *inequality of Bernoulli*, which holds for every chosen real number h (fixed in advance), where h is taken bigger than or equal to -1:

$$\forall_n[n \in \mathbb{N} : (1+h)^n \geq 1+nh] .$$

(We treat in what follows the h as a *constant*.)

The predicate $A(n)$ over which the induction must go, is the formula $(1+h)^n \geq 1+nh$. For this $A(n)$, we must first prove the *basis* $A(0)$ and thereafter the *step* $\forall_i[i \in \mathbb{N} : A(i) \Rightarrow A(i+1)]$:

• The basis is not a problem, because $(1+h)^0 = 1 = 1+0h$, and hence surely $(1+h)^0 \geq 1+0h$. (Indeed, if $a=b$, then it also holds (by the rule $\wedge$-$\vee$-weakening) that $a = b \vee a > b$, i.e. $a \geq b$.)

• The step is not difficult either; it amounts to cleverly applying some basic mathematics.

We give immediately a full proof:

    { Mathematics: }

(1) $(1+h)^0 = 1 = 1+0h$, hence $(1+h)^0 \geq 1+0h$

    { Definition of $A(0)$ on (1): }

(2) $A(0)$

    { Assume: }

(3)   var i; $i \in \mathbb{N}$

      { Assume (induction hypothesis): }

(4) $A(i)$

       { Definition of $A(i)$ on (4): }

(5) $(1+h)^i \geq 1+ih$

(6)   { Mathematics: }

$(1 + h)^{i+1} = (1 + h)^i (1 + h) \geq$ (use (5)) $(1 + ih)(1 + h) =$

$1 + (i + 1)h + ih^2 \geq 1 + (i + 1)h$

{ Hence from this it follows that: }

(7) $(1 + h)^{i+1} \geq 1 + (i + 1)h$

{ From (7), by definition of $A(i + 1)$: }

(8) $A(i + 1)$

{ $\Rightarrow$-intro on (4) and (8): }

(9) $A(i) \Rightarrow A(i + 1)$

{ $\forall$-intro on (3) and (9): }

(10) $\forall_i [i \in \mathbb{N} : A(i) \Rightarrow A(i + 1)]$

{ Induction on (2) and (10): }

(11) $\forall_n [n \in \mathbb{N} : A(n)]$

{ Definition of $A(n)$ on (11): }

(12) $\forall_n [n \in \mathbb{N} : (1 + h)^n \geq 1 + nh]$

We make some remarks on this proof:

– The proof of the 'basis' $A(0)$ finishes in line number (2), and the proof of the 'step' $\forall_i [i \in \mathbb{N} : A(i) \Rightarrow A(i + 1)]$ finishes in line number (10). These together make the conclusion $\forall_n [n \in \mathbb{N} : A(n)]$ which appears in line number (11), possible.

– The proof of the 'step' $\forall_i [i \in \mathbb{N} : A(i) \Rightarrow A(i + 1)]$ begins straightforwardly with $\forall$-intro and $\Rightarrow$-intro.

– In line number (5) we find $(1 + h)^i \geq 1 + ih$. This is a 'translation' of the induction hypothesis $A(i)$ in line number (4). But be careful, this formula holds *only* (see line number (4)) for the i which is introduced in line number (3), and hence not for *every* i, as some casual reader might come to believe. It is hence really important that one delivers a separate proof for the proposition $A(i + 1)$, which is $(1 + h)^{i+1} \geq 1 + (i + 1)h$. This takes place in lines number (6) and (7).

– In line number (6) it is indeed necessary that $h \geq -1$, which we assumed in the beginning as a condition for the inequality of Bernoulli. Hence, because we now have $1 + h \geq 0$, it follows from $(1 + h)^i \geq 1 + ih$ (see line number (5)) that we must also have: $(1 + h)^i (1 + h) \geq (1 + ih)(1 + h)$ (see line number (6)). (If also $h < -1$ was allowed, the last would not follow any more.)

Hence, induction gives us an *extra* possibility to show $\forall_n[n \in \mathbb{N} : A(n)]$, via the 'basis' and the 'step'. But do not forget that the old proof rule '$\forall$-intro' is – also in the case when the domain is $\mathbb{N}$ – still a promising method, which is moreover often much faster.

On the other hand there are many cases of true universal propositions on the domain $\mathbb{N}$ where a proof with the $\forall$-intro-rule will succeed, but will be quite painful. (Try it out with the above example!) And often, the attempt with the $\forall$-intro-rule fails altogether and induction then is the only way. See also the following sections.

Remark 19.3.3 *In proofs by induction, it is not enough to prove the 'step formula'* $\forall_k[k \in \mathbb{N} : A(k) \Rightarrow A(k+1)]$: *we also need a proof of the 'basis formula'* $A(0)$. *Take for example the following predicate:* $A(n) \equiv n < 0$. *Then, it is not very difficult to prove that*

$\forall_k[k \in \mathbb{N} : k < 0 \Rightarrow k+1 < 0]$,

because for $k < 0$ *we may substitute* False *here, from which follows that* $k < 0 \Rightarrow k+1 < 0$ *is equivalent to* True. *From this it follows also that the whole formula is* True.

If however the conclusion $\forall_n[n \in \mathbb{N} : n < 0]$ *is now drawn with an appeal to 'induction', you immediately see that something wrong is going on here. And indeed, this is not a good inductive proof, because the basis formula* $A(0)$ *has not been checked. This is where the situation fails: one cannot find a proof for* $0 < 0$.

In the induction rule that we gave above, the start point is 0: first $A(0)$ must be shown and thereafter $A(i) \Rightarrow A(i+1)$ for every i starting at 0.

It is actually possible to take another start point, for example the start point 2. So we take the 'basis' to be a proof of $A(2)$ and we take the 'step' to be a proof of $A(i) \Rightarrow A(i+1)$ for all $i \geq 2$, and so induction will deliver a proof of $A(n)$ *for all* n *from start point* 2. Intuitively this is quite obvious.

It is also possible to have a start point which is negative, for example -3. The latter appears strange at first sight, because we are no longer dealing with *natural* numbers, but are now using the *whole* numbers. However, a closer look reveals that there is nothing strange about this: the set of all whole numbers bigger than or equal to -3 looks very much like $\mathbb{N}$, only with a *shift* over -3: the start number is -3 and the successor function delivers in this case $s(-3) = -2$, $s(s(-3)) = -1$, $s(s(s(-3))) = 0$, $s(s(s(s(-3)))) = 1$, and so on. Hence $\{n \in \mathbb{Z} | n \geq -3\}$ has the same structure as $\mathbb{N}$.

In this way we can *extend* the proof method of 'induction' by applying it to an arbitrary start point $a \in \mathbb{Z}$.

induction from start point a in $\mathbb{Z}$:

$$\vdots$$

(k) $\quad A(a)$

$$\vdots$$

(l) $\quad \forall_i[i \in \mathbb{Z} \wedge i \geq a : A(i) \Rightarrow A(i+1)]$
$\quad\quad$ { Induction on (k) and (l): }
(m) $\quad \forall_n[n \in \mathbb{Z} \wedge n \geq a : A(n)]$

Remark 19.3.4 *The proof principle that we called* induction *in this section, is also known under different names. Induction as we have described above, is often called 'mathematical induction' in the literature and the term 'complete induction' is reserved for strong induction, see Section 19.5.*

19.4 Inductive definition of sets of numbers

In the *step* of a proof by induction, the *truth* of a proposition is continuously 'passed on', namely from $A(i)$ to $A(i+1)$. Indeed, $A(0)$ implies $A(1)$, and this implies $A(2)$, and this again implies $A(3)$, and so on. This means that if $A(0)$ is itself already true (the *basis*), we can pass this truth to $A(1)$, and this again to $A(2)$, and so on.

Induction – we repeat it once more – takes care of the fact that we can now conclude *in one sweep* the proof of the truth of every $A(n)$.

In the same way, the *construction* of objects in mathematics and computer science is often given by describing how object a_{i+1} can be built from object a_i. As soon as we know what the start object a_0 is, we can with this knowledge construct a_1 and with this construct a_2 and again with this construct a_3 and so on. So doing we can, at least in principle, construct *all* the a_n's. We say that this set of all the a_n's, constructed in this way, is *inductively defined*. This is comparable to how the truth of *all* propositions A_n is *inductively proved* by induction (see the previous section).

Example 19.4.1 *We construct an infinite set of objects $\{a_0, a_1, a_2, \ldots\}$, determined by the following inductive definition:*
$\quad a_0 := 5,$
$\quad a_{i+1} := 2a_i - 4 \ (i \in \mathbb{N}).$
In this definition we see a basis, *giving the value of a_0, and a* step, *which explains how we can get a_{i+1} from a_i: multiply a_i by 2 and subtract 4 from this result.*

With this inductive definition we can construct the a_n's one by one:

$a_0 = 5$ *(basis)*,
$a_1 =$ *(step)* $2a_0 - 4 = 2 \cdot 5 - 4 = 6$,
$a_2 =$ *(step)* $2a_1 - 4 = 2 \cdot 6 - 4 = 8$,
$a_3 = 12$,
$a_4 = 20$,
$a_5 = 36$, ...

Our 'mathematical feeling' says that all the a_n's are tightly constructed by the above definition, at least in principle. No one shall doubt that for example a_{100} or even $a_{1000000}$ will get a certain value by the above definition, the only issue is that it takes effort to calculate these values...

In summary, the above given 'definition by induction' determines the full set of all the a_n's.

Such an inductive definition is often used and it appears in many appli-cations. It will be obvious that propositions over such inductively defined sets are often shown by an inductive *proof.*

For example we look at the above set, with $a_0 = 5$, $a_1 = 6$, $a_2 = 8$, $a_3 = 12$, $a_4 = 20$... . The numbers a_n begin with 5 and continuously get bigger, with repeatedly bigger differences: from a_0 to a_1 the difference is 1, from a_1 to a_2, the difference is 2, from a_2 to a_3 the difference is 4, then 8, then 16... . There is a pattern here. The differences are all powers of 2 where we see that $a_{n+1} - a_n = 2^n$, for every a_n.

How do we prove this? Of course with induction! The predicate over which we will do our induction is $A(n) \equiv (a_{n+1} - a_n = 2^n)$. The core of the induction proof below consists of mathematical calculations, in which we use the inductive definition.

        { Mathematics: }

(1) $a_1 - a_0 = 6 - 5 = 1 = 2^0$

        { Definition of $A(0)$ on (1): }

(2) $A(0)$

        { Assume: }

(3) $\boxed{\underline{\text{var } i};\ i \in \mathbb{N}}$

            { Assume (induction hypothesis): }

            $\boxed{A(i)}$

               { Definition of $A(i)$ on (4): }

(5) $a_{i+1} - a_i = 2^i$

> { Mathematics, use of the definition for a_{i+2} and a_{i+1}: }

(6) $\quad a_{i+2} - a_{i+1} = (2a_{i+1} - 4) - (2a_i - 4) = 2(a_{i+1} - a_i)$

> { From (6), use (5): }

(7) $\quad a_{i+2} - a_{i+1} = 2 \cdot 2^i = 2^{i+1}$

> { Definition of $A(i + 1)$ on (7): }

(8) $\quad A(i + 1)$

> { $\Rightarrow$-intro on (4) and (8): }

(9) $\quad A(i) \Rightarrow A(i + 1)$

> { $\forall$-intro on (3) and (9): }

(10) $\quad \forall_i [i \in \mathbb{N} : A(i) \Rightarrow A(i + 1)]$

> { Induction on (2) and (10): }

(11) $\quad \forall_n [n \in \mathbb{N} : A(n)]$

> { Definition of $A(n)$ on (11): }

(12) $\quad \forall_n [n \in \mathbb{N} : a_{n+1} - a_n = 2^n]$

Note that the observation $a_{i+1} - a_i = 2^i$ *in line number* (5) *only holds for the i which is introduced in line number* (3). *It is a direct consequence of the induction hypothesis $A(i)$ from line number* (4). *The proposition $A(i + 1)$, hence* $a_{i+2} - a_{i+1} = 2^{i+1}$, *must here be proven separately, making use of $A(i)$.*

Sometimes it is possible to replace an inductive definition of a set of the form $\{a_0, a_1, a_2, \ldots\}$ with a so-called *closed formula*, that is, a formula with which an arbitrary a_n can be *directly* calculated, without first calculating all of a_0, a_1, a_2 up to a_{n-1}. Hence, such a closed formula does have neither a 'basis' nor a 'step'.

Those who look at the above sequence: $a_0 = 5$, $a_1 = 6$, $a_2 = 8$, $a_3 = 12$, $a_4 = 20$, $a_5 = 36, \ldots$, will quickly get the idea what the closed formula should be for the above example. Indeed: $5 = 1 + 4$, $6 = 2 + 4$, $8 = 4 + 4$, $12 = 8 + 4$, $20 = 16 + 4$, $36 = 32 + 4$, etc. So, we propose:

$\forall_n [n \in \mathbb{N} : a_n = 2^n + 4]$.

A *proof* of this can obviously be done by induction. (Do it yourself.) Actually, there is here a simple proof which can be given by a simple *calculation*, because for an arbitrary n we have that:

$a_{n+1} - a_n = $ (by the definition) $2a_n - 4 - a_n = a_n - 4$.

By using $\forall$-elim on what we have proved earlier in this section, viz. that $\forall_n[n \in \mathbb{N} : a_{n+1} - a_n = 2^n]$, we get for arbitrary n that $a_n - 4 = 2^n$ holds, hence indeed $\forall_n[n \in \mathbb{N} : a_n = 2^n + 4]$. This latter simply holds by the 'normal' $\forall$-intro (hence induction is not needed).

A closed formula for a_n is of course nicer than an inductive definition of a_n. For example, we can now directly say what a_{100} is, namely: $2^{100} + 4$. However, it is not always possible to find a corresponding closed formula for a given inductively defined set (it is also not possible to replace every inductive proof by a 'normal' $\forall$-intro-proof...).

Remark 19.4.2 *Inductive definitions are also called* recursive *definitions. This latter name is actually mostly used in more general settings, namely when the emphasis is not on the structure of the natural numbers – as above – but on a more general structure with a start value and one* or more *possible successors. The latter is the case for* trees, *where a node can indeed have many branches. See Part I, Section 2.3, for an example of a recursive definition. See also Section 19.6.*

In this chapter we shall always speak of inductive definitions, *even in the latter case.*

19.5   Strong induction

We saw that the 'step' of inductive proofs and inductive definitions consists of the 'passing over' of information from i to $i + 1$, hence from i to its successor. You can also turn this round: in order to know something about the situation for number k, you must have the information about the situation for the *predecessor* $k - 1$. This holds for every $k \in \mathbb{N}$, except for $k = 0$, which does not have any predecessor.

Sometimes, it can be the case that, in order to say something about the situation for k, we do not only need the situation for the *direct* predecessor $k - 1$, but also the situation for more than *one* predecessor of k, for example for both $k - 2$ and $k - 1$. Or even, for *all* the predecessors, from 0 up to and including $k - 1$. Also here it is intuitively 'logical' to obtain a conclusion for all n's by induction.

We make this plausible by looking at the following example, where we have a predicate $A(n)$ for which we know the following: for every step the truth is passed on from *all the predecessors together*. We call the corresponding formula φ:

$\forall_k[k \in \mathbb{N} : \forall_j[j \in \mathbb{N} \land j < k : A(j)] \Rightarrow A(k)]$.

Look at how the parentheses are grouped! Inside the formula φ we have the following subformula:

$\forall_j [j \in \mathbb{N} \land j < k : A(j)] \;\Rightarrow\; A(k)$.

This formula says the following: the truth of all $A(j)$'s together with j smaller than k, so for $0 \leq j < k$, implies the truth of $A(k)$ itself. In other words: the truth of the predicate for *all the predecessors* of k, implies the truth of the predicate for k itself. And this holds (as the formula φ expresses) for *arbitrary* $k \in \mathbb{N}$.

Let us look now at the consequences of formula φ by applying the rule of $\forall$-elimination with different values of k:

$k = 0$ Then $\forall$-elim gives: $\forall_j [j \in \mathbb{N} \land j < 0 : A(j)] \;\Rightarrow\; A(0)$. Now, there are no j's in $\mathbb{N}$ smaller than 0, hence $j \in \mathbb{N} \land j < 0 \overset{val}{=\!=\!=} $ **False**. It holds then that $\forall_j [\textbf{False} : A(j)] \;\Rightarrow\; A(0)$, and hence by the empty domain-rule: **True** $\Rightarrow A(0)$, which can be written as $A(0)$ by Implication and True/False-elimination.

Hence, the 'basis' of the normal induction, $A(0)$, *follows from* the formula φ for $k = 0$!

$k = 1$ Now, $\forall$-elim gives: $\forall_j [j \in \mathbb{N} \land j < 1 : A(j)] \;\Rightarrow\; A(1)$. From the mathematical fact that $j \in \mathbb{N} \land j < 1$ is equal to $j = 0$, together with the One-element rule, it follows that, $A(0) \Rightarrow A(1)$.

This is all similar to the first 'step' of normal induction! Together with $A(0)$ from above, it follows by $\Rightarrow$-elim that also $A(1)$ is true. Hence, $A(1)$ is also a consequence of formula φ.

$k = 2$ We now obtain $\forall_j [j \in \mathbb{N} \land j < 2 : A(j)] \;\Rightarrow\; A(2)$. A combination of mathematics and logic gives that $\forall_j [j \in \mathbb{N} \land j < 2 : A(j)]$ is equal to $A(0) \land A(1)$, and hence in this case we have $(A(0) \land A(1)) \Rightarrow A(2)$.

The second 'step' is in this case a bit more complex than the corresponding second step $A(1) \Rightarrow A(2)$ of the normal induction, but we already expected this. It is however the case that we have just shown that $A(0)$ and $A(1)$ are both consequences of formula φ, hence also $A(0) \land A(1)$ ($\land$-intro), and so from $(A(0) \land A(1)) \Rightarrow A(2)$ we get $A(2)$ ($\Rightarrow$-elim).

$k = 3$ The same reasoning says that $\forall_j [j \in \mathbb{N} \land j < 3 : A(j)] \;\Rightarrow\; A(3)$ is equal to $(A(0) \land A(1) \land A(2)) \Rightarrow A(3)$, from which together with the above we get that $A(3)$ is true by $\Rightarrow$-elim.

And in this manner we can continue. To summarize:

– First of all, we have that $A(0)$ is true,
– then by $A(0) \Rightarrow A(1)$, we have that $A(1)$ is true,

 – then by $(A(0) \wedge A(1)) \Rightarrow A(2)$, we have that $A(2)$ is true,
 – then by $(A(0) \wedge A(1) \wedge A(2)) \Rightarrow A(3)$, we have that $A(3)$ is true, and
so on.

 And so it is intuitively obvious that we can show, one by one, that *every* $A(n)$ is true. But we still do not have any proof *for all $n \in \mathbb{N}$ together*, because such a thing – just as in the normal induction – needs infinitely many steps. Despite this, it is reasonable to conclude from formula φ that $\forall_n[n \in \mathbb{N} : A(n)]$ holds. This is *induction* too. To distinguish it from the induction of Section 19.3, we will in this case speak of *strong induction*:

strong induction:

$$\vdots$$

(l) $\forall_k[k \in \mathbb{N} : \forall_j[j \in \mathbb{N} \wedge j < k : A(j)] \Rightarrow A(k)]$
    { Strong induction on (l): }
(m) $\forall_n[n \in \mathbb{N} : A(n)]$

 The proof which must be filled where the dots occur, will usually go in the standard way by the rules $\forall$-intro and $\Rightarrow$-intro, hence in the form as it appears in the following scheme.

     { Assume: }
(1) $\boxed{\text{var } k;\ k \in \mathbb{N}}$

      { Assume (induction hypothesis):}
(2) $\boxed{\forall_j[j \in \mathbb{N} \wedge j < k : A(j)]}$

       $\vdots$

$(l-2)$ $A(k)$
      { $\Rightarrow$-intro on (2) and $(l-2)$: }
$(l-1)$ $\forall_j[j \in \mathbb{N} \wedge j < k : A(j)] \Rightarrow A(k)$
     { $\forall$-intro on (1) and $(l-1)$: }
(l) $\forall_k[k \in \mathbb{N} : \forall_j[j \in \mathbb{N} \wedge j < k : A(j)] \Rightarrow A(k)]$
     { Strong induction on (l): }
(m) $\forall_n[n \in \mathbb{N} : A(n)]$

Remark 19.5.1 *In a proof with strong induction, the induction hypothesis is stronger than that in a proof with 'normal' induction. See line number (2)*

in the figure below: $\forall_j [j \in \mathbb{N} \wedge j < k : A(j)]$. *From this induction hypothesis it follows by $\forall$-elim that $A(j)$ can be used for* every *predecessor j of k, in the part of the proof which still needs to be delivered. This gives more possibilities than in the normal induction, where only the* direct *predecessor is considered, and hence an appeal can be made only on $A(k-1)$.*

Just like a proof by strong induction passes on the *truth* from *more than one*, or even from *all the predecessors*, so also *definition* by strong induction is possible. For the latter, the *construction* is passed on in the same way, the k-th element is built with the help of *a number* of already constructed elements, possibly with the help of *all* of them.

If we want to prove a property for a set which is defined by strong induction, then the proof will often also be by strong induction.

For example, let us look at an infinite set $\{a_0, a_1, a_2, \ldots\}$ of whole numbers. This set, also denoted by $\{a_n | n \in \mathbb{N}\}$, is defined by:

$a_0 := 0$,
$a_1 := 1$,
$a_{i+2} := 3a_{i+1} - 2a_i \ (i \in \mathbb{N})$.

This is defined by *strong induction* because, for the construction of a_{i+2} not only is the direct predecessor a_{i+1} needed, but also its (second) predecessor a_i. For this reason, we need at the start not only the definition of a_0, but also that of a_1. Otherwise we cannot get started!

We first calculate some elements:

$a_0 = 0$ (basis),
$a_1 = 1$ (second basis),
$a_2 =$ (step) $3 \cdot 1 - 2 \cdot 0 = 3$,
$a_3 =$ (step) $3 \cdot 3 - 2 \cdot 1 = 7$,
$a_4 =$ (step) $3 \cdot 7 - 2 \cdot 3 = 15$,
$a_5 = 31$, ...

These numbers are always just *one* less than the power of two, and so we conjecture that for each a_n, there is also a closed formula, namely: $a_n = 2^n - 1$, for all $n \in \mathbb{N}$. We will prove this by strong induction according to the scheme given before. As predicate $A(n)$ we take $a_n = 2^n - 1$. We must hence show that, under the induction hypothesis $\forall_j [j \in \mathbb{N} \wedge j < k : A(j)]$, it holds that $A(k)$, i.e. that $a_k = 2^k - 1$. In order to use the induction hypothesis, we need to replace a_k by *one or more* a_j's with $j < k$. This can be done by the third definition line, which says that $a_{i+2} = 3a_{i+1} - 2a_i$. Hence $a_k = 3a_{k-1} - 2a_{k-2}$. *This latter can only be acceptable if $k \geq 2$!* For this reason we must look at the cases $k = 0$ and $k = 1$ separately. See the following proof. (Comments about the reasoning in line (5) are written below the proof.)

$\{$ Assume: $\}$

(1) $\boxed{\text{var } k; \; k \in \mathbb{N}}$

$\{$ Assume (induction hypothesis): $\}$

(2) $\boxed{\forall_j[j \in \mathbb{N} \land j < k : A(j)]}$

$\{$ Case $k = 0$: $\}$

(3) $a_0 = 0 = 2^0 - 1$, hence $A(0)$ holds.

$\{$ Case $k = 1$: $\}$

(4) $a_1 = 1 = 2^1 - 1$, hence $A(1)$ holds.

$\{$ Case $k \geq 2$: $\}$

(5) $a_k = 3a_{k-1} - 2a_{k-2} =$

$\{$ $\forall$-elim on induction hyp. (2), for $j = k - 1$ and $k - 2$: $\}$

$3(2^{k-1} - 1) - 2(2^{k-2} - 1) = 3 \cdot 2^{k-1} - 3 - 2 \cdot 2^{k-2} + 2 =$

$(6 - 2)2^{k-2} - 1 = 2^k - 1$, hence $A(k)$ holds.

$\{$ So whatever k is: 0, 1 or bigger, we have: $\}$

(6) $A(k)$

$\{$ $\Rightarrow$-intro on (2) and (6): $\}$

(7) $\forall_j[j \in \mathbb{N} \land j < k : A(j)] \; \Rightarrow \; A(k)$

$\{$ $\forall$-intro on (1) and (7): $\}$

(8) $\forall_k[k \in \mathbb{N} : \forall_j[j \in \mathbb{N} \land j < k : A(j)] \; \Rightarrow \; A(k)]$

$\{$ Strong induction on (8): $\}$

(9) $\forall_n[n \in \mathbb{N} : A(n)]$

$\{$ Definition of $A(n)$: $\}$

(10) $\forall_n[n \in \mathbb{N} : a_n = 2^n - 1]$

In line number (5) we used the induction hypothesis twice, namely to apply $\forall$-elim to line number (2) with $k - 1$ for j respectively $k - 2$ for j. (This is acceptable, because both $k - 1$ and $k - 2$ are smaller than k.) This delivers the truth of $A(k - 1)$ resp. $A(k - 2)$ and hence we may employ that both $a_{k-1} = 2^{k-1} - 1$ and $a_{k-2} = 2^{k-2} - 1$.

Also for strong induction there are versions with other start points than 0, for example $a \in \mathbb{Z}$. The formulas are then a bit more complicated:

strong induction from start point a in $\mathbb{Z}$:

$$\vdots$$

(l) $\forall_k[k \in \mathbb{Z} \wedge k \geq a : \forall_j[j \in \mathbb{Z} \wedge a \leq j < k : A(j)] \Rightarrow A(k)]$

   { Strong induction on (l): }

(m) $\forall_n[n \in \mathbb{Z} \wedge n \geq a : A(n)]$

Here, k begins from start point $a \in \mathbb{Z}$. The corresponding induction hypothesis is that $A(j)$ holds for all predecessors of k in $\mathbb{Z}$ *which are greater than or equal to a.* Then, also the final conclusion holds for all n from a.

Remark 19.5.2 *(1) Although it may appear that strong induction is a stronger method than 'normal' induction, this is really not the case: everything which can be shown with strong induction can also be shown with normal induction. It is however the case that a proof with strong induction may be much shorter than (and different from) one with normal induction. (Also the opposite is possible!) Hence, it remains advisable to choose the 'appropriate' method, provided that it is possible to assess beforehand which is the shorter or more convenient.*

(2) 'Strong induction' is also called 'complete induction', and sometimes 'course-of-values induction'. The latter is a literal translation from German, where it is called 'Wertverlaufsinduktion'. With this course of values you can think of how the True*-values of the propositions $A(n)$ go from small n to big n, and similarly, how the construction of the elements a_n is passed on.*

19.6 Inductive definition of sets of formulas

In the previous two sections, we came across sets that were built inductively: after the definition of *one* or more start values (the 'basis'), a process was given in order to build the others (via the 'step'). With such an inductive definition, a set of numbers can for example be constructed, as we saw in the previous section. The proof of a property of such a set is then mostly by induction (either strong or normal).

An inductive definition can also deliver a set of formulas, as in Section 2.3. There, we gave an inductive (or recursive) definition of the set of all abstract propositions. Recall that this set contained for example the propositions a and $((a \land b) \Rightarrow (\neg c))$.

In general, an inductive definition of a set $\mathcal{F}$ of formulas looks as follows:
- There is a number of 'basis cases', where concrete formulas are indicated which certainly belong to $\mathcal{F}$.
- Next there is a number of 'step cases' which say how 'new' formulas of $\mathcal{F}$ can be built from one or more 'old' formulas of $\mathcal{F}$.

We give some examples of inductively defined sets.

Example 19.6.1 Abstract propositions. *The set $\mathcal{P}$ of abstract propositions – see Definition 2.3.1 and Definition 4.3.1 – is given by the following inductive definition:*

- Basis:
    - case 1: Every proposition variable (like a, b and c) is an element of the set $\mathcal{P}$.
        - case 2: True $\in \mathcal{P}$, False $\in \mathcal{P}$.
- Step:
    - case 1: if $P \in \mathcal{P}$, then $(\neg P) \in \mathcal{P}$.
    - case 2a: if $P \in \mathcal{P}$ and $Q \in \mathcal{P}$, then $(P \land Q) \in \mathcal{P}$.
    - case 2b: if $P \in \mathcal{P}$ and $Q \in \mathcal{P}$, then $(P \lor Q) \in \mathcal{P}$.
    - case 2c: if $P \in \mathcal{P}$ and $Q \in \mathcal{P}$, then $(P \Rightarrow Q) \in \mathcal{P}$.
    - case 2d: if $P \in \mathcal{P}$ and $Q \in \mathcal{P}$, then $(P \Leftrightarrow Q) \in \mathcal{P}$.

Example 19.6.2 Parentheses formulas. *We understand by parentheses formulas, all the formulas which consist of only opening parentheses and closing parentheses, but such that these parentheses appear in pairs: with every opening parenthesis there corresponds exactly one closing parenthesis, and vice versa. (In such a pair, the opening parenthesis must always appear before the closing parenthesis).*

Here are some examples which give an idea of what we mean:
$(), (()), ()(), (()()), (()())((())()).$

Here are some examples of formulas which are not parentheses formulas:
$)(, ()), ((), ())(()),)$.

We also add the empty *formula to the set of parentheses formulas. This has hence 0 opening parenthesis and 0 closing parentheses. Because this empty formula is actually 'invisible', we introduce a special symbol for it, viz. ε.*

The set $\mathcal{H}$ of this kind of parentheses formulas can be inductively defined as follows:
- Basis: $\varepsilon \in \mathcal{H}$.

- Step:
    - case 1: if $h \in \mathcal{H}$, then $(h) \in \mathcal{H}$.
    - case 2: if $h_1 \in \mathcal{H}$ and $h_2 \in \mathcal{H}$, then $h_1 h_2 \in \mathcal{H}$.

Here we must read $h_1 h_2$ as: write down formula h_1 and immediately thereafter formula h_2. (This process is called concatenation, from the Latin word con, 'together', and catenare, 'to chain'. The h_1 and the h_2 are hence 'chained together'.)

Remark 19.6.3 *The process of constructing a formula by an inductive definition, can often be illustrated by building a* construction tree. *For the example above,* $(()()())((())())$, *the construction tree looks as follows:*

$$\frac{\varepsilon}{()}1 \quad \frac{\varepsilon}{()}1 \\ \frac{}{()()}2 \quad \frac{\varepsilon}{()}1 \\ \frac{}{()()}2 \\ \frac{}{()()()}1 \quad \frac{\varepsilon}{()}1 \quad \frac{\varepsilon}{()}1 \\ \frac{}{(())}1 \quad \frac{\varepsilon}{()}1 \\ \frac{}{(())()}2 \\ \frac{}{((())())}2 \\ \frac{}{(()()())((())())}$$

Verify that this is indeed a construction tree, comparable for example to that of Section 2.4. It is only drawn differently: instead of the nodes, we have parentheses formulas *(which are actually the labels of the nodes) and instead of the branches we have here horizontal lines, followed by a number (1 or 2). Moreover, the tree is standing 'upside down'. Compare this tree with that of Section 2.4.*

From the construction tree, we can read from top to bottom, how the formula in question is built, starting with (a number of) ε's (this is allowed by the Basis) *and then applying step a number of times. (In the last case the 1 and 2 next to the horizontal line, mean that we are dealing with either case 1 or with case 2.) But also, by reading from bottom to top, we can see how the formula can be continuously 'parsed' into smaller pieces until we reach the 'basis parts' (here always ε).*

Finally, a question for the connoisseur: does the above diagram give the only possibility for a construction tree of $(()()())((())())$?

Example 19.6.4 Natural numbers. *In Section 19.2 we looked at the structure of the natural numbers, $\langle \mathbb{N}, 0, s \rangle$. The formula set that we used there – and which we call here $\mathcal{N}$ – has a simple inductive definition:*

- Basis: $0 \in \mathcal{N}$.
- Step: if $\varphi \in \mathcal{N}$, then $s(\varphi) \in \mathcal{N}$.

It will be obvious that the corresponding set $\mathcal{N}$ consists of the formulas: $0, s(0), s(s(0)), s(s(s(0))), \dots$.

19.7 Structural induction

The proofs of properties of inductively defined sets or formulas go by a form of induction which is usually more complex than 'normal' or strong induction, namely the so-called *structural induction*. Also for structural induction, it usually holds that the inductive definition is closely followed. We give illustrative examples below.

The first example that we give here concerns $\mathcal{H}$, the set of all parentheses formulas. We shall prove for this set that:

Every formula in $\mathcal{H}$ has the property that the number of opening parentheses is equal to the number of closing parentheses.

First note that we are not giving the proof of this proposition because we doubt it – as a matter of fact it is obvious that every $\varphi \in \mathcal{H}$ has this property. The main reason why we nevertheless give the proof is that we want to show how structural induction works.

Next, note that the proof below is given in compact form, without flags and the like; hence we deviate here from the general format employed in this book. We do this for two reasons:

(1) We are only interested in making the *idea* of structural induction clear.

(2) The format without flags and flagpoles is the usual manner to give proofs in the mathematical literature; so this is a good occasion to get acquainted with the style of proofs you find in books on mathematics and computer science.

Proof of the lemma (by structural induction):

We consider an arbitrary φ which we know to be in $\mathcal{H}$. The conclusion that $\varphi \in \mathcal{H}$, is derived from the inductive definition of $\mathcal{H}$ (see the previous section). We look now at what the *last* step was according to this definition. For this there are different possibilities:

• The final conclusion $\varphi \in \mathcal{H}$ comes from the *Basis:* $\varepsilon \in \mathcal{H}$.

Then we must have $\varphi \equiv \varepsilon$.

Because ε is the empty parentheses formula, with no single opening or closing parenthesis, the property holds for this basis case: φ has as many opening as closing parentheses (namely 0).

• The final conclusion $\varphi \in \mathcal{H}$ comes from *Step*. Then there are two possibilities:

  – *case 1:* $\varphi \in \mathcal{H}$ by the rule: *if $h \in \mathcal{H}$, then $(h) \in \mathcal{H}$.*

Hence $\varphi \equiv (h)$ for some h for which we knew already that $h \in \mathcal{H}$.

According to the *induction hypothesis* h has as many opening as closing parentheses (the formula h is constructed 'earlier' than the formula φ (which is (h) in this case) and the main point of structural induction is that we can assume that formulas which are constructed 'earlier' already have the desired properties).

But if there are in h as many opening as closing parentheses, say k of each, then this also holds for (h): it must have $k+1$ of each. So also φ has the property.

    – *case 2:* $\varphi \in \mathcal{H}$ by the rule: *if $h_1 \in \mathcal{H}$ and $h_2 \in \mathcal{H}$, then $h_1 h_2 \in \mathcal{H}$.* Then $\varphi \equiv h_1 h_2$ and we knew already that both $h_1 \in \mathcal{H}$ and $h_2 \in \mathcal{H}$.

According to the *induction hypothesis* we now have: h_1 has as many opening as closing parentheses, say m of each, and also h_2 has as many opening as closing parentheses, say n of each. (Again: this induction hypothesis is characteristic for structural induction, both h_1 and h_2 are constructed 'earlier' than φ (which in this case is $h_1 h_2$), hence we can already assume the property for both h_1 and h_2.)

But then $h_1 h_2$ has $m+n$ opening parenthesis and also $m+n$ closing parentheses, and so also φ has the property.

And so we are done. The (unique) basis case was trivial, and in the two step cases we saw how the property *has-as-many-opening-as-closing-parentheses* was passed on from earlier constructed formulas to later constructed ones (from the 'if'-side of the inductive definition to the 'then'-side).

As a second example, we start with $\mathcal{P}$, the set of all abstract propositions. What we will prove is the following simple lemma: if $\varphi \in \mathcal{P}$, and if we remove from φ everything which is not a parenthesis, then we get a pure parentheses formula, hence a formula in $\mathcal{H}$. Taking for example the abstract proposition $((a \lor \mathbf{True}) \Rightarrow (\neg(a \land b) \lor b))$, we get the parentheses formula $(()(()))$.

We *prove* this in order get more acquainted with the method of structural induction.

We first introduce a useful notation: if φ is an abstract proposition, then $\overline{\varphi}$ is the corresponding parentheses formula, so for example:

$$\overline{((a \lor \mathbf{True}) \Rightarrow (\neg(a \land b) \lor b))} \equiv (()(())).$$

The lemma that will be shown now is the following:
Every $\varphi \in \mathcal{P}$ has the property that $\overline{\varphi} \in \mathcal{H}$.

Once more, we give here a *proof by structural induction*, again in compact form:

- *Basis:*
    – *case 1:* φ is a proposition variable (for example a).
Then $\overline{\varphi} \equiv \varepsilon \in \mathcal{H}$.
    – *case 2:* $\varphi \equiv \mathbf{True}$ or $\mathbf{False}$.
Then: $\overline{\varphi} \equiv \varepsilon \in \mathcal{H}$.

- *Step:*
  - *case 1:* $\varphi \equiv (\neg P)$ and we know: $(\neg P) \in \mathcal{P}$ by the fact that $P \in \mathcal{P}$.

  This means that the abstract proposition P was constructed 'earlier'.

  Then from the *induction hypothesis* it follows that $\overline{P} \in \mathcal{H}$ (for P the property already holds). It can be easily seen that $\overline{(\neg P)} \equiv (\overline{P})$ (the '$\neg$' sign is thrown out, because it is not a parenthesis), hence $\overline{\varphi} \equiv \overline{(\neg P)} \equiv (\overline{P}) \in \mathcal{H}$ (the last comes from *step, case 1*, of the definition of $\mathcal{H}$ which says: if $\overline{P} \in \mathcal{H}$ then so is $(\overline{P}) \in \mathcal{H}$).

  - *case 2a:* $\varphi \equiv (P \wedge Q)$ and $(P \wedge Q) \in \mathcal{P}$ by the fact that $P \in \mathcal{P}$ and $Q \in \mathcal{P}$.

  From the *induction hypothesis* it now follows that both $\overline{P} \in \mathcal{H}$ and $\overline{Q} \in \mathcal{H}$.

  Now we have $\overline{(P \wedge Q)} \equiv (\overline{P}\,\overline{Q})$ (the '$\wedge$' disappears), hence it follows that: $\overline{\varphi} \equiv \overline{(P \wedge Q)} \equiv (\overline{P}\,\overline{Q}) \in \mathcal{H}$.

  This latter statement $(\overline{P}\,\overline{Q}) \in \mathcal{H}$ follows from *step, case 2* and *case 1* of the definition of $\mathcal{H}$ as follows: because both $\overline{P} \in \mathcal{H}$ and $\overline{Q} \in \mathcal{H}$, then (by *case 2:*) $\overline{P}\,\overline{Q} \in \mathcal{H}$, and hence (by *case 1:*) $(\overline{P}\,\overline{Q}) \in \mathcal{H}$.

  - *cases 2b, 2c and 2d:* are similar to *case 2a*.

It is useful to study the above proof in two ways: not only in detail (how does all the 'technicality' fit together), but also the general lines. With respect to this latter: look in particular at how the desired property
- is first studied for the basis cases (and apparently holds there),
- and then for the different steps, where the property is *passed on* (for example from P and Q to $(P \wedge Q)$). Especially this last idea is important, it is the fundamental principle for the concept of 'induction' as we have seen in the earlier sections.

Inductive definitions are also given for sets or other objects than numbers or formulas, for example for tree shaped mathematical objects or for derivations (in logic). We will not go into this here.

The induction proofs which are applicable on such sets, can be based on either normal or strong induction, but also equally well on the above called structural induction. The knowledge that we have built in the previous sections and in this one, will be enough to enable us to deliver and understand inductive proofs even in more complex situations.

19.8 Cardinality

In this section we go back to the basis of the natural numbers, *counting*. The process of counting gives actually a *ranking order* between the counted objects: when you are counting a set ('one, two, three, ...') you actually say: 'this is the first, this is the second, this is the third, ...'. You only know that a certain object is the eighty-third, if you first know what the eighty-second is. Hence, the *successor relation* plays an important role in counting: after the 82nd comes the 83rd.

The different induction principles which we described in the previous sections, are related to this successor relation. This was very clear when we described induction as a formalization of the passing on of a proof or a construction. In fact, this passing on always happens with respect *to a successor*, for example from i to the successor $i+1$ in the 'normal' induction, or from the set $\{0, 1, \ldots, j - 1\}$ to the successor j in strong induction.

Looked at in this way, the set of the natural numbers is nothing else than *a sequence of successors*, where the *ordering* 'first the first, then the second, thereafter the third, ...' is essential. To be precise, we begin with the 'zero'th'. The natural numbers following this conception, form the initial part of the so-called *ordinal numbers*. The actual theory of the ordinal numbers adds the 'infinite' (written as ω, and pronounced: omega) to the natural numbers, and then continues counting thereafter, so altogether we get: 1, 2, 3, ..., ω, $\omega + 1$, $\omega + 2$, ..., 2ω, $2\omega + 1$, ...

Counting can also serve another goal, namely not to know *how many* elements a set has, but to know if *two* sets have *as many* (or the same number of) elements. In the latter case we first count the first set and then the other. If the counting in both cases delivers the same number, then the sets are of the same size; otherwise they are not.

But in order to know whether two sets have the same number of elements (are 'of the same size'), counting is not necessary! It is equally trustworthy to state that there is a *bijection* between the sets. This has nothing to do with counting, it is purely concerned with sets and functions (like those of the earlier chapters).

Example 19.8.1

- *Assume that in a ballroom there are two groups of people: A group W which only consists of women and a group M which only consists of men. In order to know if these groups are of the same size, it is enough to ask every woman to choose one man. If by doing so, we get a new group which only consists of pairs then W and M are of the same size. If this is not the case (this means, if there is still at least one single man who has not been asked, or there is still at least one single woman which could not find a man), then the sets W and M are not of the same size.*

- *Look at the sets $\{5, 10, 15, \ldots, 155\}$ and $\{10, 20, 30, \ldots, 310\}$. These sets are of the same size, because there is a bijection between them, namely with the function f where $f(n) = 2n$.*

Note that in both examples it is unnecessary to really count the sets!

Instead of 'of the same size' one also says: *they have the same cardinality* or *they are equinumerous*. We can hence give the following definition:

Two sets V and W have the *same cardinality* (or are *equinumerous*) if there is a bijection between V and W.

We use the symbol $\sim$ to denote the relation 'have the same cardinality' (or 'are equinumerous'). Note that $\sim$ has the properties of an equivalence relation:

– *Reflexivity:* for all V we have $V \sim V$.
– *Symmetry:* for all V and W we have: if $V \sim W$, then $W \sim V$.
– *Transitivity:* for all V, W and X we have: if $V \sim W$ and $W \sim X$, then $V \sim X$.

This follows from the fact that bijectivity is reflexive, symmetric and transitive. (Check it out.)

We can now give a simple definition of what a finite set is: a set V is *finite* if V has the same cardinality as the set $\{0, 1, 2, ..., n\}$, for some $n \in \mathbb{N}$. In this case, the *number of elements* of V (or its *cardinality*) is $n + 1$.

For example, $\{\clubsuit, \diamondsuit, \heartsuit, \spadesuit\}$ is finite, because $\{\clubsuit, \diamondsuit, \heartsuit, \spadesuit\} \sim \{0, 1, 2, 3\}$. The number of its elements is $3 + 1 = 4$. Another example: the set V of the even natural numbers smaller than 40 is finite, because $V \sim \{0, 1, \ldots, 19\}$. This set has 20 elements.

19.9   Denumerability

You can also apply the concept 'are equinumerous' (or 'have the same cardinality') to *infinite* sets, but this gives unexpected results. And in this case, it is no longer clear that 'have the same cardinality' is a formalization of 'being-of-the-same-size'.

Look for example at $\mathbb{N}$ (all natural numbers, including 0) and $\mathbb{N}^+$ (all *positive* natural numbers, hence without the 0). Are these 'of the same size'? You would probably say: no, because $\mathbb{N}^+$ is a *strict* subset of $\mathbb{N}$, in fact $0 \in \mathbb{N}$ but $0 \notin \mathbb{N}^+$.

However, this is only one side of the story. Because $\mathbb{N}$ really *has the same cardinality* as $\mathbb{N}^+$, via the bijection f where $f(n) = n + 1$. Hence the elements of $\mathbb{N}$ and $\mathbb{N}^+$ can be paired together *without any one remaining unpaired*. Everything you can do with $\mathbb{N}$, you can also, in principle, do with $\mathbb{N}^+$, by just reading 1 as 0, and 2 as 1, and so on... Induction, for example, can be treated equally well with $\mathbb{N}^+$ as with $\mathbb{N}$ (that is induction from start point 1 instead of 0).

So, you may think that the intuitive concept 'being-of-the-same-size' does not apply as it is to infinite sets. However, 'having the same cardinality' is the best approximation to 'being-of-the-same-size', we cannot do better.

In the rest of this section, we will look further into sets which have the same cardinality as $\mathbb{N}$. There are surprising cases here! In the next section we will discuss whether *all* infinite sets have the same cardinality (hence are 'of the same size as' $\mathbb{N}$), or whether there are 'even bigger' infinite sets.

A set V which has the same cardinality as $\mathbb{N}$, is *infinitely countable* or *denumerable*. A counting or an *enumeration* of V is a bijection f from $\mathbb{N}$ to V. (By this enumeration f we can actually *count* or *enumerate* the elements of V, by *listing them*: $0 \mapsto f(0)$, $1 \mapsto f(1)$, $2 \mapsto f(2)$, in such a way that eventually $V = \{f(0), f(1), f(2), \ldots\}$.)

In order to show that V is denumerable, we can

– give a bijection from $\mathbb{N}$ to V (and show that this mapping is indeed a bijection),

or, because being equinumerous is symmetric:

– give a bijection from V to $\mathbb{N}$ (and show that this mapping is a bijection),

Examples of denumerable sets include:

– $\mathbb{N}^+$. We already saw that $\mathbb{N}$ has the same cardinality as $\mathbb{N}^+$.

– $\{n \in \mathbb{N} \mid n$ is even$\}$. The mapping f where $f(n) = 2n$ is a bijection from $\mathbb{N}$ to this set of the *even* natural numbers.

– $\mathbb{Z}$. Also $\mathbb{Z}$ has the same power as $\mathbb{N}$! A bijection $f : \mathbb{N} \to \mathbb{Z}$ is for example:

$$f(n) = \begin{cases} -\frac{1}{2}n & \text{if } n \text{ is even} \\ \frac{1}{2}(n+1) & \text{if } n \text{ is odd} \end{cases}$$

This bijection does the following:

n	0	1	2	3	4	5	6	...
$f(n)$	0	1	-1	2	-2	3	-3	...

– $\mathbb{N}^2$. We recall that $\mathbb{N}^2$ consists of all *pairs* of natural numbers. This set has the same power as $\mathbb{N}$ itself! In order to show this, we give an enumeration. For this, we first systematically write the elements of $\mathbb{N}^2$ as an infinite *matrix*: see the top of the following page.

Then, we will *enumerate* or *list* the elements of this matrix. Of course we must do this in a suitable way. If we start with the first row,

$0 \mapsto (0,0)$, $1 \mapsto (0,1)$, $2 \mapsto (0,2)$, ... ,

then we never reach the second row, neither the third, nor the fourth... The same also holds if we start with the first *column*. So in both cases the mapping is not a bijection (because it is not a *surjection*).

$$
\begin{array}{llllll}
(0,0) & (0,1) & (0,2) & (0,3) & (0,4) & \ldots \\
(1,0) & (1,1) & (1,2) & (1,3) & (1,4) & \ldots \\
(2,0) & (2,1) & (2,2) & (2,3) & (2,4) & \ldots \\
(3,0) & (3,1) & (3,2) & (3,3) & (3,4) & \ldots \\
(4,0) & (4,1) & (4,2) & (4,3) & (4,4) & \ldots \\
\vdots & \vdots & \vdots & \vdots & \vdots & \ddots
\end{array}
$$

But, if we list the elements in a more suitable way, we do indeed get a bijection! The trick is to list the elements *diagonally*, for example in the following direction (start with the top left):

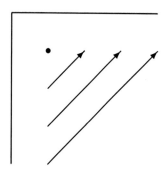

So, the listing of $\mathbb{N}^2$ is as follows:

$0 \mapsto (0,0)$	$2 \mapsto (0,1)$	$5 \mapsto (0,2)$	$9 \mapsto (0,3)$	$14 \mapsto (0,4)$	$\vdots \cdots$
$1 \mapsto (1,0)$	$4 \mapsto (1,1)$	$8 \mapsto (1,2)$	$13 \mapsto (1,3)$	$\vdots \cdots$	
$3 \mapsto (2,0)$	$7 \mapsto (2,1)$	$12 \mapsto (2,2)$	$\vdots \cdots$		
$6 \mapsto (3,0)$	$11 \mapsto (3,1)$	$\vdots \cdots$			
$10 \mapsto (4,0)$	$\vdots \cdots$				
$\vdots \cdots$					

It will be obvious that by doing so, we get a bijection from $\mathbb{N}$ to $\mathbb{N}^2$. (Can you find a formula which describes this mapping?)

— What about $\mathbb{Q}$, the set of all rational numbers? Although you may not expect it: this set is also denumerable! In order to show this we first give a listing of $\mathbb{Q}^+$, the set of the *positive* rationals. We arrange these rationals in a matrix, just as we have done with $\mathbb{N}^2$:

$$
\begin{array}{ccccccc}
\frac{1}{1} & \frac{1}{2} & \frac{1}{3} & \frac{1}{4} & \frac{1}{5} & \cdots \\[4pt]
\frac{2}{1} & \frac{2}{2} & \frac{2}{3} & \frac{2}{4} & \frac{2}{5} & \cdots \\[4pt]
\frac{3}{1} & \frac{3}{2} & \frac{3}{3} & \frac{3}{4} & \frac{3}{5} & \cdots \\[4pt]
\frac{4}{1} & \frac{4}{2} & \frac{4}{3} & \frac{4}{4} & \frac{4}{5} & \cdots \\[4pt]
\frac{5}{1} & \frac{5}{2} & \frac{5}{3} & \frac{5}{4} & \frac{5}{5} & \cdots \\[4pt]
\vdots & \vdots & \vdots & \vdots & \vdots & \vdots
\end{array}
$$

It is not difficult to see that *every* positive rational in the matrix can be located: the rational $\frac{m}{n}$ (where m and $n \in \mathbb{N}^+$) is situated at the meeting point of *row* m and *column* n. There is obviously a problem, namely that the same rational number appears in many places of the matrix. For example: $\frac{1}{2}$ is the same as $\frac{2}{4}$, $\frac{3}{6}$, and so on, and hence appears in many places in the matrix.

We solve this by forbidding all the fractions whose numerators and denominators have a common divisor other than 1. So for example we throw out $\frac{2}{4}$, $\frac{3}{6}$, and so on, and many more. We only allow those fractions whose numerators and denominators do not have any other positive common divisor than the number 1.

The matrix is now as follows:

$$
\begin{array}{ccccccc}
\frac{1}{1} & \frac{1}{2} & \frac{1}{3} & \frac{1}{4} & \frac{1}{5} & \cdots \\[4pt]
\frac{2}{1} & \times & \frac{2}{3} & \times & \frac{2}{5} & \cdots \\[4pt]
\frac{3}{1} & \frac{3}{2} & \times & \frac{3}{4} & \frac{3}{5} & \cdots \\[4pt]
\frac{4}{1} & \times & \frac{4}{3} & \times & \frac{4}{5} & \cdots \\[4pt]
\frac{5}{1} & \frac{5}{2} & \frac{5}{3} & \frac{5}{4} & \times & \cdots \\[4pt]
\vdots & \vdots & \vdots & \vdots & \vdots & \vdots
\end{array}
$$

Next, we list the elements of this matrix, in the same way as we did for $\mathbb{N}^2$, only now we will ignore the crosses:

$0 \mapsto \frac{1}{1}$	$2 \mapsto \frac{1}{2}$	$4 \mapsto \frac{1}{3}$	$8 \mapsto \frac{1}{4}$	$10 \mapsto \frac{1}{5}$	$\cdots$
$1 \mapsto \frac{2}{1}$	$\times$	$7 \mapsto \frac{2}{3}$	$\times$	$15 \mapsto \frac{2}{5}$	$\cdots$
$3 \mapsto \frac{3}{1}$	$6 \mapsto \frac{3}{2}$	$\times$	$14 \mapsto \frac{3}{4}$	$19 \mapsto \frac{3}{5}$	$\cdots$
$5 \mapsto \frac{4}{1}$	$\times$	$13 \mapsto \frac{4}{3}$	$\times$	$24 \mapsto \frac{4}{5}$	$\cdots$
$9 \mapsto \frac{5}{1}$	$12 \mapsto \frac{5}{2}$	$18 \mapsto \frac{5}{3}$	$23 \mapsto \frac{5}{4}$	$\times$	$\cdots$
$\vdots$	$\vdots$	$\vdots$	$\vdots$	$\vdots$	$\cdots$

And in this way, we get indeed an enumeration of $\mathbb{Q}^+$, which means a bijection f from $\mathbb{N}$ to $\mathbb{Q}^+$. However, it is not possible in this case to find a *formula* for the mapping f. This is not a problem, however, we defined the above mapping f precisely enough: for *every* $n \in \mathbb{N}$ it is clear how to calculate what $f(n)$ is, by expanding the matrix as far as needed!

Now that we have an enumeration of $\mathbb{Q}^+$, it is not difficult to figure out how we can use it to build an enumeration of $\mathbb{Q}$. And so, we have shown that also $\mathbb{Q}$ is denumerable.

—   Let V and W be both denumerable. Figure out (using the above) how you can now show that the Cartesian product $V \times W$ is also denumerable.

—   Do the same for the n-fold Cartesian product $V_1 \times V_2 \times \ldots \times V_n$, assuming that all of $V_1, V_2, \ldots, V_n$ are denumerable.

—   Take $\mathbb{Z}^2$, $\mathbb{Q}^2$, $\mathbb{N}^3$, $\mathbb{Z}^8$, $\mathbb{Q} \times \mathbb{Z}$. Give arguments why these sets are denumerable.

Looking at the above, one might begin to believe that *all* sets are denumerable. This is however definitely not the case, as we shall see in the following section.

19.10   Uncountability

An example of an infinite, but not denumerable set is $\{0, 1\}^{\mathbb{N}}$, the *set of all mappings from $\mathbb{N}$ to $\{0, 1\}$*.

Remark 19.10.1 *The set of all mappings from A to B is usually denoted by B^A (be careful: the A appears after (and above) the B). Hence $f \in B^A$ if and only if $f : A \to B$.*

This notation has the following 'justification'. Assume that A and B are finite, *with m resp. n elements. Then the number of elements of B^A is equal to n^m, as can be shown straightforwardly. In fact, if $A = \{x_1, x_2, \ldots, x_m\}$,* *then every $f \in B^A$ is fully characterized by the sequence of the function val-ues $\langle f(x_1), f(x_2), \ldots, f(x_m) \rangle$. For every $f(x_i)$ there are n possible choices. Hence there are n^m different such sequences possible and so, there are n^m possible functions from A to B.*

Now, for finite sets A and B we have, thanks to the notation B^A, the beautiful property that:
$$\#(B^A) = \#(B)^{\#(A)}.$$

How does an f in $\{0,1\}^{\mathbb{N}}$ look like? For every $i \in \mathbb{N}$ we have that $f(i)$ can only be either 0 or 1, so for example:

$f(0) = 1,\ f(1) = 1,\ f(2) = 0,\ f(3) = 1,\ f(4) = 0,\ f(5) = 0,\ f(6) = 1,$ $f(7) = 0,\ \ldots$.

Such a function f can hence be characterized by the infinite sequence of zeros and ones which we get if we write the sequence of the *function values* $f(0), f(1), f(2), \ldots$. For the above example we get the sequence φ with:

$\varphi = 1, 1, 0, 1, 0, 0, 1, 0, \ldots$.

The sequence φ corresponds to the above f and vice versa: f corresponds to φ. It will become clear that for *every* function in $\{0,1\}^{\mathbb{N}}$ there is exactly *one* such sequence of zeros and ones, and vice versa. So there is a bijection between $\{0,1\}^{\mathbb{N}}$ and the set of all such 0-1-sequences. Hence, in order to show that $\{0,1\}^{\mathbb{N}}$ is not denumerable, it is enough to show that the set of all such 0-1-sequences cannot be denumerable.

We are now going to show this:

{ Assume: }

| The set of all infinite 0-1-sequences is denumerable. |

Then there is a *listing* of this set, say:

$0 \mapsto \varphi_0,\ 1 \mapsto \varphi_1,\ 2 \mapsto \varphi_2,\ 3 \mapsto \varphi_3,\ \ldots$

We write these sequences as follows:

$\varphi_0\ =\ a_{00},\quad a_{01},\quad a_{02},\quad a_{03},\quad \cdots$

$\varphi_1\ =\ a_{10},\quad a_{11},\quad a_{12},\quad a_{13},\quad \cdots$

$\varphi_2\ =\ a_{20},\quad a_{21},\quad a_{22},\quad a_{23},\quad \cdots$

$\varphi_3\ =\ a_{30},\quad a_{31},\quad a_{32},\quad a_{33},\quad \cdots$

$\quad \vdots \qquad \vdots \quad \vdots \quad \vdots \quad \vdots \quad \vdots \quad \cdots$

with every a_{ij} being either 0, or 1.

Look now at the 'diagonal sequence' $\psi = a_{00},\ a_{11},\ a_{22},\ a_{33}, \ldots$.

Replace in ψ every 0 by a 1 and every 1 by a 0: we will then get the sequence $\chi = b_0,\ b_1,\ b_2,\ b_3, \dots$, where always $b_i \neq a_{ii}$.

But this means that no single φ_i is equal to χ, because in φ_i we have a_{ii} in the $i + 1$-th position, and in ψ we have b_i.

Hence χ is a 0-1-sequence which does not appear in the list, when it actually should (the listing is supposed to be a bijection)!

Contradiction (or: `False`).

{ $\Rightarrow$-intro and Negation: }

Hence the set of all infinite 0-1-sequences is *not* denumerable.

The clever point of this proof is the focus on the 'diagonal' of the a_{ij}-matrix (the infinite sequence ψ) and then *change every position of this diagonal* (this gives the sequence χ). For this χ we know that it is definitely 'new' with respect to *all* the sequences φ_i.

This proof method is called *diagonalisation* or the *diagonal argument of Cantor*, after the German mathematician and logician Georg Cantor[2]. We will once again come across this method below.

A set that is not finite and not denumerable, is called *nondenumerable*. We now know that $\{0, 1\}^{\mathbb{N}}$ is nondenumerable.

It is not difficult now to see that $\mathcal{P}(\mathbb{N})$, the powerset of $\mathbb{N}$, is nondenumerable. In fact, an element $X \in \mathcal{P}(\mathbb{N})$ is a subset of $\mathbb{N}$, which we can code uniquely as a 0-1-sequence, by checking every natural number one by one, to see if it is or is not in X, for example:

$\mathbb{N}$	0	1	2	3	4	...
in X ?	*yes*	*yes*	*no*	*yes*	*no*	...

for a subset X for which $0, 1, 3, \dots \in X$, but not $2, 4, \dots$.

The sequence *yes, yes, no, yes, no,* ... can be written as $1, 1, 0, 1, 0, \dots$, hence as a 0-1-sequence. Another example: the set $X_{\text{even}} \subseteq \mathbb{N}$ of the even natural numbers corresponds to the 0-1-sequence $1, 0, 1, 0, 1, 0, \dots$ and the set of all prime numbers corresponds to $0, 0, 1, 1, 0, 1, 0, 1, 0, 0, \dots$.

It is clear that in this way, there is a bijection between subsets of $\mathbb{N}$ and 0-1-sequences. Knowing that the latter set, $\{0, 1\}^{\mathbb{N}}$, is nondenumerable, the first $\mathcal{P}(\mathbb{N})$, must also be nondenumerable.

---

[2]G. Cantor, *Über eine elementare Frage der Mannigfaltigkeitslehre*, Jahresbericht der Deutschen Mathematiker Vereinigung, Bd. 1, 1890-1.

With a similar diagonal argument as above for $\{0,1\}^{\mathbb{N}}$, we can show also that $\mathbb{N}^{\mathbb{N}}$, the set of all functions from $\mathbb{N}$ to $\mathbb{N}$, is nondenumerable.

What about $\mathbb{R}$? Earlier, we have seen that $\mathbb{N}$, $\mathbb{Z}$ and $\mathbb{Q}$ are all *denumerable* (and hence also have the same cardinality). Is this also the case for $\mathbb{R}$, the set of all *real* numbers?

The answer is: no. In order to show this, we use again a form of Cantor's diagonal argument. We start with $I = \langle 0, 1 \rangle$, the interval of all real numbers between 0 and 1.

Assume that I is nondenumerable. Then we can list the elements of I.

Now, it is possible to write every number in I as an infinite decimal fraction, for example

$$\frac{3}{4} = 0,7500000\ldots,$$
$$\frac{\pi}{10} = 0,31415926535\ldots.$$

Hence, a possible listing of I looks in decimal notation as follows:

$$r_0 \;=\; 0, d_{00}\, d_{01}\, d_{02}\, d_{03} \cdots$$

$$r_1 \;=\; 0, d_{10}\, d_{11}\, d_{12}\, d_{13} \cdots$$

$$r_2 \;=\; 0, d_{20}\, d_{21}\, d_{22}\, d_{23} \cdots$$

$$r_3 \;=\; 0, d_{30}\, d_{31}\, d_{32}\, d_{33} \cdots$$
$$\vdots \quad \vdots \quad \vdots \quad \vdots \quad \vdots \quad \vdots \quad \vdots \quad \vdots \cdots$$

with every d_{ij} a 'decimal', hence a digit from the set $\{0, 1, 2, \ldots, 9\}$ of possible decimals.

Look now again at the *diagonal*, and more precisely look at the diagonal which starts after the 0 and the comma. From this, we can make the real number s with

$$s \;=\; 0, d_{00}\, d_{11}\, d_{22}\, d_{33} \cdots.$$

Replace now all the decimals d_{ii} of s by *other* decimals, for example by adding *one* to every decimal except 9, and replacing all 9s by 0s. In this way we get a new real number, say

$$t \;=\; 0, \delta_0\, \delta_1\, \delta_2\, \delta_3 \cdots,$$

with the property that $\forall_i [i \in \mathbb{N} : d_{ii} \neq \delta_i]$.

From this it follows that no single r_j can be equal to t, in fact, the j-th decimal of r_j (namely d_{jj}) is different from the j-th decimal of t (namely δ_j). Hence t is a real number between 0 and 1, which is clearly not in the above listing $r_0, r_1, r_2, \ldots$. But that was a listing of the *full* interval $\langle 0, 1 \rangle$! Contradiction.

Conclusion: $\langle 0, 1 \rangle$ is not denumerable, and because the interval $\langle 0, 1 \rangle$ is naturally also not finite, it must be nondenumerable.

Remark 19.10.2 *There is a small complication in the above, because there are real numbers which have* two *different representations as decimal numbers. Take for example the real number* $\frac{3}{20}$. *We can write this as* $0,15000\ldots$, *but also as* $0,14999\ldots$. *If in such situations we agree to always choose the first (hence with an infinite 'tail' of zeros), then we can guarantee the unicity of the representation.*

We can now easily show that also the whole set $\mathbb{R}$ must be nondenumerable. There is actually a bijection between $\langle 0,1 \rangle$ and $\mathbb{R}$, namely the mapping $f : \langle 0,1 \rangle \to \mathbb{R}$ where $f(x) = \tan(\pi(x - \frac{1}{2}))$. (Draw the graph yourself of this mapping: It will look like *one* 'swing' of the tangent function, between the asymptots $x = 0$ and $x = 1$.) Hence $\langle 0,1 \rangle$ is equinumerous to $\mathbb{R}$. If now $\mathbb{R}$ was denumerable (that is: $\mathbb{R}$ is equinumerous to $\mathbb{N}$), then $\langle 0,1 \rangle$ would also be equinumerous to $\mathbb{N}$ (actually: being equinumerous is transitive). But this latter is not the case, as we have just seen.

We have hence shown that $\{0,1\}^{\mathbb{N}}$, $\mathcal{P}(\mathbb{N})$, $\mathbb{N}^{\mathbb{N}}$, $\langle 0,1 \rangle$ and $\mathbb{R}$ are all nondenumerable. Moreover, the first three have the same cardinality, and so do the last two. But do *all five* have the same cardinality? The answer is: yes, but the proof of this is quite complicated and hence will not be given here.

Another question which offers itself now is the following. We know that all *denumerable* sets have the same cardinality, because they all stand in bijections with $\mathbb{N}$. Do we have something similar now for the *nondenumerable* sets? This means: do *all* nondenumerable sets have the same cardinality, for example via a bijection with $\mathbb{R}$?

The answer to this question is no. This follows from a lemma which says that every set V has a smaller cardinality than $\mathcal{P}(V)$, where 'V *has smaller cardinality than* W ' means: there is an injection from of V to W, but no surjection from V to W (hence also no bijection). We do not give a proof of this lemma. Verify that this lemma holds for *finite* sets (for example: $\emptyset$ has a smaller cardinality than $\mathcal{P}(\emptyset)$ and $\{1,2,3\}$ has a smaller cardinality than $\mathcal{P}(\{1,2,3\})$) and that the lemma also holds for $\mathbb{N}$.

It especially holds that: $\mathbb{R}$ has a smaller cardinality than $\mathcal{P}(\mathbb{R})$, which means that $\mathbb{R}$ and $\mathcal{P}(\mathbb{R})$ are *not* equinumerous: the set $\mathcal{P}(\mathbb{R})$ is *really* 'larger' than the set $\mathbb{R}$.

The class of all *denumerable* sets, hence the sets which have the same cardinality as $\mathbb{N}$, is represented with $\aleph_0$ (pronounced: aleph-zero). The class of the sets which have the same cardinality as $\mathbb{R}$ is called $\aleph_1$ (aleph-one), and so we can go on. Hence:

– $\aleph_0$ consists of $\mathbb{N}$, $\mathbb{Z}$, $\mathbb{Q}$ and other examples like $\mathbb{N}^+$, $\{n \in \mathbb{N} | n$ is even $\}$, $\mathbb{N}^2$, $\mathbb{Z}^2$, $\mathbb{Z}^8$, $\mathbb{Q}^2$, $\mathbb{Q} \times \mathbb{Z}$, $\ldots$.

– $\aleph_1$ consists of $\mathbb{R}$, $\mathcal{P}(\mathbb{N})$ and other examples like $\{0,1\}^\mathbb{N}$, $\mathbb{N}^\mathbb{N}$, $\langle 0,1 \rangle$, $[0,1]$, $\mathbb{R}^2$, $\mathcal{P}(\mathbb{N}^2)$, ...

– $\aleph_2$ consists of $\mathcal{P}(\mathbb{R})$, $\mathcal{P}(\mathcal{P}(\mathbb{N}))$, ...

– $\mathcal{P}(\mathcal{P}(\mathcal{P}(\mathbb{N})))$ is in $\aleph_3$, and so on.

(Some *proofs* of the above facts are very complicated and are beyond the scope of this book.)

19.11   Exercises

19.1 Define on the structure $\langle \mathbb{N}, 0, s \rangle$ the function v by

$$v(0) := 0,$$
$$v(s(i)) := i \quad (i \in \mathbb{N}) .$$

(a) How can the function v be described?

(b) Is v a bijection? How can you make from s and v together a bijection?

19.2 (a) Let s, $v \in \mathbb{R}$. The *arithmetic sequence* with *start value s* and *common difference v* is the sequence $a_0, a_1, a_2, \ldots$ where
$a_i = s + i \cdot v \ (i \in \mathbb{N})$.
Prove that: $\forall_n [n \in \mathbb{N} : \sum_{k=0}^{n} a_k = (n+1)s + \frac{1}{2}n(n+1)v]$.

(b) Let s, $r \in \mathbb{R}$ where $r \neq 1$. The *geometric sequence* with *start value s* and *common ratio r* is the sequence $a_0, a_1, a_2, \ldots$ where
$a_i = s \cdot r^i \ (i \in \mathbb{N})$.
Prove that: $\forall_n [n \in \mathbb{N} : \sum_{k=0}^{n} a_k = s \frac{1-r^{n+1}}{1-r}]$.

19.3 Prove by induction:

(a) $\forall_n [n \in \mathbb{N} : \sum_{k=0}^{n} (k \cdot k!) = (n+1)! - 1]$.

(b) $\forall_n [n \in \mathbb{N} : \ 9$ is a divisor of $n^3 + (n+1)^3 + (n+2)^3 \ ]$.

19.4 Prove by induction:

(a) $\forall_n [n \in \mathbb{N} \wedge n \geq 1 : 1 + 3 + \ldots + (2n-1) = n^2]$.

(b) $\forall_n [n \in \mathbb{N} \wedge n \geq 1 : \sum_{k=0}^{n-1} k^2 = \frac{1}{3}n^3 - \frac{1}{2}n^2 + \frac{1}{6}n]$.

(c) $\forall_n [n \in \mathbb{N} \wedge n > 0 : \sum_{k=0}^{n-1} k^3 = \frac{1}{4}n^2(n-1)^2]$.

19.5 Prove by induction:

$\forall_n [n \in \mathbb{N} \wedge n \geq 1 : \sum_{k=1}^{n} \frac{1}{\sqrt{k}} \leq 2\sqrt{n} - 1]$.

19.6 The sequence $a_0, a_1, a_2, \ldots$ is inductively defined by

$a_0 := 0$,

$a_{i+1} := a_i + (i+1)(i+2)(i+3)$ $(i \in \mathbb{N})$.

Prove that: $\forall_n [n \in \mathbb{N} : a_n = \frac{1}{4}n(n+1)(n+2)(n+3)]$.

19.7 The set $\{a_n | n \in \mathbb{N}\}$ is inductively defined by

$a_0 := 2$,

$a_{i+1} := 3a_i - 3$ $(i \in \mathbb{N})$.

Find a closed formula for $a_{i+1} - a_i$, and thereafter one for a_n. Prove the correctness of both answers.

19.8 The set $\{a_n | n \in \mathbb{N}\}$ is inductively defined by

$a_0 := 0$,

$a_1 := 1$,

$a_{i+2} := 2a_{i+1} - a_i$ $(i \in \mathbb{N})$.

Find a closed formula for a_n and prove the correctness of your answer.

19.9 The sequence $a_0, a_1, a_2, \ldots$ is inductively defined by

$a_0 := 0$,

$a_1 := 1$,

$a_{i+2} := a_{i+1} + a_i$ $(i \in \mathbb{N})$.

(This is called the *Fibonacci sequence*.)

Prove:

(a) $\forall_n [n \in \mathbb{N} : a_{n+2} = a_n + a_{n-1} + \ldots + a_1 + a_0 + 1]$.

(b) $\forall_n [n \in \mathbb{N} : a_{3n}$ is even$]$.

19.10 (a) The set $\{a_n | n \in \mathbb{N}\}$ is inductively defined by

$a_0 := 0$,

$a_1 := 4$,

$a_{i+2} := 4(a_{i+1} - a_i)$ $(i \in \mathbb{N})$.

Prove that: $\forall_n [n \in \mathbb{N} : a_n = n \cdot 2^{n+1}]$.

(b) The set $\{a_n | n \in \mathbb{N}\}$ is inductively defined by

$a_0 := 1$,

$a_1 := 1$,

$a_{i+2} := 5a_{i+1} - 6a_i$ $(i \in \mathbb{N})$.

Prove that: $\forall_n [n \in \mathbb{N} : a_n = 2^{n+1} - 3^n]$.

(c) The sequence $a_0, a_1, a_2 \ldots$ is inductively defined by

$a_0 := 1,$

$a_{i+1} := \frac{1}{i+1}(a_0 + a_1 + \ldots + a_i)$ $(i \in \mathbb{N}).$

Prove that: $\forall_n[n \in \mathbb{N} : a_n = 1].$

(d) The sequence $a_0, a_1, a_2, \ldots$ is inductively defined by

$a_0 := 1,$

$a_{i+1} := a_0 + a_1 + \ldots + a_i - i + 1$ $(i \in \mathbb{N}).$

Prove that: $\forall_n[n \in \mathbb{N}\backslash\{0\} : a_n = 2^{n-1} + 1].$

19.11 The set C of digits is the set $\{0, 1, 2, \ldots, 9\}.$

The formula set $\mathcal{G}$ is given by the following inductive definition:

- *Basis:*

- *Every $c \in C\backslash\{0\}$ is an element of $\mathcal{G}$.*

- *Step:*

- *if $\varphi \in \mathcal{G}$ and $c \in C$, then $\varphi c \in \mathcal{G}$.*

(With φc we mean the concatenation of φ and c.)

(a) How can the set $\mathcal{G}$ be described?

(b) Draw a construction tree of the formula 35061.

(c) Is there for every formula in $\mathcal{G}$ only one construction tree possible?

19.12 Every element n belonging to the structure $\langle \mathbb{N}, 0, s \rangle$, has the following form: $s(s(\ldots(0)\ldots))$, where the number of s's is bigger than or equal to 0.

In this structure, we can inductively define *addition* as follows:

$m + 0 := m,$

$m + s(n) := s(n + m).$

(a) Calculate $s(s(0)) + s(s(s(0)))$ using this definition.

(b) Prove by structural induction: $0 + n = n$, for all n in the structure.

(c) Define the *multiplication* in $\langle \mathbb{N}, 0, s \rangle$, using addition.

19.13 As set L of *letters* we take $\{x, y, z\}.$

The formula set $\mathcal{M}$ is given by the following inductive definition:

- *Basis:*
  - *Every $l \in L$ is element of $\mathcal{M}$.*
- *Step:*
  - *case 1: if $\varphi_1 \in \mathcal{M}$ and $\varphi_2 \in \mathcal{M}$, then $\varphi_1 + \varphi_2 \in \mathcal{M}$.*
  - *case 2: if $\varphi_1 \in \mathcal{M}$ and $\varphi_2 \in \mathcal{M}$, then $\varphi_1 - \varphi_2 \in \mathcal{M}$.*

  (a) Is there for every formula in $\mathcal{M}$ only one construction tree possible?

  (b) Prove by structural induction that in every formula of $\mathcal{M}$ the number of plus and minus signs are *together* one less than the number of letters in the formula.

19.14 Take the set of parentheses formulas, $\mathcal{H}$, from Section 19.6.

Prove that: if $\varphi \in \mathcal{H}$ and $\varphi \equiv \psi_1 \psi_2$ (hence φ is the concatenation of two subformulas, which by the way need not be in $\mathcal{H}$), then the number of opening parentheses in ψ_1 is bigger than or equal to the number of closing parentheses in ψ_1.

19.15 The formula set $\mathcal{V}$ is given by the following inductive definition:

- *Basis:*
  - *01 is an element of $\mathcal{V}$.*
- *Step:*
  - *case 1: if $\varphi \in \mathcal{V}$ and we replace a 1 in φ by 101, then the result is again an element of $\mathcal{V}$.*
  - *case 2: if $\varphi \in \mathcal{V}$ and we replace a 1 in φ by 011, then the result is again an element of $\mathcal{V}$.*

  (a) Construct all elements in $\mathcal{V}$ which consist of six digits.

  (b) Prove that: every $\varphi \in \mathcal{V}$ has as many zeros as ones.

  (c) Give a relation between $\mathcal{V}$ and the set $\mathcal{H}$ of parentheses formulas of Section 19.6 (only the answer).

19.16 (a) Give an enumeration (i.e., a listing) of the odd whole numbers.

  (b) Prove that every class of the equivalence relation $\equiv_6$ is denumerable.

  (c) Prove that $\mathbb{N} \times \{0, 1\}$ is denumerable.

19.17 (a) Prove that, if V and W are denumerable, then also $V \times W$ is denumerable.

(b) Assume that V is denumerable, that $W \subseteq V$ and that W has infinitely many elements.

Prove that also W is denumerable.

(c) Prove that the set of all subsets of $\mathbb{N}$ which have three elements, is denumerable.

19.18 (a) Prove that: if V is denumerable and $a \notin V$, then $V \cup \{a\}$ is also denumerable.

(b) Let W be the set of all *squares* of rational numbers. (So $\frac{1}{2} \notin W$, but $\frac{1}{4} \in W$.)

Prove that W is denumerable.

19.19 Consider an infinite sequence of sets: $A_0, A_1, \ldots$.

By definition, we take $\bigcup_{i \in \mathbb{N}} A_i$ to be the set which contains *all* elements of *all* A_i's (and no others). Hence it holds that $x \in \bigcup_{i \in \mathbb{N}} A_i$ if and only if $\exists_k [k \in \mathbb{N} : x \in A_k]$.

Assume that every A_i is denumerable. Prove that $\bigcup_{i \in \mathbb{N}} A_i$ is then also denumerable.

19.20 (a) Prove that $\mathbb{R}^+$ has the same cardinality as $\mathbb{R}$.

(b) Prove that $[0, 1\rangle$ has the same cardinality as $\mathbb{R}^+ \cup \{0\}$.

(c) Prove that $\mathbb{N}^{\mathbb{N}}$ is nondenumerable.

Chapter 20

Ordered sets

`All received in good order`

20.1 Quasi-ordering

In this chapter we are concerned with the concept of 'ordering', which is important in many areas of mathematics and computer science (and also outside these!). If we say that a set is *ordered*, then we mean that there is a relation on this set which deals with a 'relative order' of the elements. This can be: 'an element *appears before* (*precedes*) another', but also 'an element *appears after* (*succeeds*) another' (an order can go either way!).

An 'ordering' is hence a *relation* (see Chapter 17) with special properties. What these properties are exactly, depends on the *kind* of ordering in question. In this section, we will look at the so-called *quasi-ordering*, which is a relation which has some of the essential properties of ordering, but not all.

In the other sections of this chapter, we discuss different kinds of orderings. It appears that also for *sets of numbers* like $\mathbb{N}$, $\mathbb{Q}$ and $\mathbb{R}$, ordering relations can be given. (And so there is a connection with the previous chapter). Think for example, of the relation 'smaller than', which gives an ordering on $\mathbb{N}$: if $x < y$ then x *precedes* y; for the 'bigger than' relation the situation is otherwise: if $x > y$ then x *succeeds* y.

A set with an ordering is a *structure*, comparable to the structures of Chapter 19 (see for example Section 19.2). In this way the set $\mathbb{N}$ forms with the ordering relation 'smaller than', the structure $\langle \mathbb{N}, < \rangle$. Such a structure is also called an *ordered set*.

The different kinds of (quasi-)orderings which exist, fall under two main groups: the *reflexive* and the *irreflexive* ones. A structure $\langle A, S \rangle$ in the latter group has the following property:

$$\forall_x [x \in A : \neg(xSx)],$$

called *irreflexivity*, which can be considered as a kind of absolute opposite of *reflexivity* (see Section 17.3 and here below). In fact, in case of a reflexive R we *always* have xRx, and in case of an irreflexive S we *never* have xSx.

For an irreflexive relation S we can only have aSb if a and b are *different*, either a 'precedes' b, or a 'succeeds' b. Irreflexivity is surely a natural property of an ordering: if you say that Anna is longer than Bert, then you explicitly mean that she cannot be *as long*; if c is smaller than d, then c is *not equal* to d. In the ordered set $\langle \mathbb{N}, < \rangle$, for example, the ordering '$<$' is irreflexive (no natural number is smaller than itself).

Nevertheless, it is often convenient to stretch a bit the concept 'precedes' and to extend it with 'being equal to'. For numbers for example, the irreflexive ordering relation '$<$' plays an important role, but so does the ordering relation '$\leq$', which is reflexive (in fact we always have $x \leq x$).

A *reflexive* relation R on a set A, as we already saw in Section 17.3, can be characterized by the property:

$$\forall_x [x \in A : xRx].$$

In what follows we shall deal with both kinds of ordering relations, reflexive and irreflexive. Below, we will see that to every reflexive ordering relation there corresponds in a 'natural' way an *ir*reflexive one, and vice versa.

Let's for now concentrate on *reflexive* relations R on A. If such a relation R is to be an ordering on A, then R must also be *transitive* (this concept is also known from Section 17.3):

$$\forall_{x,y,z} [x, y, z \in A : (xRy \wedge yRz) \Rightarrow xRz].$$

In fact, it is quite obvious that an ordering has the *transitivity property*: if x precedes y and y precedes z, then x will also precede z (as R is reflexive, we have to be broad-minded: 'being equal to' is a special case of 'preceding'). In $\langle \mathbb{N}, \leq \rangle$, for example we have : if $x \leq y$ and $y \leq z$, then $x \leq z$. In the first sentence of this paragraph, you can replace 'precedes' everywhere by 'succeeds', and the property will still hold; for example in $\langle \mathbb{N}, \geq \rangle$: if $x \geq y$ and $y \geq z$, then $x \geq z$.

Note that the transitivity property is also a natural requirement for *ir*reflexive ordering relations, for example: if $x < y$ and $y < z$, then $x < z$.

With the properties 'reflexivity/irreflexivity' and 'transitivity', one can define two classes of relations: the reflexive quasi-orderings and the irreflexive quasi-orderings:

(1) A relation R on A (or: the structure $\langle R, A \rangle$) is a *reflexive quasi-ordering* if R is both reflexive and transitive. Other names for such relations are: *pre-ordering* or *pre-order*.

(2) A relation S on A (or: the structure $\langle S, A \rangle$) is an *irreflexive quasi-ordering* if S is both *irreflexive* and transitive. Other names for such relations are: *strict pre-ordering* or *strict pre-order*.

However, generally spoken, a quasi-ordering is not treated as a 'real' ordering. For this we need more; see the following section.

20.2   Orderings

In Section 17.4 we saw that an *equivalence relation* is a relation which is reflexive, symmetric and transitive. If a reflexive quasi-ordering is hence also *symmetric*, then it is an equivalence relation. But this is not a real ordering, and the reason for this is symmetry: if x precedes y, and if y in turn precedes x, then something strange is happening (assuming that $x \neq y$): we get into a circle, and the concept 'order' does not make much sense any more.

And so for a reflexive relation R to be a real ordering, it is undesirable that it be symmetric. Hence *not always*: if xRy then yRx. Even stronger, the situation that at the same time both xRy and yRx can hold, must *never* take place (unless of course x is the same as y). We express this in the following property, which is called *antisymmetry* (a kind of absolute opposite of symmetry). In the case of a reflexive relation this looks as follows:

$$\forall_{x,y}[x, y \in A : (xRy \wedge yRx) \Rightarrow x = y].$$

Now we have the first important kind of ordering, which is called *reflexive partial ordering*, or in short: *reflexive ordering*. (Sometimes one also leaves out the word 'reflexive' and simply speaks of *ordering*.)

A reflexive (partial) ordering R on A is hence:

(1) *reflexive:* $\forall_x[x \in A : xRx]$,
(2) *antisymmetric:* $\forall_{x,y}[x, y \in A : (xRy \wedge yRx) \Rightarrow x = y]$, and
(3) *transitive:* $\forall_{x,y,z}[x, y, z \in A : (xRy \wedge yRz) \Rightarrow xRz]$.

We also say in this case: *the structure $\langle A, R \rangle$ is reflexively (partially) ordered* or *the set A is reflexively (partially) ordered by R*.

Often one abbreviates 'partially ordered set' as *poset*.

The second major group of orderings is based on *irr*eflexivity. So let S be an irreflexive relation. Then, as a consequence of the *irr*eflexivity, the antisymmetry is replaced by *strict antisymmetry*:

$$\forall_{x,y}[x, y \in A : \neg(xSy \wedge ySx)].$$

This is so because now in the case where both xSy and ySx hold, the 'trivial' possibility '$x = y$' fails (xSx is not allowed by irreflexivity!). The assumption of transitivity is the same for irreflexive orderings as for reflexive ones.

Also for *irreflexive* relations one talks about 'partial orderings', or in short: 'orderings'. An *irreflexive (partial) ordering* S on A is hence:

(1) **ir***reflexive:* $\forall_x[x \in A : \neg(xSx)]$,
(2) **strictly** *antisymmetric:* $\forall_{x,y}[x, y \in A : \neg(xSy \wedge ySx)]$, and
(3) *transitive:* $\forall_{x,y,z}[x, y, z \in A : (xSy \wedge ySz) \Rightarrow xSz]$.

In what follows, we will always make it clear which kind of ordering we are using: a *reflexive* or an *irreflexive* one.

Example 20.2.1

- *The structures* $\langle \mathbb{N}, \leq \rangle$, $\langle \mathbb{Z}, \leq \rangle$ *and* $\langle \mathbb{R}, \leq \rangle$ *are reflexive orderings. In fact, we 'always' have:* $x \leq x$ *(reflexivity),* $(x \leq y \wedge y \leq x) \Rightarrow x = y$ *(antisymmetry) and* $(x \leq y \wedge y \leq z) \Rightarrow x \leq z$ *(transitivity).*

  The above structures remain reflexive orderings if we replace '$\leq$' by '$\geq$'.

- *Structures like* $\langle \mathbb{R}, < \rangle$ *and* $\langle \mathbb{R}, > \rangle$ *are* irreflexive *orderings.*

- *Look at the relation 'is-divisor-of' on* $\mathbb{N}^+$, *with symbol '$|$'. So for example:* $3|15$ *and* $15|15$, *but not* $3|16$ *or* $15|3$. *In formula form:*

  $m|n$ *if and only if* $\exists_k[k \in \mathbb{N}^+ : k \cdot m = n]$.
  Then $\langle \mathbb{N}^+, | \rangle$ *is a reflexive ordering.*

It is easy to check that the structure $\langle \mathbb{N}^+, | \rangle$, described above, is indeed a reflexive ordering. We give as an example the proofs of *reflexivity* and *antisymmetry* (do the proof of transitivity on your own, in the same way).

– *Reflexivity:*

{ Assume: }

(1) | var x; $x \in \mathbb{N}^+$

{ Mathematics: }

(2) | $1 \cdot x = x$ and $1 \in \mathbb{N}^+$

{ ∃*-intro on (2): }

(3) | $\exists_k [k \in \mathbb{N}^+ : k \cdot x = x]$

{ Definition of | on (3): }

(4) | $x | x$

{ ∀-intro: }

(5) $\forall_x [x \in \mathbb{N}^+ : x | x]$

– *Antisymmetry:*

{ Assume: }

(1) | var x, y; $x, y \in \mathbb{N}^+$

{ Assume: }

(2) | | $x | y \wedge y | x$

{ ∧-elim on (2): }

(3) | | $x | y$

{ Definition of | on (3): }

(4) | | $\exists_k [k \in \mathbb{N}^+ : k \cdot x = y]$, say k

{ ∧-elim on (2): }

(5) | | $y | x$

{ Definition of | on (5): }

(6) | | $\exists_l [l \in \mathbb{N}^+ : l \cdot y = x]$, say l

{ Mathematics on (4) and (6): }

(7) | | $l \cdot k \cdot x = l \cdot y = x$

{ Mathematics on (7); because $x \neq 0$: }

(8) | | $l \cdot k = 1$, hence $l = 1$ and $k = 1$

{ Mathematics, since $k \cdot x = y$, (4), and $k = 1$, (8): }

(9) | | $x = y$

{ ⇒-intro: }

(10) | $(x | y \wedge y | x) \Rightarrow x = y$

{ ∀-intro (twice): }

(11) $\forall_{x,y}[x, y \in \mathbb{N}^+ : (x|y \wedge y|x) \Rightarrow x = y]$

Note that we used in the lines numbered (4) and (6), a short form of
$\exists^*$-elimination, via the word 'say', instead of with a sentence like 'pick a
$k \in \mathbb{N}^+$ with $k \cdot x = y$'.

We continue our set of examples:

Example 20.2.2

- *For every set A we have that $\langle \mathcal{P}(A), \subseteq \rangle$ is a reflexive ordering. In
fact:*

  *(1) For every $X \in \mathcal{P}(A)$ (hence: X is a subset of A) we have $X \subseteq X$
  (reflexivity),*

  *(2) For every pair X and $Y \in \mathcal{P}(A)$ we have: if $X \subseteq Y$ and $Y \subseteq X$,
  then $X = Y$ (antisymmetry),*

  *(3) and for every triple X, Y and $Z \in \mathcal{P}(A)$ we have: if $X \subseteq Y$ and
  $Y \subseteq Z$, then $X \subseteq Z$ (transitivity).*

  (These are not real *proofs, we have only summarized what the three
  proofs should actually show. It should however be clear how the complete proofs can approximately look like, where proof techniques from
  Part II are used: flags, introduction- and elimination rules.)*

- *Let M be the set of all people (both the living and the dead) and S the
relation 'is-ancestor-of', hence $m_1 S m_2$ if m_1 is an ancestor of m_2.
Then $\langle M, S \rangle$ is an irreflexive ordering. Check this.*

Remark 20.2.3 *From a reflexive ordered structure $\langle V, R \rangle$ we can easily
construct the corresponding* irreflexive *ordered structure $\langle V, S \rangle$ by defining:*

$x \, S \, y$ *if and only if* $xRy \wedge x \neq y$.

*Conversely, we can construct from an irreflexive ordered structure $\langle V, S \rangle$
the corresponding reflexive ordered structure $\langle V, R \rangle$, by defining:*

$x \, R \, y$ *if and only if* $xSy \vee x = y$.

(This R is called the reflexive closure *of S; see also Section 17.6.)*

*Verify for example that the reflexive ordering $\langle \mathbb{Z}, \leq \rangle$ corresponds to the
irreflexive ordering $\langle \mathbb{Z}, < \rangle$, and vice versa.*

Remark 20.2.4 *In order to establish that a relation is either a* reflexive
or an irreflexive *ordering, we stated – in both cases – three requirements:
(1) (ir-)reflexivity, (2) (strict) antisymmetry and (3) transitivity.*

It turns out that we can save on this in the case of irreflexive *orderings: it happens that (2) strict antisymmetry is a* consequence *of (1) irreflexivity and (3) transitivity!*

We prove this 'in words', leaving it to the reader to turn this verbal proof into a proof in flag format.

Proof: *Assume that S is an irreflexive and transitive relation. We shall show that S then also is strictly antisymmetric, i.e.:*

$\forall_{x,y}[x, y \in A : \neg(xSy \land ySx)]$.

So take $x, y \in A$. (To prove: $\neg(xSy \land ySx)$.) So assume the opposite: $xSy \land ySx$. From $xSy \land ySx$ and transitivity, follows xSx. But irreflexivity says that xSx is impossible! Hence our final assumption $xSy \land ySx$ leads to a contradiction, which brings along that $\neg(xSy \land ySx)$ must hold. Q.e.d. (meaning: 'quod erat demonstrandum', being Latin for 'which had to be proven'). Otherwise said: we're done! □

(The □ means: 'end of proof'.)

So when having to show that some relation S is an irreflexive *ordering, we may suffice with showing irreflexivity and transitivity only, omitting a proof of strict antisymmetry.*

Unfortunately, a similar thing does not happen for reflexive *relations: in the latter case it is always necessary to prove reflexivity and antisymmetry and transitivity.*

20.3 Linear orderings

Assume that we have an arbitrary structure $\langle A, R \rangle$, which consists of a set A and a relation R on A. If we take two arbitrary, *different* elements x and y in A, then these can:

- be related in one direction: xRy, or
- be related in the other direction: yRx, or
- *not* be related.

In the first two cases, we say that x and y are *comparable*, in the last case they are *incomparable*, except if $x = y$. If x and y are *equal* then one considers them always *comparable*, even if R is irreflexive.

Example 20.3.1

- *In $\langle \mathcal{P}(\mathbb{N}), \subseteq \rangle$ the sets $\{0, 2, 3\}$ and $\{0, 3\}$ are comparable, because obviously $\{0, 3\} \subseteq \{0, 2, 3\}$.*

  Also $\{0, 2, 3\}$ is comparable with itself and with for example $\{0, 1, 2, 3\}$. But $\{0, 2, 3\}$ is incomparable with $\{0, 1, 3\}$.

- *In* $\langle \mathbb{N}^+, \mid \, \rangle$ *we have that* 3 *is comparable with* 15, *also* 15 *with* 3 *and* 15 *with* 15, *but not* 3 *with* 16.

- *In* $\langle \mathbb{R}, < \rangle$, *every* two *elements are comparable! This is because for arbitrary* x *and* y *we always have: either* $x < y$, *or* $y < x$, *or* $x = y$. *Also in* $\langle \mathbb{R}, \leq \rangle$ *every two elements are comparable.*

The relations $<$ and $\leq$ on $\mathbb{R}$, see the last example, bring with them the nice property that every two elements are comparable. In general a relation with this property is called *linear*. Hence R on A is linear if:

$$\forall_{x,y}[x, y \in A : xRy \lor yRx \lor x = y].$$

(If R is *reflexive*, we can replace this by

$$\forall_{x,y}[x, y \in A : xRy \lor yRx].)$$

If the relation R on A is both linear and an ordering, then it is called a *linear ordering* (other names are: a *total ordering* or a *chain*).

Hence the structure $\langle A, R \rangle$ is a *reflexive linear ordering* if R is (1) reflexive and (2) antisymmetric and (3) transitive and (4) linear.

There are also *irreflexive* linear orderings, which are (1) *ir*reflexive and (2) *strictly* antisymmetric and (3) transitive and (4) linear.

In a *diagram* these relations can often be presented by a straight line (hence the name 'linear'). Below, in Figure 20.1, we respectively give the diagrams of the reflexive linear orderings $\langle \mathbb{N}, \leq \rangle$, $\langle \mathbb{Z}, \leq \rangle$ and $\langle \mathbb{R}, \leq \rangle$. (The same diagrams correspond to the *irreflexive* linear orderings $\langle \mathbb{N}, < \rangle$, $\langle \mathbb{Z}, < \rangle$ and $\langle \mathbb{R}, < \rangle$.)

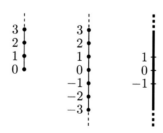

Figure 20.1: Diagrams of the linear orderings $\langle \mathbb{N}, \leq \rangle$, $\langle \mathbb{Z}, \leq \rangle$ and $\langle \mathbb{R}, \leq \rangle$

20.4 Lexicographic orderings

There are also orderings that are a bit more complicated. In this section we consider the so-called *lexicographic ordering*, which in fact is a convenient way to bring an ordering into the *Cartesian product* of two given orderings.

Again, there are two variants: the *reflexive* lexicographic orderings and the *irreflexive* ones. Since the latter one is easier to describe than the former, we start with the *irreflexive lexicographic ordering*.

The definition of this lexicographic ordering is as follows.

Assume that $\langle A, S_1 \rangle$ and $\langle B, S_2 \rangle$ are both *irreflexive orderings*. For the Cartesian product $A \times B$ we define now the relation S_3 by:

$(x, y) S_3 (x', y')$ if $x S_1 x' \vee (x = x' \wedge y S_2 y')$.

In words: the pairs (x, y) and (x', y') in $A \times B$ are in the S_3-relation, if:

– the *first* 'coordinates' x and x' (which are both elements of A) are in the S_1-relation,

– but also, in case these first coordinates are equal $(x = x')$, if the *second* coordinates y and y' (which are in B) are in the S_2-relation.

With this definition, the structure $\langle A \times B, S_3 \rangle$ becomes again an irreflexive ordering. We come back to this at the end of this section.

We illustrate how such a lexicographic ordering is built by looking at an example.

We take A and B both equal to $\mathbb{N}$ and the irreflexive relations S_1 and S_2 to be both '<'. Then each of the orderings $\langle A, S_1 \rangle$ and $\langle B, S_2 \rangle$ is equal to $\langle \mathbb{N}, < \rangle$, an irreflexive ordering.

The lexicographic relation S_3 according to the above definition, on the Cartesian product $\mathbb{N} \times \mathbb{N}$, will also be denoted by the symbol '<'. (This is obviously 'overloading' of the symbol '<'.)

In the structure $\langle \mathbb{N} \times \mathbb{N}, < \rangle$ we have now for example:

– $(5, 8) < (7, 2)$, because $5 < 7$, but also:

– $(5, 8) < (5, 11)$, because $5 = 5$ and $8 < 11$.

It does *not* hold for example that: $(5, 8) < (4, 12)$, $(5, 8) < (5, 7)$ or $(5, 8) < (5, 8)$.

Remark 20.4.1 *In the last mentioned example, both relations S_1 and S_2 are also* linear. *It can be shown, that in such a case the corresponding lexicographic ordering S_3 is linear, as well.*

So $\langle \mathbb{N} \times \mathbb{N}, < \rangle$ must be linear. This fact cannot be expressed well in a diagram. The best that we can do to show the linear character, is as follows:

$(0, 0) < (0, 1) < (0, 2) < \ldots < (1, 0) < (1, 1) < (1, 2) < \ldots < (2, 0) < (2, 1) < (2, 2) < \ldots < \ldots$

*At the sequences of dots there are infinitely many pairs of numbers! With
the obvious mapping $0 \mapsto (0,0)$, $1 \mapsto (0,1)$, and so on – which 'respects' this
ordering – we never even reach $(1,0)$, so how about those pairs of number
which are 'situated higher up'? They'll never be reached! (We already saw
this in Section 19.9.) Nevertheless, it is not hard to* prove *that this $\langle \mathbb{N} \times \mathbb{N}, < \rangle$
is linear. (It is of course better still, to prove in general that, if the irreflexive
orderings $\langle A, S_1 \rangle$ and $\langle B, S_2 \rangle$ are both linear, then also the corresponding
lexicographic ordering $\langle A \times B, S_3 \rangle$ is linear.)*

The name *lexicographic ordering* is related to the word-ordering in a
lexicon or a *dictionary*.

The connection can be made clear as follows. Look at the letter set
$L = \{a, b, c, \ldots, z\}$ with the 'usual' ordering relation '$<$', hence $a < b < c <
\ldots < z$. Then $\langle L, < \rangle$ is an irreflexive (linear) ordering. As stated above,
the structure $\langle L \times L, < \rangle$ is an irreflexive (linear) ordering, as well, with a
'new' relation '$<$' defined between *pairs* of letters.

In $\langle L \times L, < \rangle$ we now have for example:

$(g, o) < (m, e)$, because $g < m$.

$(i, f) < (i, n)$, because $(i = i \wedge f < n)$.

In this way we get indeed the dictionary ordering of all two-letter words,
for example, *go* appears before *me*, and *if* appears before *in*.

This can be directly generalized to the dictionary ordering of arbitrary
length (take also the space symbol in the alphabet L, in order to be able to
compare words of different lengths).

We continue with the *reflexive* variant of the lexicographic ordering. So
let $\langle A, R_1 \rangle$ and $\langle B, R_2 \rangle$ be reflexive orderings. Then the corresponding
lexicographic ordering R_3 on $A \times B$ is defined as follows:

$(x, y)R_3(x', y')$ if $xR_1x' \wedge (x = x' \Rightarrow yR_2y')$.

In words: the pairs (x, y) and (x', y') are in the R_3-relation, if:

–   the first coordinates x and x' are in the R_1-relation, *and also*

–   in case these first coordinates are *equal*, then the second coordinates
must be in the R_2-relation.

Then $\langle A \times B, R_3 \rangle$ becomes, again, a reflexive ordering.

We take a similar example as above, now with *reflexive* relations $\leq$:
$\langle A, R_1 \rangle = \langle \mathbb{N}, \leq \rangle$ and $\langle B, R_2 \rangle = \langle \mathbb{N}, \leq \rangle$.

Then, in the structure $\langle \mathbb{N} \times \mathbb{N}, \leq \rangle$ we have for example:

– $(5, 8) \leq (7, 2)$, because $5 \leq 7$ and *not* $5 = 7$,

– $(5, 8) \leq (5, 11)$, because $5 \leq 5$ and $5 = 5 \Rightarrow 8 \leq 11$, and also

- $(5,8) \leq (5,8)$, because $5 \leq 5$ and $5 = 5 \Rightarrow 8 \leq 8$.

It does *not* hold that, for example, $(5,8) \leq (4,12)$, $(5,8) \leq (4,8)$ or $(5,8) \leq (5,7)$.

Remark 20.4.2 *Of course, there is a relation between the definitions of lexicographic orderings in the* irreflexive *and the* reflexive *cases. The reflexive definition as given above, can also be* calculated *on the basis of the irreflexive one (this can also be done the other way round).*

So it can be proved that:

When we 'know' that

(1) $(x,y)S_3(x',y') \overset{\text{def}}{=} xS_1x' \lor (x = x' \land yS_2y')$,

then we can show *that*

(2) $(x,y)R_3(x',y') \overset{\text{val}}{=} xR_1x' \land (x = x' \Rightarrow yR_2y')$,

where the reflexive orderings R_1 and R_2 correspond to the irreflexive orderings S_1 and S_2, respectively (see Remark 20.2.3). Moreover, R_3 is the reflexive lexicographic ordering corresponding to the irreflexive lexicographic ordering S_3.

The proof, which heavily depends on the correspondences between reflexive and irreflexive orderings, will be omitted.

We still have not shown – as we mentioned above – that the irreflexive lexicographic ordering $\langle A \times B, S_3 \rangle$ built from the irreflexive orderings $\langle A, S_1 \rangle$ and $\langle B, S_2 \rangle$, is itself an *irreflexive ordering*. For this, S_3 must also be irreflexive, strictly antisymmetric and transitive. The proofs of this are a bit complicated, especially because we are dealing with many constants (A, B, S_1, S_2, S_3) and variables (x, y, x', y', ...).

In order to clarify the idea of the proofs, we give below one of these proofs: that of transitivity. We give a compact version of the proof, and assume that the reader is in a position to fill the details where necessary.

Transitivity of S_3:

{ Assume: }

> var $(x,y), (x',y'), (x'',y'')$; $(x,y), (x',y'), (x'',y'') \in A \times B$
>
> > { Assume: }
> >
> > > $(x,y)S_3(x',y') \land (x',y')S_3(x'',y'')$
> >
> > Then we have: $(x,y)S_3(x',y')$, for this there are two possible

reasons: $(1a)$ xS_1x', or $(1b)$ $x = x' \wedge yS_2y'$.

We also have: $(x', y')S_3(x'', y'')$, for this there are two possible

reasons: $(2a)$ $x'S_1x''$, or $(2b)$ $x' = x'' \wedge y'S_2y''$.

Hence, there are in total four possible cases:

$(1a) + (2a)$: then by transitivity of S_1 we have that xS_1x''.

$(1a) + (2b)$: then by xS_1x' and $x' = x''$ we have that xS_1x''.

$(1b) + (2a)$: then by $x = x'$ and $x'S_1x''$ we have that xS_1x''.

$(1b) + (2b)$: then it directly follows that $x = x''$, and by the

transitivity of S_2 it also follows that yS_2y''.

<u>Conclusion:</u> We always have either xS_1x'', or $(x = x'' \wedge yS_2y'')$,

hence by the definition of S_3 we have: $(x, y)S_3(x'', y'')$

{ $\Rightarrow$-intro and $\forall$-intro: }

$$\forall_{(x,y),(x',y'),(x'',y'')}[(x, y), (x', y'), (x'', y'') \in A \times B :$$
$$((x, y)S_3(x', y') \wedge (x', y')S_3(x'', y'')) \Rightarrow (x, y)S_3(x'', y'')]$$

The proof written above already starts to look like a proof from a mathematics book!

In the same vein, one may prove that the lexicographic ordering constructed from two *reflexive* orderings, is again reflexive. And moreover, that the lexicographic ordering built from two *linear* orderings, is linear, again.

20.5   Hasse diagrams

At the start of this chapter we introduced the concept of 'ordering' by associating it to a 'relative order' between elements of a set. Later, we noticed that there may be pairs of elements that follow the relation (in either of the two directions), *but there may also be elements that don't.* (This explains why one often speaks of *partial* order, instead of just 'order'.)

In the present section we concentrate on those pairs of elements that *are* related in a special manner: they live so to say 'next to each other'. We shall call such elements *direct successors/predecessors*.

We first recall that the *successor relation* as we have in $\mathbb{N}$ (see Chapter 19), has a direct connection with ordering: the successor function s

appoints to every natural number n a *direct successor* $s(n)$, and this latter also has $s(s(n))$ as direct successor, and so on. You can say that $n < m$ if and only if $m = s(...(s(n))...)$ for a certain number of s's (at least *one*). The ordering which corresponds to this is the *irreflexive* ordering $\langle \mathbb{N}, < \rangle$. (This is a *linear* ordering.)

In general we call the element $y \in A$ a *direct successor* of $x \in A$, given an *irreflexive* ordering relation S on the set A, if:

$$xSy \wedge \neg\exists_z[z \in A : xSz \wedge zSy],$$

This means that x precedes y, *and there is no element in between.*

For a reflexive ordering relation R we must replace in the above formula the symbol S by the corresponding R. This makes the formula more complex, since we have to make sure that x, y and z are really *different*:

$$xRy \wedge x \neq y \wedge \neg\exists_z[z \in A : (xRz \wedge x \neq z) \wedge (zRy \wedge z \neq y)].$$

In a linear ordering, every element has at most *one* direct successor, as can be easily checked. In the structure $\langle \mathbb{N}^+, \mid \rangle$, however – a reflexive ordering which is *not* linear – you can also talk about direct successors. But here, every number has *many* direct successors. The number 5, for example, has as direct successors 10, 15, 25, 35, 55, but not: 20, 30, 40, 45 or 50. In fact: $5|10$ and $10|20$, hence 20 is not the *direct* successor of 5 (because 10 is in between), and so on.

Something completely different happens in the structure $\langle \mathbb{R}, < \rangle$, the irreflexive (linear) ordering structure of the real numbers with the relation 'smaller than': there, every number has many *successors* (all the numbers which are bigger than this number), but *no single* number has a *direct* successor. In fact, assume that y is a direct successor of x. Then $x < y$ and nothing can be in between x and y. But this is impossible, because in this case we always have for example that

$$x < \tfrac{x+y}{2} < y,$$

and $\tfrac{x+y}{2}$ is also in $\mathbb{R}$.

Next to the 'direct successor' we obviously have the concept 'direct predecessor'. Some examples:

Example 20.5.1

- In the irreflexive structure $\langle \mathbb{N}, < \rangle$ (and hence also in the reflexive structure $\langle \mathbb{N}, \leq \rangle$) every element n has a direct predecessor (namely $n - 1$), except the number 0.

- In $\langle \mathbb{N}^+, \mid \rangle$ every element has at least one direct predecessor, except the number 1. For example, 3 and 2 are both direct predecessors of 6, and 1 is a direct predecessor of 7.

- *No single element of* ⟨ℝ, <⟩ *(resp.* ⟨ℝ, ≤⟩*) has a direct predecessor.*

- *In the lexicographic ordering on* ℕ × ℕ*, described in the previous section, every element* (k, l) *has a direct successor, namely* $(k, l+1)$*. But not every element has a direct predecessor. For* $(0, 0)$ *this is obvious, because* $(0, 0)$ *is the 'smallest' element, which has no single predecessor. But also* $(1, 0)$*, and* $(2, 0)$*, and so on, don't have any direct predecessors (whereas they each have an infinite number of 'normal' predecessors)!*

Hence, for some orderings, the concept 'direct successor' (or 'direct predecessor') is useful, for others this is not the case. If we can speak about direct successors (or direct predecessors), then the ordering structure can often be given with a diagram, a so-called *Hasse diagram*.[1] Hasse diagrams are especially informative for *finite* sets.

We give a couple of examples in order to illustrate what a Hasse diagram looks like and how convenient such a diagram can be in order to get an 'image' of the structure.

First, we draw a diagram of the set $\{1, 2, \ldots, 10\}$ with the divisibility ordering ' | '. Cf. Figure 20.2.

We see there how every labeled node is related in *upward* direction (via a branch) to the nodes of the direct successors of that label.

For example: the node with label 2 is related in upward direction, by three branches, to the nodes with labels 4, 6 and 10. These last three are precisely the direct successors of 2 inside $\{1, 2, \ldots, 10\}$.

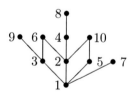

Figure 20.2: A Hasse diagram for ⟨$\{1, 2, \ldots, 10\}$, | ⟩

If we allow to go higher up along the branches, we find *all* the successors. If we look at 2, then above it we find 6, 4, 10, and also 8 – the successors

---

[1]Helmut Hasse (1898 - 1979) was a known German number theorist. The diagrams called after him, appear in his book *Vorlesungen über Klassenkörpertheorie*, Physica-Verlag, Universität Marburg, 1967.

of 2 in this structure are hence 4, 6, 8 and 10. Also the *direct predecessors* can be immediately read: 2 has 1 as (unique) direct predecessor, and 10 has both 2 and 5.

From the Hasse diagram we can also read that for example 3 and 10 are *incomparable*: there is no 'ascending path' (along the branches of the diagram) from 3 to 10 or from 10 to 3.

Our next example is the structure $\langle \mathcal{P}(A), \subseteq \rangle$, where we take for A the three elements set $\{0, 1, 2\}$. The number of elements of $\mathcal{P}(A)$ is 8, and the corresponding Hasse diagram is given in Figure 20.3. From that diagram it appears that 'crossing over of branches' is sometimes inevitable.

For big sets it becomes difficult and sometimes impossible to draw conveniently arranged Hasse diagrams. For infinite sets we can at best give an idea of the ordering, see for example the left hand side and the middle diagram in Figure 20.1. (The right hand side diagram in that figure is *not* a Hasse diagram, because there are no direct successors in $\langle \mathbb{R}, \leq \rangle$.)

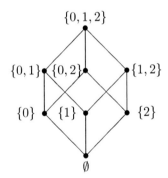

Figure 20.3: A Hasse diagram for $\langle \mathcal{P}(\{0, 1, 2\}), \subseteq \rangle$

20.6 Extreme elements

Often, for a given reflexive ordering $\langle A, R \rangle$, one is interested in a *subset* A' of the original A (hence $A' \subseteq A$). The 'substructure' $\langle A', R \rangle$ is then also a reflexive ordering, as can be easily shown (in fact, the properties reflexivity, antisymmetry and transitivity remain valid for A').

Similar observations hold for *ir*reflexive orderings: if $\langle A, S \rangle$ is an irreflexive ordering and A' is a subset of A, then also $\langle A', S \rangle$ is an irreflexive ordering.

Interesting objects in such subsets A' are *extreme elements* of A', with respect to the order relation. These can be for example elements which have no successor (or no predecessor). In Figure 20.2, for example, none of 6, 7, 8, 9 and 10 has any successor and 1 does not have any predecessor. Such elements are respectively called *maximal* and *minimal* in the subset $\{1, 2, \ldots, 10\}$ of $\mathbb{N}^+$.

We can summarize these concepts in formula form, as follows.

Let $\langle A, R \rangle$ be a *reflexive* ordering and let A' be a subset of A. Then $m \in A'$ is a *maximal element* if

$$\forall_x[x \in A' : mRx \Rightarrow m = x],$$

(hence m has no successor in A': the only possible x with mRx is m itself), and $m \in A'$ is a *minimal element* if

$$\forall_x[x \in A' : xRm \Rightarrow x = m]$$

(hence m has no predecessor in A').

For an *irreflexive* ordering S, the 'escape clause' $m = x$ is cut off. Then we say:

$m \in A'$ is a maximal element of $\langle A, S \rangle$, if $\forall_x[x \in A' : \neg(mSx)]$;
$m \in A'$ is a minimal element of $\langle A, S \rangle$, if $\forall_x[x \in A' : \neg(xSm)]$.

Maximal respectively minimal elements can be described as a kind of *local* (or *relative*) extremes: there are no 'higher' or 'lower' elements *nearby*.

Sometimes, in a structure $\langle A, R \rangle$ with $A' \subseteq A$, there may exist a *global* (or *absolute*) extreme in the subset A', for example a *maximum*. Element $m \in A'$ is called a maximum of A' if it is the successor of ('it is bigger than') *all other* elements of A'.

Hence, in a *reflexive* structure $\langle A, R \rangle$ with $A' \subseteq A$, we have that $m \in A'$ is a maximum of A' if

$$\forall_x[x \in A' : xRm].$$

In an *irreflexive* structure $\langle A, S \rangle$ (where we do not allow mSm), this becomes: $m \in A'$ is a maximum of A' if

$$\forall_x[x \in A' \wedge x \neq m : xSm].$$

It is not difficult to see that such a maximum, if it exists, is also *unique*. There is hence *at most one* maximum. For this we give a short proof, which we write in a compact form (see Section 18.2 for how the concept 'at most one' is formalized, which we apply here in the last line of the proof below).

Let $\langle A, R \rangle$ be a reflexive ordering with $A' \subseteq A$. (A proof for an *irreflexive* ordering goes similarly.)

{ Assume: }

> var m_1, m_2; $m_1, m_2 \in A'$
>
> > { Assume: }
> >
> > > m_1 is a maximum of A' and so is m_2
> > >
> > > > { Definition of 'maximum', twice: }
> > > >
> > > > $\forall_x[x \in A' : xRm_1]$ and $\forall_x[x \in A' : xRm_2]$
> > > >
> > > > { $\forall$-elim, twice, where $x = m_2$ resp. $x = m_1$: }
> > > >
> > > > m_2Rm_1 and m_1Rm_2
> > > >
> > > > { By antisymmetry of R: }
> > > >
> > > > $m_1 = m_2$
>
> { $\Rightarrow$-intro, $\forall$-intro: }
>
> $\forall_{m_1,m_2}[m_1, m_2 \in A' :$
>
> $(m_1$ is a maximum of A' and so is $m_2) \Rightarrow m_1 = m_2]$

Because such a maximum is unique, if it exists, we speak of *the* maximum. It is also called the *top*, and denoted by: $\top$.

Similarly, we can define when $m \in A'$ is the *minimum* of A' (or *bottom* of A', denoted by: $\bot$). In the reflexive/irreflexive case this becomes: $m \in A'$ is the minimum of A' if

$\forall_x[x \in A' : mRx]$ (for reflexive R);

$\forall_x[x \in A' \wedge x \neq m : mSx]$ (for irreflexive S).

Example 20.6.1

- *The reflexive ordering $\langle \{1, 2, \ldots, 10\}, \mid \rangle$ of Figure 20.2 does not have any top, but does have a bottom, namely 1. It has 1 as bottom because $1 \mid x$ for all $x \in \{1, 2, \ldots, 10\}$.*

- *The reflexive ordering $\langle \mathcal{P}(\{0, 1, 2\}), \subseteq \rangle$ of Figure 20.3 has both a top: $\{0, 1, 2\}$ and a bottom: $\emptyset$.*

- *In the irreflexive ordering $\langle \mathbb{N}, < \rangle$ we have that 0 is a minimal element and also even the minimum (the bottom), whereas there is no maximal element in $\langle \mathbb{N}, < \rangle$, let alone a maximum (or top), precisely as we expected.*

- *The orderings $\langle \mathbb{Z}, R \rangle$ where R is equal to $<$, $>$, $\leq$ or $\geq$, don't have any maximal or minimal elements, and hence no tops or bottoms. The same holds if we replace $\mathbb{Z}$ by $\mathbb{R}$.*

Remark 20.6.2 *The words 'maximal element', 'minimal element', 'maximum' and 'minimum' go well with relations which we read as 'smaller than' or 'precedes'. But the same words can be extremely deceptive for a relation R which we read as 'bigger than' or 'succeeds'. For example:*

Look at $\langle \mathbb{N}, > \rangle$, with the relation '$>$'. Now, 0 is a maximal *element! In fact, for no single $n \in \mathbb{N}$ we have $0 > n$. Even more, 0 is the maximum, because for all $x \in \mathbb{N}$ where $x \neq 0$ we have $x > 0$.*

Moreover, it is easy to see that this structure has no *minimal element(!), hence also no minimum.*

20.7   Upper and lower bounds

In the previous section, we investigated extreme elements *inside* a subset A' of a set A, with respect to a reflexive ordering $\langle A, R \rangle$ (or an irreflexive ordering $\langle A, S \rangle$).

In the present section, however, we relate the elements of A' to elements which also may be *outside* A' (but still inside the original set A).

For example, we can look at how A' is embedded in the bigger A with respect to the ordering. A first possibility is to look for those elements of the 'big' set A which are 'above' *all* the elements of the subset A' . Such elements are called upper bounds.

Hence, $b \in A$ is an *upper bound* of (the whole) A', with respect to the reflexive ordering relation R, if

$$\forall_x [x \in A' : xRb].$$

Moreover, we say that $a \in A$ is a *lower bound* of A' if

$$\forall_x [x \in A' : aRx].$$

Remark 20.7.1 *If A' has a* maximum, *then obviously this element is immediately an upper bound of A'. This is the only case where the upper bound of A' is also in A'. All other possible upper bounds are outside A' (but obviously in A). (A similar remark holds for a* minimum.)

Generally, one only speaks of upper and lower bounds if the relation is a *reflexive* ordering. Therefore, in the rest of this section, we concentrate on *reflexive orderings only*; however, similar notions as described below, exist for *ir*reflexive orderings.

Example 20.7.2

- *Take* $A' = \{1, 2, \ldots, 10\}$, *a subset of* $\mathbb{N}^+$. *Then the reflexive ordering* $\langle A', \mid \rangle$ *(see the Hasse diagram in Figure 20.2) is a 'subordering' of* $\langle \mathbb{N}^+, \mid \rangle$. *What are the upper bounds of A' in $\mathbb{N}^+$ with respect to the division relation '$\mid$'? If b is such an upper bound, then all $x \in A'$ must be divisors of b. A bit of arithmetic will give the result that b must be at least $2^3 \cdot 3^2 \cdot 5 \cdot 7 = 2520$! Every multiple of 2520 is then obviously also an upper bound.*

  For the lower bounds we are done quicker: 1 is a lower bound (because 1 is divisor of 1 up to and including 10), and it is the only one.

- *Take $\langle \mathcal{P}(\{0, 1, 2\}), \subseteq \rangle$ (see Figure 20.3) as 'subordering' of for example* $\langle \mathcal{P}(\mathbb{N}), \subseteq \rangle$. *Then $\{0, 1, 2\}$ is an upper bound, because all 8 elements of $\mathcal{P}(\{0, 1, 2\})$ are in the $\subseteq$-relation with $\{0, 1, 2\}$, as can be seen in* the figure. *(Note that $\{0, 1, 2\}$ is also* the maximum *of $\mathcal{P}(\{0, 1, 2\})$.)* Are there any more upper bounds? Yes, all subsets of $\mathbb{N}$ which contain $\{0, 1, 2\}$.

  Also here, there is a unique lower bound, namely $\emptyset$.

- *Look at the reflexive ordering $\langle \mathbb{Z}, \leq \rangle$ and let $A' = \{-2, 0, 2\} \subseteq \mathbb{Z}$. Then the structure $\langle A', \leq \rangle$ is a reflexive 'subordering' of $\langle \mathbb{Z}, \leq \rangle$. Now all the whole numbers which are bigger than or equal to 2 are upper bounds of A', and all the whole numbers which are smaller than or equal to -2 are lower bounds.*

  If on the other hand, we take A' to be the set of all *even numbers (either positive, zero or negative) of $\mathbb{Z}$, then A' will have no upper bounds in $\mathbb{Z}$, and also no lower bounds.*

- *Look at the reflexive ordering $\langle \mathbb{R}, \leq \rangle$ and take $A' = \langle 0, 1 \rangle$, the* open interval *of all real numbers between 0 and 1. The upper bounds of A' are now 1 and all the real numbers above it, the lower bounds are 0 and all the real numbers below it.*

  If we take $A' = [0, 1]$, the closed *interval of all real numbers between 0 and 1 (including 0 and 1), then this gives the same set of upper bounds and the same set of lower bounds! This also holds if we we take A' to be the two elements set $\{0, 1\}$, or the set $[0, \frac{1}{4}] \cup [\frac{3}{4}, 1]$ or the set $\{1, \frac{1}{2}, \frac{1}{3}, \frac{1}{4}, \ldots\}$. If on the other hand we take $A' = \mathbb{N}$, then we will have the same set of lower bounds, but an* empty *set of upper bounds.*

Often, a non-empty set of upper bounds has a minimum, according to the definition of the previous section. Such a minimum is called '*least upper bound'*, or *'supremum'*. The word 'least upper bound' is usually shortened to *lub*.

Similarly, if a non-empty set of lower bounds has a maximum, then it is called *'greatest lower bound'* or *'infimum'*. Again, one usually shortens the word 'greatest lower bound', viz. to *glb*.

Example 20.7.3 *(See also Example 20.7.2):*

- *The least upper bound of* $\{1, 2, \ldots, 10\}$ *in* $\mathbb{N}^!$ *with respect to the relation '* $\mid$ *', is* 2520. *The greatest lower bound is* 1.

- *The least upper bound of* $\mathcal{P}(\{0, 1, 2\})$ *in* $\mathcal{P}(\mathbb{N})$ *with respect to* $\subseteq$ *is* $\{0, 1, 2\}$, *the greatest upper bound is* $\emptyset$.

- *For the open interval* $\langle 0, 1 \rangle$, *the least upper bound in* $\mathbb{R}$ *(with respect to* $\leq$*) is* 1 *and the greatest lower bound is* 0. *If on the other hand we are only allowed to look in* $\mathbb{R}^+$ *(the set of the positive real numbers), then* $\langle 0, 1 \rangle$ *still has the least upper bound* 1, *but no greatest lower bound (even no lower bounds at all).*

Remark 20.7.4 *It is a bit tricky to see that a non empty set of upper bounds does not always have a* minimum. *For a counterexample, look at the sets* $V = \{-1, -\frac{1}{2}, -\frac{1}{3}, -\frac{1}{4}, \ldots\}$ *and* $W = \{1, \frac{1}{2}, \frac{1}{3}, \frac{1}{4}, \ldots\}$. *Consider now* V *as a subset of* $V \cup W$, *both with the usual ordering* $\leq$. *Then* every element of W *is an upper bound of* V, *or, said differently: the set of all upper bounds of* V *which come from* $V \cup W$, *is precisely this* W. *But obviously* W *does not have any minimum, hence* V *has no* least upper bound *in* $V \cup W$.

In order to see how proofs of upper and lower bounds go, we show the following:

Lemma 20.7.5 *Let* $\langle A, R \rangle$ *be a reflexive ordering and* A' *be a non-empty subset of* A. *Then for every lower bound* a *of* A' *and for every upper bound* b *of* A' *we have that* aRb.

Proof:

{ Assume: }

| var a, b; $a, b \in A$ |

    { Assume: }

| a is a lower bound of A' and b is an upper bound of A' |

      { Definition of 'lower bound' resp. 'upper bound': }

(1): $\forall_x[x \in A' : aRx]$ and (2): $\forall_x[x \in A' : xRb]$.

{ Given: }

A' is not empty.

{ Property of $\emptyset$, and Remark 16.7.1: }

$\exists_y[y \in A']$

{ $\exists^*$-elim: }

Pick a y with $y \in A'$.

{ $\forall$-elim, twice, on (1) and (2): }

aRy and yRb

{ By transitivity of R: }

aRb

{ $\Rightarrow$-intro, $\forall$-intro: }

$\forall_{a,b}[a, b \in A$:

    $(a$ is a lower bound of A' and b is an upper bound of $A') \Rightarrow aRb]$

Hence, indeed as we expected: every lower bound is 'under' every upper bound (and the whole A' is 'in between'). Note that in this proof it was enough to use an '*arbitrary*' y of the non-empty A' in order to derive by transitivity that aRb. Which y this is does not matter: every y in A' is good.

20.8 Well-ordering and well-foundedness

In this section we will see that there is a general form of 'induction' which helps us to deliver proofs for irreflexive ordered sets, provided that *the ordering ensures that there always is a kind of 'basis'*.

The last-mentioned requirement is intuitively obvious: induction must always *start* somewhere before it can continue further via the *steps*. This holds for both the 'normal' induction (see Section 19.3) and the strong induction (Section 19.5, see the case $k = 0$): without the *Basis* you cannot take off.

(See also the Remark in Section 19.3, where we give an example of an inductive proof which does not work, because the basis fails.)

We only consider *irreflexive* orderings in the present section, and start with *linear* ones.

How can we ensure for an irreflexive linear ordering $\langle A, S \rangle$ that a kind of basis exists, in order to be able to use 'induction'?

This amounts to the following *minimum property*:

$$\forall_{A'}[A' \subseteq A \wedge A' \neq \emptyset : \exists_m[m \in A' : m \text{ is the minimum of } A']] ,$$

in words: 'every non-empty subset of A has a minimum'.

An irreflexive linear ordering which also has the minimum property, is called a *well-ordering*. Hence the structure $\langle A, S \rangle$ is a well-ordering (or a 'well-ordered structure') if $\langle A, S \rangle$ satisfies the four properties of an irreflexive linear ordering – hence (1) is irreflexive, (2) strictly antisymmetric, (3) transitive and (4) linear – and also (5) satisfies the minimum property.

Remark 20.8.1 *The word well-ordering is a translation from German, where it is called 'Wohlordnung'.*

Seen intuitively: in a well-ordering, the minimum property ensures that there is always a *Basis* (which is that *minimum*). The ordering properties ensure that there always is a possible *Step*.

Example 20.8.2

- *The structure $\langle \mathbb{N}, < \rangle$ is a well-ordering (every non-empty subset of $\mathbb{N}$ has a minimum, which is a mathematical fact), but $\langle \mathbb{Z}, < \rangle$ is not a well-ordering ($\mathbb{Z}$ itself for example does not have any minimum). For this reason, induction in $\mathbb{N}$ is possible (see Section 19.3), and even strong induction (see Section 19.5), but this is not the case for $\mathbb{Z}$.*

- *Another example of well-ordering is the structure $\langle \{n \in \mathbb{Z} | n \geq a\}, < \rangle$, for every $a \in \mathbb{Z}$. The set $\{n \in \mathbb{Z} | n \geq a\}$ is actually a kind of a 'copy' of $\mathbb{N}$, but then 'shifted' by a distance a. You can also say: if you 'cut off' everything in $\mathbb{Z}$ which is under a, then what remains will have the minimum property.*

  In $\{n \in \mathbb{Z} | n \geq a\}$, induction is hence again possible. Indeed, see the methods 'induction from start point a' and 'strong induction from start point a', in Section 19.3 resp. 19.5.

- *Also the irreflexive lexicographic ordering on $\mathbb{N} \times \mathbb{N}$ is a well-ordering. We have seen in Section 20.5 that in these orderings there are elements like $(1,0)$, $(2,0)$, ... – which have predecessors, but no direct predecessors (such elements do not exist in $\mathbb{N}$ and $\{n \in \mathbb{Z} | n \geq a\}$). Still, here too induction can be applied, which is a consequence of the following.*

Induction can be applied on every well-ordering $\langle A, S \rangle$. In such a case, one speaks of *transfinite induction*, which is a direct generalization of what we called *strong induction* in Section 19.5. It can be formulated as follows.

Let P be a predicate on A in the well-ordering $\langle A, S \rangle$. Then the principle of transfinite induction says:

if $\forall_k [k \in A : \forall_j [j \in A \land jSk : P(j)] \Rightarrow P(k)]$,
then $\forall_n [n \in A : P(n)]$.

Note here that indeed we have 'the same' formulas as in Section 19.5, but with $\mathbb{N}$ generalized to the arbitrary set A, and $<$ to the well-ordered relation S on A.

The *induction hypothesis* is hence in this case: $\forall_j [j \in A \land jSk : P(j)]$. So: for all '$S$-predecessors' of k the predicate P already holds.

Remark 20.8.3 *The word 'transfinite' points to the fact that with this form of induction we can go 'past finiteness'. Look for example at the irreflexive lexicographic ordering $\langle \mathbb{N} \times \mathbb{N}, < \rangle$, where the ordering can be described as follows (see Section 20.3):*
$$(0,0) < (0,1) < (0,2) < \ldots < (1,0) < (1,1) < (1,2) < \ldots < (2,0) <$$
$$(2,1) < (2,2) < \ldots < \ldots .$$
This lexicographic ordering is a well-ordering, hence the being-true of a predicate Q on $\mathbb{N} \times \mathbb{N}$ for all $(n,m) \in \mathbb{N} \times \mathbb{N}$ can be proven with transfinite induction. The 'step' of the induction is now not always 'finite', in order for example to be able to reach $(1,0)$, we must jump over an 'infinite hole'.

The principle of transfinite induction can also be applied in a more general form, namely for *non-linear* irreflexive orderings like tree constructing orderings. These latter we came across, for example, with inductive definitions of formula sets (see Section 19.6). The set $\mathcal{H}$ of parentheses formulas, as was defined in Example 2 of that section, has a 'natural' irreflexive ordering S which we can describe by: $h_1 S h_2$ if the construction of h_1 precedes (and is needed for) the construction of h_2. Then we have for example (see also the construction tree as drawn in that section):

$\varepsilon \; S \; () \; S \; (()) \; S \; (())() \; S \; ((())()) \; S \; (()()())((())()) \; .$

Now, the general case that we mentioned is the following: the principle of transfinite induction holds for every irreflexive ordering $\langle A, S \rangle$ which has the property that it is *well-founded*; where 'well-foundedness' means:

every sequence $\ldots, x_2, x_1, x_0$ of elements of A, where $x_{n+1} S x_n$ for all $n \in \mathbb{N}$, must be *finite*.

Hence the following must hold: if we start with an arbitrary $x_0 \in A$, and then we look for an $x_1 \in A$ where $x_1 S x_0$, and then again an x_2 where

$x_2 S x_1$, and so on, then we reach a certain moment where we cannot go further. (Compare with $\mathbb{N}$ and the relation $<$: if we start with an arbitrary $n_0 \in \mathbb{N}$, and then take an n_1 where $n_1 < n_0$, and then an n_2 where $n_2 < n_1$, and so on, then definitely this must stop after some time.)

The set $\mathcal{H}$ of parentheses formulas with the ordering just described is well-founded, as can be checked easily. Intuitively speaking, well-foundedness ensures that with recursion (hence 'going backwards') we are always halted by a 'Basis', and this is why induction becomes possible. Structures like $\langle \mathbb{Z}, < \rangle$, where the basis is missing, are obviously not suitable for this.

This principle of transfinite induction for well-founded orderings, as described here, has a lot to do with the structural induction that we have described in Section 19.7. We leave out the full details and assume that the above is sufficient to get the idea.

20.9   Exercises

20.1 Consider on $\mathbb{N}^+$ the relation R where xRy if the number of divisors of x is smaller than or equal to the number of divisors of y.

   (a) Show that $1Rx$ for every $x \in \mathbb{N}^+$, and that for every prime number p and every $x \neq 1$ we have that pRx.

   (b) Show that $\langle \mathbb{N}^+, R \rangle$ is a reflexive quasi-ordering.

   (c) Is $\langle \mathbb{N}^+, R \rangle$ also a reflexive ordering?

20.2 Let S be a relation on A which is irreflexive and transitive. Give a derivation in flag format, following the lines of the proof in Remark 20.2.4, that S is strictly antisymmetric.

20.3 Given the reflexive orderings $\langle A, R_1 \rangle$ and $\langle B, R_2 \rangle$, we define R_3 on $A \times B$ by:

$(x, y) R_3 (x', y')$ if xR_1x' and yR_2y'.

   (a) Prove that $\langle A \times B, R_3 \rangle$ is a reflexive ordering, again (the so-called reflexive *Cartesian* ordering).

   (b) Let $A = B = \mathbb{R}$ and $R_1 = R_2 = \,\leq$. We also denote R_3 by the symbol '$\leq$'. How can one geometrically see in $\mathbb{R}^2$, the flat plane, that $(x, y) \leq (x', y')$?

   (c) Assume, moreover, that $\langle A, R_1 \rangle$ and $\langle B, R_2 \rangle$ are *linear*. Is the Cartesian ordering $\langle A \times B, R_3 \rangle$ then necessarily linear?

20.4 Let Φ be the set of all functions $f : \mathbb{R} \to \mathbb{R}$.

We define on Φ the relation $<$ by:

$f < g$ if $\forall_x [x \in \mathbb{R} : f(x) < g(x)]$.

(a) Let i be the *identity function*, that is the function for which we have:

$\forall_x [x \in \mathbb{R} : i(x) = x]$.

Find two functions g and h such that $g < i < h$.

(b) Prove that $\langle \Phi, < \rangle$ is an irreflexive ordering.

(c) Is it also a *linear* ordering?

20.5 Check that the following *reflexive* lexicographic orderings are linear:

(a) $\langle \mathbb{Z} \times \mathbb{Z}, \le \rangle$.

(b) $\langle \mathbb{N}^+ \times \mathbb{N}^+, \, | \, \rangle$.

(c) $\langle \mathcal{P}(\mathbb{N}^+) \times \mathcal{P}(\mathbb{N}^+), \subseteq \rangle$.

20.6 For every $n \in \mathbb{N}^+$ we define A_n as the set of all positive divisors of n.

(a) Draw a Hasse-diagram for $\langle A_{36}, \, | \, \rangle$.

(b) For which $n \in \mathbb{N}^+$ does $\langle A_n, \, | \, \rangle$ produce a Hasse diagram with the same graph structure as $\langle A_{36}, \, | \, \rangle$?

(c) For which $n \in \mathbb{N}^+$ is $\langle A_n, \, | \, \rangle$ a *linear* ordering?

20.7 Take n to be an element of $\mathbb{N}^+$ which is greater than 1. The set $\{0, 1\}^n$ consists of all sequences $(x_1, \ldots, x_n)$ where $x_i \in \{0, 1\}$.

On $\{0, 1\}^n$ we define the relation $\le$ by

$(x_1, \ldots, x_n) \le (x_1', \ldots, x_n')$ if $\forall_i [1 \le i \le n : x_i \le x_i']$.

(a) Prove that $\langle \{0, 1\}^n, \le \rangle$ is a reflexive ordering.

(b) Show that there are incomparable elements in $\langle \{0, 1\}^n, \le \rangle$.

(c) Draw a Hasse diagram for $\langle \{0, 1\}^3, \le \rangle$.

(d) Compare this diagram with that of $\langle \mathcal{P}(\{1, 2, 3\}), \subseteq \rangle$ and clarify the common features.

(e) For which $n \in \mathbb{N}^+$ does the reflexive ordering $\langle A_n, \, | \, \rangle$ of Exercise 20.6 lead to a Hasse-diagram with the same graph structure as the two above described structures?

20.8 (a) Let $A := \{2, 3, 4, 6, 8, 12\}$. Draw a Hasse diagram of $\langle A, \, | \, \rangle$.

(b) Let $B := \{ \{2\}, \{2,4\}, \{2,4,8\}, \{3\}, \{2,3,6\}, \{2,3,4,6,12\} \}$. Draw a Hasse diagram for $\langle B, \subseteq \rangle$.

(c) Give a process with which from a reflexive ordering $\langle A, R \rangle$ with a Hasse diagram, we can always make another reflexive ordering $\langle B, \subseteq \rangle$, also with a Hasse diagram, such that,
- the Hasse diagrams have the same graph structures,

and
- B consists of a collection of subsets of A.

20.9 A *partition* of a number $n \in \mathbb{N}^+$ is a division of n into a number of summands. So for example $12 = 5 + 7$ and $12 = 2 + 2 + 3 + 5$ are two partitions of 12. The order of the summands does not make any difference, so $2 + 2 + 3 + 5$ and $5 + 2 + 3 + 2$ are *the same* partitions of 12 (but $5 + 7$ is another one).

If in such a partition, we partition further one of the summands, we get a *subpartition* of the old partition, also if we continue this process. So, $1 + 2 + 2 + 7$ is a subpartition of $1 + 4 + 7$ and also of $5 + 7$.

Give a Hasse diagram which consists of all partitions of 6 and gives the subpartition relation between these partitions.

20.10 Σ^* is the set of all finite sequences of zeros and/or ones, including the empty sequence ε. We order Σ^* by:

$u \leq v$ if u is a *prefix* of v.

(A prefix is an unbroken starting piece of length ≥ 0, example: ε, 0, 01, 010 and 0100 are all prefixes of 0100.)

(a) Prove that $\langle \Sigma^*, \leq \rangle$ is a reflexive ordering.

(b) Draw a Hasse diagram which describes the prefix ordering of all sequences of Σ^* of length ≤ 3.

(c) Does $\langle \Sigma^*, \leq \rangle$ have maximal or minimal elements? What about if we limit Σ^* to the sequences of length ≤ 3?

(d) The same questions for maximum and minimum.

20.11 Let $\langle A, R \rangle$ be a reflexive ordering and $A' \subseteq A$.

(a) Assume that A' has a maximum a' and A has a maximum a. Prove that $a' R a$.

(b) Find out whether we always have: if A has a maximum, then A' does too.

(c) Idem: if A' has a maximum, then A does too.

20.12 Consider the reflexive structure $\langle \{2,3,6\} \times \{2,3,6\}, \mid \rangle$.

   (a) Give Hasse diagrams for this structure, one for the case the ordering is lexicographic, and another for the case that the ordering is Cartesian (see the above Exercise 20.3).

   (b) Say in both cases what the maximal and minimal elements are, and what the maximum and minimum are (if they exist).

20.13 Let $\langle A, R_1 \rangle$ and $\langle B, R_2 \rangle$ be reflexive orderings and R_3 be the reflexive lexicographic ordering on $A \times B$.

   Prove that: if (x,y) is a maximal element of $\langle A \times B, R_3 \rangle$, then x is a maximal element of $\langle A, R_1 \rangle$ and y is a maximal element of $\langle B, R_2 \rangle$.

20.14 Determine in $\langle \mathbb{R}, \leq \rangle$ the greatest lower bound and the least upper bound (if they exist) of the following subsets:

   (a) The n-points set $\{a_0, a_1, \ldots a_{n-1}\}$ where $a_i \in \mathbb{R}$.

   (b) $[0, 1]$.

   (c) $\langle 0, 1 \rangle$.

   (d) $\{1, \frac{1}{2}, \frac{1}{3}, \ldots\}$.

   (e) $\{\frac{1}{2}, -\frac{2}{3}, \frac{3}{4}, -\frac{4}{5}, \frac{5}{6}, -\frac{6}{7}, \ldots\}$.

   (f) $\mathbb{N}$.

20.15 (a) Let $\langle A, R \rangle$ be a reflexive ordering. Prove that every subset A' of A can only have at most *one* least upper bound.

   (b) Give a general description of the least upper bound of a two-element set $\{k, l\}$ in $\langle \mathbb{N}^+, \mid \rangle$.

   (c) The same question for the least upper bound of a two-element set $\{A', A''\}$ in the reflexive ordering $\langle \mathcal{P}(A), \subseteq \rangle$.

   (d) What is the least upper bound of the following set (consisting of three elements): $\{(x_1, \ldots, x_n), (x'_1, \ldots, x'_n), (x''_1, \ldots, x''_n)\}$, in the reflexive ordering $\langle \{0,1\}^n, \leq \rangle$ of Exercise 20.7?

20.16 Consider $\mathbb{N}^2$ with the reflexive lexicographic ordering. Determine the greatest lower bound and the least upper bound (if they exist) of the following subsets:

   (a) $\{(x,y) \in \mathbb{N}^2 \mid x = 3\}$.

(b) $\{(x, y) \in \mathbb{N}^2 | y = 3\}$.

(c) $\{(x, y) \in \mathbb{N}^2 | x + y = 5\}$.

20.17 Consider the following irreflexive ordering relation S on $\mathbb{N}$ where:

xSy if (x is even and y is odd) or

(x is even and y is even and $x < y$) or

(x is odd and y is odd and $x < y$).

(a) Show that this ordering is linear.

(b) Show that it is a well-ordering.

(c) Does every $n \in \mathbb{N}$ has a direct successor with this ordering? Or a direct predecessor?

20.18 (a) Prove that for every denumerable set A we can find a relation S such that $\langle A, S \rangle$ is a well-ordering.

(b) Let $\langle A, S \rangle$ be a well-ordering. Show that $\langle A, S \rangle$ is well-founded.

Further reading

If you have reached so far, then you already have acquired a good knowledge of logic as a reasoning tool. Congratulations for coming so far, you are now well equipped to be a better student of mathematics or of computer science. The tools you have learnt in this book will be of use for you throughout your undergraduate studies, and very likely also in the different graduate directions you will take.

During your course, you may have decided that you like something more than another and that you want to learn more about a particular topic that you met in this book. This chapter will introduce some other books that you may want to read to help you both in this course, and to build a more profound knowledge for your future directions. There are many books written on the subject and as logic has wide ranging applications, and hence so much is written on logic and its applications, it is not feasible for us to list all these books. Instead, we chose a very small number of the available books. As these books have more references inside them too, soon you will be able to decide which books are the right ones for you.

We classify the books according to the subjects they represent best. Happy reading.

General introductions

W. Hodges, *Logic*, Penguin books, 1977. Reprinted 1978, 1980, 1981, 1982, 1984, 1985, 1986, 1988.

G. Priest, *Logic, a very short introduction*, Oxford University Press, 2000.

Z. Sardar, J. Ravetz and B. van Loon, *Introducing Mathematics*, Totem Books, 1999.

Introductory textbooks

P. Eccles, *An introduction to mathematical reasoning*, Cambridge University

Press, 2000.

K. Devlin, *Sets, Functions and logic, An introduction to abstract mathematics*, Chapman & Hall, 1981. Reprinted in 2000 by CRC.

A. Stolyar, *Introduction to elementary mathematical logic*, Dover, 1970.

M. Haight, *The snake & the fox, an introduction to logic*, Routledge, 1999.

P. Tomassi, *Logic*, Routledge, 1999.

The flag notation and Fitch style

R. Thomason, *Symbolic Logic, an introduction*, MacMillan publishing, 1970.

F. Fitch, *Symbolic Logic*, The Ronald Press Company, 1952.

Historical

G. Boole, *The mathematical analysis of logic*, 1847. Reprinted by Hallescher Verlag in 2001.

N. Bourbaki, *Elements of the history of mathematics*, Springer Verlag, 1999.

A. Tarski, *Introduction to Logic and to the methodology of deductive sciences*, Dover, 1995. Reprinted from the 1941 edition by OUP.

W. Quine, *Elementary logic*, Harvard University Press, 1941.

Bibliographical

M. Detlefsen, D. McCarty, J. Bacon, *Logic from A to Z*, Routledge, 1999.

Puzzles and brainteasers

L. Carroll, *Mathematical Recreations of Lewis Carroll: Symbolic Logic, Game of Logic*, Dover, 1958. Reprinted from two books of Carroll published by MacMillan & Co., in 1897 and 1887.

R. Moore (ed.), *The Dell book of logic problems*, Dell publishers, 1984.

R. Moore (ed.), *The Dell book of logic problems #2*, Dell publishers, 1986.

Set theory, lattices and order

E. Kamke, *Theory of sets*, Dover, 1950.

M. Machover, *Set theory, logic and their limitations*, Cambridge University Press, 1996.

B. Davey and H. Priestly, *Introduction to lattices and order*, Cambridge University Press, 2002.

Advanced

G. Boolos, *Logic, Logic, and Logic*, Harvard University Press, 1998.

G. Boolos and R. Jeffrey, *Computability and Logic*, Cambridge University Press, 1980.

R. Cori and D. Lascar, *Mathematical Logic, A course with exercises, Part I*, Oxford University Press, 2000.

R. Cori and D. Lascar, *Mathematical Logic, A course with exercises, Part II*, Oxford University Press, 2001.

Applications and other logics

A. Nerode and R. Shore, *Logic for applications*, Springer-Verlag, 1997.

P. Hájek, *Metamathematics of fuzzy logic*, Kluwer Academic Publishers, 1998.

S. Popkorn, *First steps in Modal Logic*, Cambridge University Press, 1994.

D. van Dalen, *Logic and Structure*, Springer, 1997.

Structured programming

D. Gries, *The Science of Programming*, Springer-Verlag, 1981.

E. Dijkstra and W. Feijen, *A Method of Programming*, Addison-Wesley, 1988.

A. Kaldewaij, *Programming, The Derivation of Algorithms*, Prentice Hall, 1990.

List of symbols

Index

absolute extreme, 336
abstract function-value, 104
abstract predicate, 87
abstract proposition, 10, 35, 71, 300
abstract reasoning, 137
abstract set, 203
addition, 284
addition of classes, 245
aleph-one, 314
aleph-zero, 314
algebra
    Boolean, 24, 45
alternative $\vee$-elim, 174
alternative $\exists$-elim, 191
alternative $\exists$-intro, 187
and, 9
antisymmetric relation, 323
antisymmetric relation
    strictly, 324
antisymmetry, 323, 325
arbitrary number, 178
arbitrary variable, 124
Aristotle, 3, 5
arrow, 21, 41, 235, 253
arrow
    double, 22
arrow graph, 233, 254
as many, 305
associativity, 39
Associativity
    rule of the, 40, 41

associativity of $\cap$ and $\cup$, 210
assume, 43, 99
assumption, 43
assumption
    induction, 287
at least one, 257, 264
at most one, 256, 257, 264, 266
axioms of Peano, 284, 286

backward reasoning, 133, 134
bag, 104
Barbara, 3, 5
basis, 10, 286, 289–291, 301–303, 341
basis case, 300
Bernoulli
    inequality of, 288
bi-implication, 22, 23, 43
Bi-implication
    rule of the, 48
bijection, 264, 267, 272
binary, 73
binary relation, 231
binder
    scope of, 110
binding of variable, 103, 105, 109
Boole, 5
Boolean algebra, 24, 45
Boolean function, 28
Boolean logic, 5
Boolean value, 17, 253
Booleans, 74
bottom, 337

Tables

Part I

Truth-Tables						
P	Q	$P \wedge Q$	$P \vee Q$	$\neg P$	$P \Rightarrow Q$	$P \Leftrightarrow Q$
0	0	0	0	1	1	1
0	1	0	1		1	0
1	0	0	1	0	0	0
1	1	1	1		1	1

Equivalences for connectives

Commutativity:	Associativity:
$P \wedge Q \overset{val}{=\!=} Q \wedge P,$	$(P \wedge Q) \wedge R \overset{val}{=\!=} P \wedge (Q \wedge R),$
$P \vee Q \overset{val}{=\!=} Q \vee P,$	$(P \vee Q) \vee R \overset{val}{=\!=} P \vee (Q \vee R),$
$P \Leftrightarrow Q \overset{val}{=\!=} Q \Leftrightarrow P$	$(P \Leftrightarrow Q) \Leftrightarrow R \overset{val}{=\!=}$
	$\qquad\qquad P \Leftrightarrow (Q \Leftrightarrow R)$

Idempotence:	Double Negation:
$P \wedge P \overset{val}{=\!=} P,$	$\neg\neg P \overset{val}{=\!=} P$
$P \vee P \overset{val}{=\!=} P$	

Inversion:	True/False-elimination:
$\neg \text{True} \overset{val}{=\!=} \text{False},$	$P \wedge \text{True} \overset{val}{=\!=} P,$
$\neg \text{False} \overset{val}{=\!=} \text{True}$	$P \wedge \text{False} \overset{val}{=\!=} \text{False},$
	$P \vee \text{True} \overset{val}{=\!=} \text{True},$
	$P \vee \text{False} \overset{val}{=\!=} P$

Negation:	Contradiction:
$\neg P \overset{val}{=\!=} P \Rightarrow \text{False}$	$P \wedge \neg P \overset{val}{=\!=} \text{False}$
	Excluded Middle:
	$P \vee \neg P \overset{val}{=\!=} \text{True}$

Distributivity:	De Morgan:
$P \wedge (Q \vee R) \overset{val}{=\!=} (P \wedge Q) \vee (P \wedge R),$	$\neg(P \wedge Q) \overset{val}{=\!=} \neg P \vee \neg Q,$
$P \vee (Q \wedge R) \overset{val}{=\!=} (P \vee Q) \wedge (P \vee R)$	$\neg(P \vee Q) \overset{val}{=\!=} \neg P \wedge \neg Q$

Implication:	Contraposition:
$P \Rightarrow Q \overset{val}{=\!=} \neg P \vee Q,$	$P \Rightarrow Q \overset{val}{=\!=} \neg Q \Rightarrow \neg P$
$P \vee Q \overset{val}{=\!=} \neg P \Rightarrow Q$	

Bi-implication:	Self-equivalence:
$P \Leftrightarrow Q \overset{val}{=\!=} (P \Rightarrow Q) \wedge (Q \Rightarrow P)$	$P \Leftrightarrow P \overset{val}{=\!=} \text{True}$

Weakening rules

∧-∨-weakening:	Extremes:
$P \wedge Q \overset{val}{\models} P,$ $P \overset{val}{\models} P \vee Q$	False $\overset{val}{\models} P,$ $P \overset{val}{\models}$ True
Monotonicity: If $P \overset{val}{\models} Q$, then $P \wedge R \overset{val}{\models} Q \wedge R,$ If $P \overset{val}{\models} Q$, then $P \vee R \overset{val}{\models} Q \vee R$	

Equivalences for quantifiers

Bound Variable:

$\forall_x[P : Q] \overset{val}{=\!=\!=} \forall_y[P[y \text{ for } x] : Q[y \text{ for } x]],$

$\exists_x[P : Q] \overset{val}{=\!=\!=} \exists_y[P[y \text{ for } x] : Q[y \text{ for } x]]$

Domain Splitting:

$\forall_x[P \vee Q : R] \overset{val}{=\!=\!=} \forall_x[P : R] \wedge \forall_x[Q : R],$

$\exists_x[P \vee Q : R] \overset{val}{=\!=\!=} \exists_x[P : R] \vee \exists_x[Q : R]$

One-element:	Empty Domain:
$\forall_x[x = n : Q] \overset{val}{=\!=\!=} Q[n \text{ for } x],$ $\exists_x[x = n : Q] \overset{val}{=\!=\!=} Q[n \text{ for } x]$	$\forall_x[\text{False} : Q] \overset{val}{=\!=\!=} \text{True},$ $\exists_x[\text{False} : Q] \overset{val}{=\!=\!=} \text{False}$
Domain Weakening: $\forall_x[P \wedge Q : R] \overset{val}{=\!=\!=} \forall_x[P : Q \Rightarrow R],$ $\exists_x[P \wedge Q : R] \overset{val}{=\!=\!=} \exists_x[P : Q \wedge R]$	**De Morgan:** $\neg\forall_x[P : Q] \overset{val}{=\!=\!=} \exists_x[P : \neg Q],$ $\neg\exists_x[P : Q] \overset{val}{=\!=\!=} \forall_x[P : \neg Q]$

Part II

Standard derivation rules for $\wedge$ and $\Rightarrow$	
$\wedge$-introduction:	**$\wedge$-elimination:**
$\quad\quad\vdots$ $(k) \quad P$ $\quad\quad\vdots$ $(l) \quad Q$ $\quad$ { $\wedge$-intro on (k) and (l): } $(m) \quad P \wedge Q$	$\quad\quad \|\|\|$ $(k) \quad P \wedge Q$ $\quad\quad \|\|\|$ $\quad$ { $\wedge$-elim on (k): } $(m) \quad P$ resp. Q
$\Rightarrow$-introduction:	**$\Rightarrow$-elimination:**
$\quad\quad$ { Assume: } $(k) \quad \boxed{P}$ $\quad\quad\quad \vdots$ $(m{-}1) \quad Q$ $\quad$ { $\Rightarrow$-intro on $\quad\quad\quad (k)$ and $(m{-}1)$: } $(m) \quad P \Rightarrow Q$	$\quad\quad \|\|\|$ $(k) \quad P \Rightarrow Q$ $\quad\quad \|\|\|$ $(l) \quad P$ $\quad\quad \|\|\|$ $\quad$ { $\Rightarrow$-elim on $\quad\quad\quad (k)$ and (l): } $(m) \quad Q$

Reasoning with $\neg$, $\neg\neg$, $\vee$ and $\Leftrightarrow$
'$\neg$-intro' and '$\neg$-elim'   via Negation: $\neg P \stackrel{val}{=\!=} P \Rightarrow \texttt{False}$
'$\neg\neg$-intro' and '$\neg\neg$-elim'   via Double Negation: $\neg\neg P \stackrel{val}{=\!=} P$
'$\vee$-intro' and '$\vee$-elim'   via Implication: $P \vee Q \stackrel{val}{=\!=} \neg P \Rightarrow Q$ resp. $P \vee Q \stackrel{val}{=\!=} \neg Q \Rightarrow P$
'$\Leftrightarrow$-intro' and '$\Leftrightarrow$-elim'   via Bi-implication: $P \Leftrightarrow Q \stackrel{val}{=\!=} (P \Rightarrow Q) \wedge (Q \Rightarrow P)$

Reasoning with False

'False-intro' via Contradiction:	'False-elim' via Extremes:
$\vdots$	$\|\|\|$
$(l) \quad \neg P$	$(l) \quad$ **False**
$\vdots$	$\|\|\|$
$(m-1) \quad P$	$\{$ Extremes on (l): $\}$
$\{$ Contradiction on $(m-1)$ and (l): $\}$	$(m) \quad P$
$(m) \quad$ **False**	

Reasoning by contradiction

$\{$ Assume: $\}$

$(l) \quad \boxed{\neg P}$

$\qquad \vdots$

$(n-2) \quad$ False

$\{ \Rightarrow$-intro on (l) and $(n-2)$, and Negation: $\}$

$(n-1) \quad \neg\neg P$

$\{$ Double Negation on $(n-1)$: $\}$

$(n) \quad P$

Standard derivation rules for ∀

∀-introduction:	∀-elimination:

∀-introduction:

$$\{ \text{Assume:} \}$$

(k) $\boxed{\underline{\text{var}}\ x;\ P(x)}$

$\vdots$

$(m-1)$ $Q(x)$

$\{$ ∀-intro on

(k) and $(m-1)$: $\}$

(m) $\forall_x[P(x) : Q(x)]$

∀-elimination:

$||||$

(k) $\forall_x[P(x) : Q(x)]$

$||||$

(l) $P(a)$

$||||$

$\{$ ∀-elim on

(k) and (l): $\}$

(m) $Q(a)$

Reasoning with ∃

'∃-intro' and '∃-elim'
via Double Negation and De Morgan:

$$\exists_x[P(x) : Q(x)] \overset{val}{=\!=} \neg\forall_x[P(x) : \neg Q(x)]$$

Alternatives for ∃

∃*-introduction:	∃*-elimination:

∃*-introduction:

$\vdots$

(k) $P(a)$

$\vdots$

(l) $Q(a)$

$\{$ ∃*-intro on

(k) and (l): $\}$

(m) $\exists_x[P(x) : Q(x)]$

∃*-elimination:

$||||$

(k) $\exists_x[P(x) : Q(x)]$

$||||$

$\{$ ∃*-elim on (k): $\}$

(l) Pick an x with

$P(x)$ and $Q(x)$.

(x in line (l) must be 'new'.)

Part III

Sets	
$A \subseteq B \overset{\text{def}}{=} \forall_x [x \in A : x \in B]$	$A = B \overset{\text{def}}{=} A \subseteq B \land B \subseteq A$
$A \cap B \overset{\text{def}}{=}$ $\{x \in \mathbf{U} \mid x \in A \land x \in B\}$	$A \cup B \overset{\text{def}}{=}$ $\{x \in \mathbf{U} \mid x \in A \lor x \in B\}$
$A^{\mathrm{c}} \overset{\text{def}}{=} \{x \in \mathbf{U} \mid \neg(x \in A)\}$	$A \backslash B \overset{\text{def}}{=} \{x \in \mathbf{U} \mid x \in A \land \neg(x \in B)\}$
$\mathbf{U} = \{\, x \in \mathbf{U} \mid \mathtt{True}\}$	$\emptyset = \{\, x \in \mathbf{U} \mid \mathtt{False}\}$
Property of $\in$: $t \in \{x \in \mathbf{D} \mid P(x)\} \overset{val}{=\!=} t \in \mathbf{D} \land P(t)$	
Property of $\subseteq$: $A \subseteq B \land t \in A \overset{val}{\models} t \in B$	**Properties of $=$:** $A = B \overset{val}{=\!=} \forall_x [x \in A \Leftrightarrow x \in B]$ $A = B \land t \in A \overset{val}{\models} t \in B$ $A = B \land t \in B \overset{val}{\models} t \in A$
Property of $\cap$: $t \in A \cap B \overset{val}{=\!=} t \in A \land t \in B$	**Property of $\cup$:** $t \in A \cup B \overset{val}{=\!=} t \in A \lor t \in B$
Property of ^{c}: $t \in A^{\mathrm{c}} \overset{val}{=\!=} \neg(t \in A)$	**Property of $\backslash$:** $t \in A \backslash B \overset{val}{=\!=} t \in A \land \neg(t \in B)$
Properties of $\mathbf{U}$: $t \in \mathbf{U} \overset{val}{=\!=} \mathtt{True}$ $A = \mathbf{U} \overset{val}{=\!=} \forall_x [x \in A : \mathtt{True}]$	**Properties of $\emptyset$:** $t \in \emptyset \overset{val}{=\!=} \mathtt{False}$ $A = \emptyset \overset{val}{=\!=} \forall_x [x \in A : \mathtt{False}]$
Property of $\mathcal{P}$: $C \in \mathcal{P}(A) \overset{val}{=\!=} C \subseteq A$	**Properties of $\times$:** $(a,b) \in A \times B \overset{val}{=\!=}$ $\qquad\qquad a \in A \land b \in B$ $(a,b) = (a',b') \overset{val}{=\!=} a = a' \land b = b'$

Mappings
Property of 'mapping' $F : A \to B$: $\forall_x[x \in A : \exists^1_y[y \in B : F(x) = y]]$

Image and source	
Let $F : A \to B$ be a mapping, $A' \subseteq A$ and $B' \subseteq B$	
the *image* of A': $F(A') =$ $\quad \{b \in B \mid \exists_x[x \in A' : F(x) = b]\}$	the *source* of B': $F^{\leftarrow}(B') =$ $\quad \{a \in A \mid F(a) \in B'\}$
Properties of 'image': $x \in A' \overset{val}{\models} F(x) \in F(A')$ $y \in F(A') \overset{val}{=\!=}$ $\quad \exists_x[x \in A' : F(x) = y]$	**Property of 'source':** $x \in F^{\leftarrow}(B') \overset{val}{=\!=} F(x) \in B'$

Special mappings	
Property of 'surjection' $\quad$ **for** $F : A \to B$: $\forall_y[y \in B :$ $\quad \exists_x[x \in A : F(x) = y]]$	**Property of 'injection'** $\quad$ **for** $F : A \to B$: $\forall_{x_1, x_2}[x_1, x_2 \in A :$ $\quad (F(x_1) = F(x_2)) \Rightarrow (x_1 = x_2)]$
Property of 'bijection' for $F : A \to B$: $\forall_y[y \in B : \exists^1_x[x \in A : F(x) = y]]$	
Property of 'inverse function' $F^{-1} : B \to A$ $\quad$ **for bijection** $F : A \to B$: $F(x) = y \overset{val}{=\!=} F^{-1}(y) = x$	
Property of 'composite mapping' $G \circ F : A \to C$ $\quad$ **for** $F : A \to B$ **and** $G : B \to C$: $G \circ F(x) = z \overset{val}{=\!=} G(F(x)) = z$	

Standard derivation rules for induction

Induction:	**Induction from** $a \in \mathbb{Z}$ **:**
$\quad\vdots$	$\quad\vdots$
$(k) \qquad A(0)$	$(k) \qquad A(a)$
$\quad\vdots$	$\quad\vdots$
$(l) \qquad \forall_i[i \in \mathbb{N}:$	$(l) \qquad \forall_i[i \in \mathbb{Z} \wedge i \geq a:$
$\qquad\qquad A(i) \Rightarrow A(i{+}1)]$	$\qquad\qquad A(i) \Rightarrow A(i{+}1)]$
$\qquad$ { Induction on	$\qquad$ { Induction on
$\qquad\qquad (k)$ and $(l):$ }	$\qquad\qquad (k)$ and $(l):$ }
$(m) \qquad \forall_n[n \in \mathbb{N} : A(n)]$	$(m) \qquad \forall_n[n \in \mathbb{Z} \wedge n \geq a : A(n)]$
Strong induction:	**Strong induction from** $a \in \mathbb{Z}$ **:**
$\quad\vdots$	$\quad\vdots$
$(l) \qquad \forall_k[k \in \mathbb{N}:$	$(l) \qquad \forall_k[k \in \mathbb{Z} \wedge k \geq a:$
$\qquad\qquad \forall_j[j \in \mathbb{N} \wedge j{<}k : A(j)]$	$\qquad\qquad \forall_j[j \in \mathbb{Z} \wedge a{\leq}j{<}k : A(j)]$
$\qquad\qquad \Rightarrow A(k)]$	$\qquad\qquad \Rightarrow A(k)]$
$\qquad$ { Strong induction on	$\qquad$ { Strong induction on
$\qquad\qquad (l):$ }	$\qquad\qquad (l):$ }
$(m) \qquad \forall_n[n \in \mathbb{N} : A(n)]$	$(m) \qquad \forall_n[n \in \mathbb{Z} \wedge n \geq a : A(n)]$

Special relations I

R on A is *reflexive* if $\forall_x[x \in A : xRx]$

R on A is *symmetric* if $\forall_{x,y}[x,y \in A : xRy \Rightarrow yRx]$

R on A is *transitive* if $\forall_{x,y,z}[x,y,z \in A : (xRy \wedge yRz) \Rightarrow xRz]$

R on A is an *equivalence relation* if
$\quad R$ is reflexive and symmetric and transitive

Special relations II

S on A is *irreflexive* if $\forall_x[x \in A : \neg(xSx)]$

R on A is *antisymmetric* if $\forall_{x,y}[x,y \in A : (xRy \wedge yRx) \Rightarrow x = y]$

S on A is *strictly antisymmetric* if $\forall_{x,y}[x,y \in A : \neg(xSy \wedge ySx)]$

R on A is *linear* if $\forall_{x,y}[x,y \in A : xRy \vee yRx \vee x = y]$

R on A is a *reflexive quasi-ordering* if R is reflexive and transitive

S on A is an *irreflexive quasi-ordering* if S is irreflexive and transitive

R on A is a *reflexive ordering* if
$\quad R$ is reflexive, antisymmetric and transitive

S on A is an *irreflexive ordering* if
$\quad S$ is irreflexive, strictly antisymmetric and transitive

$\quad$ Let $\langle A, S_1 \rangle$ and $\langle B, S_2 \rangle$ be irreflexive orderings.
The corresponding *lexicographic ordering* $\langle A \times B, S_3 \rangle$ is defined by:
$(x,y)S_3(x',y')$ if $xS_1x' \vee (x = x' \wedge yS_2y')$

Extreme elements
Let $\langle A, R \rangle$ be a **reflexive ordering** and $A' \subseteq A$
$m \in A'$ is a *maximal element* of A' if $\forall_x [x \in A' : mRx \Rightarrow x = m]$ $m \in A'$ is a *minimal element* of A' if $\forall_x [x \in A' : xRm \Rightarrow x = m]$
$m \in A'$ is the *maximum* of A' if $\forall_x [x \in A' : xRm]$ $m \in A'$ is the *minimum* of A' if $\forall_x [x \in A' : mRx]$
Let $\langle A, S \rangle$ be an **irreflexive ordering** and $A' \subseteq A$
$m \in A'$ is a *maximal element* of A' if $\forall_x [x \in A' : \neg(mSx)]$ $m \in A'$ is a *minimal element* of A' if $\forall_x [x \in A' : \neg(xSm)]$
$m \in A'$ is the *maximum* of A' if $\forall_x [x \in A' \wedge x \neq m : xSm]$ $m \in A'$ is the *minimum* of A' if $\forall_x [x \in A' \wedge x \neq m : mSx]$

Upper and lower bounds
Let $\langle A, R \rangle$ be a **reflexive ordering** and $A' \subseteq A$
$b \in A$ is an *upper bound* of A' if $\forall_x [x \in A' : xRb]$ $a \in A$ is a *lower bound* of A' if $\forall_x [x \in A' : aRx]$